FATHER OF THE SUBMARINE

Father of the Submarine

The Life of the Reverend
George Garrett Pasha

William Scanlan Murphy

WILLIAM KIMBER · LONDON

First published in 1987 by
WILLIAM KIMBER & CO. LIMITED
100 Jermyn Street, London SW1Y 6EE

© William Scanlan Murphy, 1987

ISBN 0-7183-0654-6

Photoset in North Wales by
Derek Doyle & Associates Mold, Clwyd
and printed in Great Britain by
Billing and Sons Limited, Worcester

Gu mo bhean
Gus am bris an là agus an teich na sgàilean …

Contents

List of Illustrations

DIAGRAMS IN THE TEXT

Author's Preface and Acknowledgements

On 26 February 1902, a 49-year-old fireman, lately a corporal in the United States Army, coughed himself to death in a New York slum, all but destitute and entirely ignored. He had started out as a Church of England clergyman in a parish near Manchester. He designed the world's first mechanically-propelled submarine and rose to considerable wealth and a Commission in the Imperial Ottoman Navy. His friends and acquaintances included royalty and J.J. Astor. His business colleagues included Basil Zaharoff, Knight of the Bath and *owner* of Monte Carlo. Yet he was thrown into an unmarked grave, where he lies to this day.

This preposterous curriculum vitae is that of the Reverend George Garrett – or, as he preferred, Commander the Reverend George Garrett Pasha, BA. The fact that he was ultimately nobody's idea of a Victorian success story has kept him almost entirely out of the history books, but his achievements as a pioneer in the early development of the submarine are undeniable. Equally undeniable, unfortunately, are the regrettable effects of his own personality on his fortunes and subsequent reputation. Yet one might think that a man who was one-third genius, one-third crank and one-third charlatan would be famous for being just that – but no. Garrett is one of the great lost figures of the Victorian age, and the single most puzzling absentee from most histories of the modern warship. It might well be said that he was no Faraday or Brunel – but, if modern historical scholarship is to be believed, neither were Faraday and Brunel. As to his tendency to – so to speak – over-promote his wares, his sin may have been to err on the side of temperance. Had he possessed Edison's talent for thumping the tub, he would probably have died much wealthier, but he lacked the last ounce of nerve in this respect, and suffered accordingly. He epitomised much that we now think of as the Victorian Myth, and died largely as a casualty of the American one. Perhaps we should take note.

For a man who died only 85 years ago, George Garrett left a

remarkably faint impression on the world in terms of documents: official British documentation of his life and work is scanty in the extreme. I have therefore been led down a long trail through the archives of a wide variety of institutions in six countries, in a daunting array of languages and scripts. This has made the book rather more of an adventure than might have been expected in writing a biography of a late nineteenth-century clergyman. I have been more than fortunate in finding guides to help me through the wilderness of Garrett's life.

George Garrett's great-grandson, William T. Garrett, supplied me with invaluable photographs, family documentation and information, including the cheering fact that the Garrett family originated in Ballymote, County Sligo. So did mine – *salve, magna parens*! Mr Garrett's enthusiasm for the project and unstinting help were in no way hindered by the small matter of 3,000 miles between us.

It would also be impossible to exaggerate the help and encouragement offered by my good friend Commander Richard Compton-Hall, MBE, RN (ret'd) and his staff at the Royal Navy Submarine Museum, Gosport. It was Commander Compton-Hall's superb book *Submarine Boats* which originally put me on the trail of George Garrett and prompted an exploratory dip into the Submarine Museum's archive – my first step into the Garrett wonderland.

Much help, information and tolerance in the face of obsessive persistence have also been forthcoming from the following libraries and archives: British Library; Brown and Picton Libraries, Liverpool; Central Military and Naval Museum, Leningrad; Clwyd County Record Office; Manchester Central Library and Archive; Manchester Diocesan Registry; Manchester Grammar School; National Maritime Museum; Naval Institute of Greece, Piraeus; Public Record Office; Sjöhistoriska Museet, Stockholm; Smithsonian Institution, Washington; Trinity College Library, Dublin.

Apart from the staff of these august institutions, many individuals have contributed to the cause, notably Rifat Bilsel; Mark Redknap and his MAS band; Mike Holt; Gillian Hush; Keith Jordan; Bernard Murphy; Charles Norrie; Rev. Harry Ogden; Pat and Mary Tyler. My wife Caroline had to put up with the near-physical presence of Reverend Garrett for longer than one would normally tolerate a particularly intrusive ghost.

I have occasionally thought that Garrett needed an H.P. Lovecraft to do him justice on his own level, but, in the name of scholarship and residual good taste, I have refrained from applying the adjective 'eldritch' even to John Garrett's church accounts: any similar excesses have resulted purely from astonishment in the face of a story that makes one wonder why the Victorians bothered with fiction. In many respects, George Garrett's story is an epic of failure, but I for one have found him good (if occasionally dubious) company while writing this book. We could do worse for a hero.

William Scanlan Murphy

Manchester, 1987

CHAPTER ONE

The Parson, the Pimp and the Duck-pond

Like Gilbert's Modern Major-General, the student of the early days of submarine warfare needs a pretty taste for paradox. Many (one is tempted to say *most*) of the prime movers in the genesis of what became the most lethal weapons system of all were clergymen. While, as we shall see, this was as much due to the educational and financial opportunities available to the European non-millionaire as to military tendencies in theology, it remains something of a puzzle that so many men of the cloth took an interest in submarine navigation.

Long before the advent of the ironclad, the putative target of the earliest practical submarines, the Church was heavily represented on the cutting edge of underwater technology. In 1634, two French priests, Fathers Mersenne and Fournier, combined science and religion in an educational round-trip entitled *Questions Théologiques, Physiques, Morales et Mathématiques*, which included a fairly detailed design (by Father Mersenne) for a submarine. This very remarkable leap in the dark recommended a fish-shaped hull, spindle-shaped at both ends for ease of movement in either direction; armament was to consist of large cannon, mounted in the conventional broadside figuration. The boat would creep up on its unfortunate (probably English) prey, surface unannounced and blaze away: the recoil from the guns would be used to close the gun-ports and thus facilitate a rapid underwater retreat. While the good Fathers did not trouble themselves with the dreary technicalities of underwater propulsion or stability, their concept of a big-gun submarine would make a twentieth-century comeback in the shape of the British M-boats, post-First World War submarines mounting a single 12-inch gun and relying for their military effect on precisely the tactics outlined in 1634.

The Protestant clergy supplied a vigorous early contributor to the literature in John Wilkins, who published his *Mathematicall Magick* in 1648. Not content with what must have been the urgent day-to-day problems involved in being Oliver Cromwell's brother-in-law (and subsequently bishop of Chester, an interesting combination), Wilkins discussed at some length the possibilities of a 'Submarine Ark', but, disappointingly, offered no actual designs, presumably leaving these details to the engineering branch of the Church Militant. He did, however, anticipate the airy optimism of many of the early submariners in his clear belief that the technical problems of submarine navigation were not beyond the reach of science and faith, and that his 'Submarine Ark' (apparently the first such use of 'submarine', by the way) would eventually be a reality.

In 1685 the Jesuits made their bid in the shape of Father Giuseppe Ciminius, who offered the King of France a rather vague design (more a scenario than a blueprint) for a machine to take fully-armed men to the bottom of the sea, where they would be able to move about, sit down and fight for between seven hours and a full day.

The Church, then, was not slow to see the military possibilities of customising the whale and giving Jonah a cannon. Reverend Shrapnel would even design a shell to speed the enemy to Heaven (or wherever). The Church would, however, make its greatest – and definitive – contribution to underwater warfare in the nineteenth century, not in the age of the cannon but in the infancy of the torpedo, the submarine weapon *par excellence*.

Two figures, both clergymen, stand out in the early development of the modern submarine. One, John Holland, a renegade Irish monk, struggled for nearly thirty years before convincing the world's navies of the usefulness of his boats. Holland originally intended to use his submarines to blast the hated British Navy out of the water, and, by extension, the British at large out of Ireland. After emigrating to the United States in 1873, he set about raising funds for his work from the Irish Republican Brotherhood, the nascent IRA, who shared his lack of enthusiasm for the Union. Holland was not alone in the underwater clergy; historically, it would have been a surprise if he had been. With a curious symmetry rare in real life, Holland's main industrial competitor also personally symbolised everything he detested; he was an Anglo-Irish Protestant Curate – the son, to boot, of an Ascendancy clergyman.

The Reverend George Garrett was Holland's direct antithesis in virtually every sense imaginable. As far as is known, they never met, though they certainly knew of each other's existence once they finally became aware of each other's work, surprisingly late in the day and at a point when direct rivalry was inevitable; by then, they had worked in the same field for years, but on parallel tracks. Their submarine designs, however, differed fundamentally and irreconcilably. In the end, the modern submarine took more from Holland's idea of the submarine than Garrett's. But Garrett, in every aspect of the process – the design, construction, acceptance and military deployment of the modern submarine – was first.

The ultimate fates of the two clerics, however, represented the grimmest of contrast, erasing any of the glamour that might be expected to flow from Garrett's precedence in such an important field. While Holland would be outflanked in the boardroom, dying a disgruntled and grudging member of the American lower middle classes, Garrett would almost literally starve to death, a classic case of rising like the rocket and falling like the stick. The depths of personal squalor and social degradation to which he finally sank almost beggar belief. Garrett fell from social heights that Holland never achieved to a level of Dickensian misery that the very worst Victorian novelist would have blushed to depict. Scientific and industrial defeat – and sheer bad luck – apart, Garrett was a victim of the fearsome mixture of his own extraordinary personality and the effects of choosing for his partners a cast of characters from the most lurid Victorian-Ruritanian melodrama. The fact that some of those characters held leading roles on the stage of European history is our tragedy as much as Garrett's: unlike him, we are still paying for their performance.

On 4 July 1852, George William Littler Garrett was born at 45 Waterloo Road, Lambeth, the third son of John Garrett, curate of St Mary's Church, and his wife Georgina. Although the St Mary's curacy was a comparatively lowly post, John Garrett's ecclesiastical career was far from commonplace. An Irishman from Ballymote, County Sligo, he was one of fifteen children, and one of three tall Garrett brothers who became clergymen and were known within the family as the 'Three Pillars of the Church'. John had shot to ecclesiastical stardom in 1847, when a booklet he had written on National Education had made a strong impression on Albert, the Prince Consort. The Prince had taken a benevolent personal interest in his churchly doings ever since.

This out-of-the-blue royal interest in an apparently obscure clergyman bears closer inspection. The Garretts firmly believed themselves to be very abstruse relatives of King George IV: if so, the connection is now impossible to establish. A more likely explanation is easily found, however. There are strong indications that the place where the booklet (actually a fairly humdrum résumé of Liberal policy) fell into the hands of the Queen's husband was the Lodge. The Garretts, like many of the Anglican clergy in this period, included in their number many prominent Freemasons, of whom John, like the other 'Pillars' (a rather Masonic concept) was one. Freemasonry was a powerful ingredient in the social cement of high Victorian society, a much-overlooked means of bringing together men with different but mutually beneficial interests who might not have met otherwise. At a time when professional (as opposed to learned) bodies either did not exist or were in their infancy, the Lodge's function as a forum in which important decisions were made has been little understood and even begrudged. As a force for uniting clergymen with engineers and politicians with chemists, it was undoubtedly a mostly positive force in the Victorian period; nothing else fulfilled this extension of 'one nation' into intellectual life. The importance of the Craft in the furtherance of George Garrett's future career was considerable.

Young George was not to know the grime of London for long – indeed, he would barely know it at all. Following George's birth, his father, who had started out as an Inspector of Schools at the astonishing age of twenty, held a succession of short-term curacies and chaplaincies, establishing schools for the poor at Egham and Alton; he ended this impressive period of his ministry as rector of Biscathorpe, in Lincolnshire. For most clergymen in 1857, this very respectable living would have been a reasonable place for a 35-year-old priest to dig in and await the millennium, but John Garrett, now a Doctor of Divinity, was clearly headed for higher things. On the direct recommendation of the Prince Consort, he was appointed vicar of St Paul's, Penzance, a £600-per-annum place in the sun, with a fairly clear implication of a bishopric to follow in the fullness of time. The Church commanded a superb view of Mount's Bay; it is not unreasonable to suggest that the seven years spent there by the Garretts may have given George an interest in things nautical. He would certainly have got to know what a shipwreck looked like, living by one of the world's prime maritime blackspots. This would be useful knowledge for the future.

While at St. Paul's, Dr Garrett consolidated his now very considerable political influence. A lifelong Liberal, Dr Garrett had several important friends to whom he would turn for advice and help in the years to come. Foremost among these was Angela Burdett-Coutts, who also counted Charles Dickens among her friends and was reputed to have jilted Prince Louis Napoleon. Miss (ultimately Baroness) Burdett-Coutts virtually personified Victorian philanthropy: she personally endowed a barely credible number of hospitals and assorted good causes, as well as providing the funds to establish the bishoprics of Adelaide and Cape Town. In 1859 she added the bishopric of (British) Columbia to this list, and thus indirectly gave another boost of the career of the Vicar of Penzance.

John Garrett and his brother Alexander were both appointed commissaries to George Hills, the newly-appointed bishop of Columbia. The seven-year-old George Garrett was present at the enthronement of Dr Hills at a lavish ceremony at Westminster Abbey on St Mathias' Day, 1859, and was introduced, or rather dragged, to the Prince Consort. Somewhat less traumatically, he was brought before his father's political guru Mr Gladstone, then Chancellor of the Exchequer. From his earliest childhood, he was accustomed to meeting the great and famous; the problem was that the Garretts would never have the financial collateral that was assumed to accompany such a social life. The family talent for currying favour with the influential was matched only by a woeful inability to manage money; when the financial sky fell in, there were never any reserves to speak of. This deadly personal deficiency eventually ruined both Dr Garrett and his inventive son.

In John Garrett's case, being a commissary was a desk job, if a powerful one; the heroics fell to Alexander. Young George was soon hearing hair-raising tales of Uncle Alexander's voyage round the Horn to undertake his mission to the Indians. This mission to the Victorian equivalent of Outer Space was successful enough to earn him, eventually, a less hectic position as bishop of North Texas. He also rose to the very stratosphere of Masonry, reaching the semi-legendary thirty-third degree; three 'A.C. Garrett' Lodges were founded in his honour after his death. Another of George's early heroes was Bishop Machray of Rupertsland, who left the Indians (actually quite pacific souls in Canada, unlike their brethren further South) to the fainter hearts, and stomped off into the Tundra to convert the Eskimos. All the while, John Garrett wielded immense influence as the new diocese's representative in Britain, frequently making the long journey to London on diocesan business.

In 1861, however, the Garrett family's fortunes took a severe turn for the worse. While Dr Garrett was up in London, Prince Albert died, leaving him, as he saw it, stuck in the Cornish wilderness without a patron. However, a fellow Mason (one George Hamilton) told him of a clergyman (and presumably Brother) in Manchester who would be interested in exchanging livings with him. Dr Carpenter, of Christ Church, Moss Side, was in failing health, and wished to retire, while Dr Garrett felt the need to be nearer the centre of things: the Lancastrian boom-town looked like a good offer.

The Manchester of the early 1860s was the Shangri-La of Free Trade, beyond reasonable doubt the world's industrial capital, with all the advantages and evils that such a status implied. Whether it was ever quite the Hell-hole that Dickens's 'Coketown' makes it appear is now impossible to determine: certainly, things had changed since Engels (who had an axe to grind and a prophet to support) buried the city's reputation under his own polemic of 1845 – and then left. When Marx published *Capital* in 1867, the admittedly appalling Manchester that Engels handed him as ammunition had already substantially gone, but this has not prevented his portrayal of a near-Satanic Manchester being extended in modern minds to nineteenth-century Manchester in general.

While the Garretts, owners of an autographed copy of Samuel Smiles' *Self Help* and fervent keepers of the author's flame, would hardly have read *Capital* (who does?), they would have found its contents puzzling – wildly out of date and difficult to relate to the city around them, and *Hard Times* no less so. By the time the Garretts arrived, Mr Gradgrind was near to joining the Schools Board; the humdrum but essential petty bureaucracies and social structures of modern life were beginning to take shape. The Church's role in the city was important – and highly political, as the Garretts would find to their cost.

With our view of 1860s Manchester (if we have one) so coloured by the myth of the Urban Hades, it may seem strange that Dr Garrett's primary reservation was the prospect, not of taking the Gospel to the Abyss, but of taking it to a zoo; Manchester people had a reputation for coarseness, avarice and brutality that worried him. He thought that Brother Carpenter may have been made ill by despair in the face of un-Christian greed and abuse of luxury. Perhaps, apart from being the escape route from his Cornish siding, this was the challenge of his pastoral career.

However, ill or not, Dr Carpenter made the journey to Cornwall

with what now appears to be highly suspect haste, and showed Dr
Garrett the Christ Church parish books – or rather, a page of
figures compiled by himself, no doubt for ease of reference. It was
all very impressive: the parish income was £713 a year, which
compared well with St. Paul's £600, making due allowance for the
higher cost of living in Manchester and the lack of a house attached
to the Church. Dr Garrett was convinced that the exchange was
'one which came to me from the unseen Friend in whom I had
learnt so implicitly to trust.'[1]

Once he and his family had arrived at Christ Church in July
1861. Dr Garrett soon realised that this was a mistaken impression.
He had, in fact, been more or less swindled. Dr Carpenter's figures
for the parish's income turned out to have been highly imaginative:
the enticing figure of £713 had not been reached for five years, and
even £500 per annum was optimistic. The long story of the
Garretts' financial miseries had begun.

Moss Side was then a village, two miles south of Manchester.
Surrounded by a cluster of small farms, it was in the early stages of
the transition from semi-rural township to suburb. The final stage
of the process (slum) was a long way off; the riots that brought
what was now an 'inner city area' to dubious fame in the 1980s
were beyond imagination. Little of the smoke from the city's mills
reached Moss Side, which then even stretched to its own little river
– the Corn Brook, now long since culverted, which passed close by
Greenheys Hall, the Garretts' future home. The parish's population
consisted mostly of skilled artisans and semi-professionals, with a
hefty sprinkling of the better-off; these lived on the fringes of the
parish, and peered longingly into the middle-class Promised Land
of Rusholme and Fallowfield, to which (as it happened) most of Dr
Carpenter's major contributors had gone.

Both ends of the city's manufacturing spectrum were represented
in or near the parish. There was a sprinkling of mill-owners, drawn
from the solid rather than the very wealthy, while at the north end
of the parish was an enclave of mill workers, referred to throughout
the period by the now rather American-sounding term 'operatives'.
But even these were not of the very poorest class, who were in fact
Irish migrants, in whom the rector seems to have shown no interest
whatever, despite his own origins. While he would often preach
highly sentimental sermons, verging dangerously on sob-stories,
about the strengths, sorrows and imagined future of his
countrymen in Ireland, the ones on his doorstep were actually *just*

inside the next parish, and therefore someone else's problem. As for Christ Church itself, Garrett described the parish, fairly enough, as 'neither very poor nor very wealthy'.

It is interesting to compare the Garretts' experience of moving into Manchester from the country with that of the novelist Elizabeth Gaskell, who came from the rural village of Knutsford to marry William Gaskell, minister of Cross Street (Unitarian) Chapel, in 1832. She found conditions in the city brutish beyond belief, and went on to publish *Mary Barton*, the definitive Manchester-as-Inferno novel. However, years of change, and contact with James Nasmyth, an enlightened manufacturer who was briefly a resident of Moss Side, produced *North and South*, a convincing portrait of the Manchester the Garretts knew, in which the society as a whole was just beginning to climb into the light, if somewhat reluctantly. Unfortunately, the affinity with the Garretts stopped precisely there; William Gaskell and Dr Garrett were all but enemies, clergymen on either side of a religious gulf that was all the deeper for not being particularly wide. Gaskell was not among Garrett's supporters when Dr Garrett's legal nightmares began in 1867.

In the meantime, Dr Garrett's new church had turned out to be a different kind of nightmare – a decrepit, jerry-built pile of used bricks under an unconvincing coat of pseudo-stone paint. Christ Church had been thrown up on a speculative basis by a Manchester property developer called Heath in the late 1840s. Mr Heath originally intended to have the place consecrated, then sell the church and its living to some upwardly-aspiring gentleman, who would in turn appoint a rector in the usual manner – a buy-yourself-a-squiredom deal. This highly original concept fell foul, however, of the Patronage Act, and Mr Heath, after an unpleasant exchange of opinions with the bishop of Chester, was forced to sell for £2,700 to Robert Gardner, a long-established Mancunian church patron. Christ Church was finally consecrated in 1850, and Dr Carpenter installed as rector. Dr Carpenter seems to have been looking for alternative employment long before his trip to Cornwall. It is not difficult to see why. Dr Garrett, referring to his new church with bitter irony as 'this Zion', wailed to his Sunday morning congregation:

> It was a wretched place for Divine Worship ... the walls were standing in ditches of clay, which held about 18 inches of water, always soaking into the bricks ... the water [rose] all round the Church as high as the backs of the pews.[2]

Garrett was saddled with the huge and ruinously expensive task of draining the church, shoring it up and rendering it barely habitable, which was as high as this appalling building ever aspired. The impact on his own finances (for most purposes inextricable from those of the parish) was crippling, though he did at least find himself an imposing home in Greenheys Hall, a rambling mansion that would henceforth serve as Christ Church Rectory. But this vital capital expenditure did nothing for his cash-flow, which remained stubbornly arthritic. The family funds were badly over-stretched.

Dr Garrett still had his friends in this valley of monetary darkness, however – some more Unseen than others. One of his most pressing problems – the education of his sons – was comparatively easily dealt with. Even before leaving Cornwall, his sons Oliver and Henry had been awarded places at Rossall School on highly favourable terms, and Dr Garrett now achieved the same for young George. Two-year-old Thomas and baby William could manage at home for the moment.

Rossall had been another beneficiary of the bounty of Miss Burdett-Coutts, who used her power of nomination to install the young Garretts. Her vote was supported by John Abel Smith, the MP for Chichester, who was another director of the school and a close friend, personal, political and Masonic, of Dr Garrett. One of the closest-kept secrets of the family at this time was the fact that Abel Smith paid most of the Garrett boys' school fees; from the family's earliest days in the parish, the impressive facade of Greenheys Hall was all too symbolic of their economic standing. An unkind soul might point to the church's bogus walls as being equally symbolic.

Rossall School was founded in 1844, and had soon established itself as a major public school, offering a classical education to the sons of gentlemen and clergymen in the buildings and grounds of Rossall Hall. The Hall had once been the home of Sir Peter Hesketh Fleetwood, who was forced to restructure his affairs when his vision of a seaside railway metropolis at Fleetwood proved over-optimistic.

The young George Garrett's headmaster was the Rev W.A. Osborne, who introduced the house system, organised games and prefects, all just in time for George, who was in fact fortunate to be at a school that spent all of £29 10s per boy per annum on food – far more than many others of the period. What sounds like the slimming establishment at Hurstpierpoint lavished a stomach-rumbling £18 2s per boy. However, an obviously ungrateful former pupil (F.A. Simpson) later described the Rossall boys as 'scandalously underfed'. A glimpse of George's daily diet is instructive:

> Breakfast: Tea or coffee and bread; or milk, bread and butter
> Dinner: Beef or mutton; pudding or pastry daily
> Tea: As breakfast
> Supper: Bread and cheese, or meat occasionally.[3]

George showed an interest in and aptitude for the sciences very early, but scientific subjects played very little part in the school curriculum. Rossall, in fact, produced only one other scientist of any note in the whole Victorian period – the geologist William Dawkins.

It is one of the many oddities of Garrett's life that his scientific future was secured by a financial disaster that struck the Garretts in 1867. Had the family remained prosperous, we might never have heard of him.

One of the Dr Garrett's many political enthusiasms was the temperance movement, largely as a result of the drink-inflamed horrors that he had witnessed so often in his Sligo childhood. His position, however, was always one of regulation rather than prohibition. So, when John Abel Smith presented his Sunday Closing Act (a measure to restrict drink sales on the Sabbath) to Parliament in 1867, Dr Garrett was one of the first to offer active support. He became a leading figure in the Central Association for Sunday Closing. Almost immediately, he found himself in conflict with a group of vengefully anti-alcohol extremists, who seem to have thought the Association's Committee, and Dr Garrett in particular, something approaching a brewers' front organisation.

While Dr Garrett was in London conferring with Abel Smith, there was a hard-line coup on the Manchester Committee of the Central Association, leaving it committed to a totally abolitionist stand: Dr Garrett resigned, and set up his own 'London Association'. At a temperance meeting in Gloucester between these two events, Dr Garrett collected about £30, which duly went to the coffers of the London Association. Unfortunately, he seems to have neglected to inform his contributors of the precise destination of their money: the Central Association accused him of embezzling

George Garrett (right) as a child, with his brothers Henry (left) and Thomas and their proud father Dr John Garrett.

(Above) The young graduate. It is not known whether the mortar-board is armoured.

(Left) Garrett the Trinity College pugilist, c. 1874.

the money, and flooded Manchester with leaflets saying as much. Dr Garrett sued for libel.

There then followed one of the odder convulsions of the nineteenth-century English legal system. The assizes found for Dr Garrett, and handed the matter to an assessor to determine damages. But the assessor's final decision was astonishing: although it was conceded that Garrett had been wronged, he was awarded no damages and hostile costs were levied against him – he had to pay *both* sides' legal fees. This was probably a variation on the halfpenny-damages ruse beloved of the courts in later years: while Garrett may have been technically in the right, the fact remained that he had been in Gloucester under the Central Association's auspices and at their expense. In the meantime, he had also set up the 'United Association for Sunday Closing', of which he was chairman, treasurer and entire committee, and whose offices were given simply as 'Greenheys Hall'. This new body had an elaborate and fiscally exotic relationship with the London Association that wafted a strong whiff of fraud over the whole proceedings. Something, in fact, was going on. Dr Garrett, confronted with closer inspection of his affairs, abandoned further legal action, lest worse ensue.

Suddenly finding himself with a bill for £2,500, Dr Garrett was forced to make drastic economies. The creditors' first move was to sell the Garretts' horse and carriage, largely as a gesture of ill-will. Dr Garrett was faced with the necessity of withdrawing George and Henry from Rossall. Even with the substantial help he was receiving from Abel Smith, he could no longer afford the fees, but it is at least possible that Abel Smith, faced with scandal if the link should come into the open now that Garrett was disgraced, may have been forced to withdraw his support. In any case, both boys were sent to Manchester Grammar School, about a mile from Greenheys Hall, as day-boys.

Back at Greenheys Hall, the Garretts were forced to take in lodgers to make ends meet. Paradoxically, this was far from being a catastrophe from George's point of view. It turned the Hall from a provincial rectory into a particularly unlikely outpost of cosmopolitan cultural exchange, as Dr Garrett chose his paying guests from among the many foreign businessmen who visited Manchester. When George came home in the evening, he would find merchants from Greece and Armenia, Turkey and the USA, shipping-agents and international commodity-dealers: he witnessed the world of international finance in the least likely surroundings at a very impressionable age. The fact that he once came home to find the famous Dr Pusey billeted in his bedroom ('Think of that, ye fanatical Party-Sabbath men!' roared Dr Garrett) must have been almost a disappointment after the colourful crowd he was used to.

George's new school offered him a completely different response to his scientific leanings, which had been tolerated rather than encouraged at Rossall: added to this, the polyglot mercantile and industrial atmosphere at home was a far cry from Rossall's rarified gentrification. The business world was now as much a part of his daily life as school and the Church.

Manchester Grammar School was an early leader in the scientific training of schoolboys. To the classics, French and English that formed his entire curriculum at Rossall were now added mathematics and physics. Garrett was taught physics by William Marshall Watts at the school's murky laboratory at Long Millgate. Watts was a DSc from London University, and, as the British pioneer of spectroscopy, was a considerable scientific authority in his own right. He soon spotted young Garrett's talents, and recommended him to Henry Roscoe, Professor of Chemistry at nearby Owen's College, the infant Manchester University; Roscoe recognised that the boy was something out of the ordinary.

Garrett left Manchester Grammar School in June 1869. He was immediately sent to Seighford, near Stafford, where he taught in the village school for nine months – his first taste of stoking his father's voracious economic furnace. He proved a remarkably good teacher; his glowing testimonial from the Vicar, Mr Perry, impressive enough in any case, is all the more so for a boy of seventeen:

> He is good natured, most obliging, and enjoyed the approbation of the Boys. One of my Pupils who received instructions in Classics from Mr Garrett gained honours in the Cambridge Local Examination ...[4]

It must be noted in all candour that this is the one and only document still in existence that describes George Garrett's character in anything like conventionally complimentary terms. Later, even his friends can be seen, quite unmistakably, to be choosing their words carefully. Subsequent descriptions of Garrett noted a nervousness and tendency to anxiety that were easily taken for nervous energy when things were going well, but were more worrying in other circumstances. Some people found him a little frightening – the stereotype, one fears, of the mad inventor. Be that as it may, Garrett's fortunate student would probably have passed easily into further education with this sort of qualification, but Garrett himself would have to take the long route to the top. His two older brothers were now both studying medicine: it was quite impossible for the family to bear the cost of another son at university.

Faced with George's undeniable intellectual talents, Dr Garrett was in fact confronted with a considerable problem. George could not attend University full-time – even nearby Owen's College, where Roscoe would certainly have accepted him – for the embarrassing but compelling reason that George represented earning-power which the family simply could not do without. After due consultation with friends and Friend, Dr Garrett turned to the source of his doctorate of Divinity:

> It was rendered necessary by circumstances that [George] should begin practical work at an early age, so that he entered the University of Dublin, where students can pass their courses by examinations, and in the meantime employ themselves in active occupations, if advisable.[5]

These 'absentee' students formed about 10% of the students at Trinity at the time, and were the subject of much heated controversy until the system was finally abandoned – as late, amazingly, as the 1940s. With the vague suspicion that the college was acting as a degree-mill in these cases, there was always a certain ambiguity to the degrees obtained by the 'pensioners', as students like Garrett were known, though from the outset there was never any doubt of his scholastic capabilities: 'My son was able, at the age of 17, to pass all the examinations required for the whole of his first year's course during one week'.[6] In other words, he was left with a year to spend as he wished or his father needed. Roscoe enrolled Garrett as an evening student in his chemistry class at Owen's, where his occupation was recorded as 'schoolmaster'. He was, in fact, Fourth Master in the Boys' Commercial and Scientific Day School at Manchester Mechanics' Institute, a post he secured on Roscoe's recommendation.

Roscoe's chemistry group at Owen's was no glorified evening class: Garrett's fellow students included at least one doctor and several industrial chemists, all come to sit at Roscoe's feet. Roscoe might have been forgiven for an aversion to clergymen. An earlier student of his (a Reverend Pearson) had embezzled church funds, raped a chambermaid, ransacked her master's house *and* falsified his research into the atomic weight of uranium (sin of sins) before fleeing to Wyoming, where he was eventually lynched for horse-stealing. With this behind him, Roscoe's acceptance of Garrett is *almost* evidence for a lack of obvious parsonical intent on Garrett's part; it is certainly evidence for the proposition that Manchester turned out a very singular breed of scientific clergyman in this period.

Classes were held in anatomy and physiology as well as chemistry and physics; foreign languages were also compulsory, particularly German, as much of the most important scientific work of the time had been done in Germany, where Roscoe himself had studied with the famous Bunsen, of burner fame. Work done at Owen's could be credited towards a London University (or, as in Garrett's case, Dublin) degree. Garrett's early scientific interests lay not in submarine navigation, but in the common ground between chemistry and physiology – specifically, the chemistry of breathing and the problems of breathing in confined spaces. While the relevance of this to submarines is obvious, that interest would manifest itself later. Roscoe's own first published work at Owen's had been on the subject of carbon dioxide and suffocation. It is impossible to tell whether he actually inspired this interest in Garrett, but he certainly encouraged it.

Roscoe's predecessor at Owen's had been Edward Frankland, who had (not entirely mistakenly) felt tremors in the financial ground under Owen's and had moved on to a professorship at South Kensington Museum. He combined this with a lectureship at the Royal School of Mines – and indeed several other full-time posts – in a show of pluralism that would have done a medieval priest proud. Somehow, he also found the time to develop the concept of chemical valency, a vital contribution to modern chemistry.

Mines (the definitive enclosed space before the submarine) and chemistry, however, were the combination that drew Garrett to the museum in 1872, having left the Mechanics' Institute after the vaguest hint of personal differences with the management; such discontent on the lower decks was common at the institute, which, several metamorphoses later, is now the University of Manchester Institute of Science and Technology (UMIST).

At Kensington Museum, under Frankland, Garrett carried out some of the earliest systematic research on human respiration:

> During these investigations, [he] allowed himself to be enclosed in an
> hermetically sealed chamber, which contained besides himself a bird,

rabbit, guinea pig and a lighted candle. He took samples of the air in
the chamber every fifteen minutes, as well as working out mathematical
problems [to see how his consciousness was being affected]. He
remained under observation until he lost consciousness, which was not
until the animals had passed out and the candle extinguished.[7]

The 20-year-old Garrett used the results of this work to design the
world's first self-contained breathing apparatus, using caustic
potash to 'scrub' carbon dioxide from exhaled air, an invention that
would finally appear five years later as the vital element of his
Pneumatophore. Although his work at Kensington was credited to
his degree, it was otherwise completely forgotten after the
Pneumatophore was dropped from Garrett's submarines in 1883.
Nearly forty years later, Haldane, apparently ignorant of Garrett's
work, would repeat much of it, to the same ends, and has since been
credited with achievements that belonged at least partially to this
roving undergraduate, who, again driven by his father's legal
problems, now moved on to Pocock College, County Kilkenny,
where, aged twenty-one, he became headmaster.

The Ireland of the early 1870s was a far from happy place. Many
students at Trinity found it necessary to arm themselves against
assaults by the Fenians, who saw the young Protestants of Trinity
as personifying the evils of British rule. As it happened, the college
began to accept Catholics in 1873, but the Catholic Church's
decision to forbid its members to attend Trinity saw to it that there
were few takers, so the confrontations continued.

Things were no better at Pocock – they were worse. County
Kilkenny had seen bloody rioting in the streets: Garrett had to
march his students to church on Sunday with the older boys
shouldering rifles, though mercifully things never came to a
shoot-out. What appears to have been Garrett's first warlike
invention stems from his time at Pocock:

> When out of college grounds, [the students] armed themselves with a
> peculiarly innocent looking but deadly weapon, made by removing the
> cardboard from the square flat tops of their mortar board caps and
> inserting a piece of sheet steel in its place. With the addition of a loop to
> slip over the wrist, this made a handy weapon at close quarters.[8]

However, Garrett did not spend all of his time conducting scientific
research (in this case, fearlessly anticipating our modern anti-hero
Oddjob) or urban warfare. It was during his time – eighteen
months – at Pocock that he met Jane Parker, the daughter of a

Waterford County Magistrate, at her home village of Tallow. The news of George's engagement to the daughter of a wealthy Irish lawyer was met with jubilation at Christ Church: apart from celebrating the forthcoming marriage, Dr Garrett may have dimly perceived some financial relief in the offing, and to some extent he seems to have been right. It appears that Jane's family took George under their collective wing, as he abruptly resigned from Pocock and actually took up residence at Trinity in 1874/5, thus qualifying for an honours degree, rather than the pass BA to which his absentee status would have restricted him. The necessary money certainly did not and (with Dr Garrett's beady-eyed creditors ever vigilant) could not originate at Greenheys Hall. However, not all of Garrett's time was spent in the laboratory:

> He gained a special medal for being the first lightweight to ever win the heavyweight championship in the annual boxing matches. At that time these contests were fought with bare knuckles. His Instructor in this gentle art was Jem Mace, at that time the foremost exponent of skill as against brute force in this game. [Garrett] seemed to prove this fact, as he weighed only 142 pounds and was able to beat men weighing as much as 216.[9]

In the summer of 1875, Garrett, at twenty-three an oldish undergraduate by any standards, faced a battery of examinations: Mathematical and Experimental Physics, Astronomy, Experimental Science and Ethics, the last a regrettable absentee from modern science degrees. A more positive symptom of the march of science is the content of the papers, which are pitched at a level slightly lower than the modern British A-level. It is amusing to note that he gained full marks for a question on latent heat and 'freezing machines', the diametrically opposite application of the principle to the one that would make him famous. The crews of his submarines would have sold their souls for a 'freezing machine' at the end of a dive.

On 30 June, Garrett graduated from Trinity with his BA in Experimental Sciences, second in his class of *Respondentes* and sixth in his year – a very creditable performance. He did not, however, immediately plunge into a scientific or technical career; the convoluted affairs of his father led him elsewhere.

Because of the ferocious pressures on his income, Dr Garrett was having to run the parish on his own – without a curate. This state of affairs bore heavily on a man whose Gothic finances were audibly creaking under the weight of his debts. Dr Garrett's long experience in educational affairs had brought him to a seat on the Manchester Schools Board, only to come under fire from his own parishioners when he seemed less than anxious to set up a day school in his own parish. In the usual Victorian (and John Garrett) fashion, a pamphlet war broke out. Dr Garrett flooded the parish with copies of his references from twenty years of church work, testifying to his efficiency in such matters – a rather odd way of defending his reluctance to build a school, which was largely due to the state of the parish's (i.e. his) finances. The school was built, and money became even scarcer.

With a large parish and a school to run, Dr Garrett needed a curate. If a curate could be found who was cheap on the one hand, and had a potentially lucrative sideline on the other, so much the better. Whether George Garrett ever had a true vocation to the Church has often been debated: we cannot, however, doubt his loyalty to his father. The line-up was simple enough. George's eldest brother Oliver was now practising medicine in France; Henry was starting out as an obstetrician (and, ironically, epic boozer). George pulled the short straw.

Whatever his activities did to his sons, it is certainly true that Dr Garrett's doings wore down his wife, who suffered all her life from *grand mal* epileptic fits: there are genuinely heart-rending tales of Dr Garrett having literally to sit on Georgina during her convulsions, to prevent her hurting herself. With its very weird finances, its spare rooms occupied by Armenian merchants (or reserve supplies of Dr Garrett's pamphlets) and the lady of the house suffering from this ghastly complaint, Greenheys Hall was a far cry from a 'normal' rectory. It is therefore scarcely surprising that the parish would not have a 'normal' curate.

George's immediate response to his father's invitation to join the clergy is not recorded. Soon after graduating, however, he appears to have fallen into deep conclave with his fiancée's family, convincing them of his need to further his scientific education in some form or other. In the event, this took the form of a year in Fiji and New Zealand, spent, as his father later recorded, 'teaching and practising navigation in all its branches'.[10] We will learn later that George's many talents never quite encompassed navigation: his reluctance to face this limitation would cause him a great deal of sorrow. Jonah, at least, could trust the whale to know where it was going: the worst upheavals in Garrett's submarining career would

be caused by navigational errors, caused, in turn, by blind faith in
his own navigational abilities.

A presumably bronzed George Garrett returned to England in
1876 and married Jane Parker at Tallow on 17 August. He then
enrolled at Trinity College, Cambridge, to study for the Cambridge
Theological Examination, the Anglican clergyman's driving
licence. This comparatively undemanding course caused him no
difficulty: on 27 May 1877, the bishop of Manchester ordained him
a deacon and appointed him to the curacy of Moss Side, on a
stipend of £100 per annum. The Church, which had presumably
seen the in-house curate trick before, expressly forbade him to take
less than this in a clause printed on the cover of his licence; doing
so was punishable by dismissal. The rector, however, was a
talented amateur accountant; such sums were easily lost in the
steaming jungles of the Christ Church accounts.

Reverend George and Mrs Garrett began what should have been
low-budget clerical life in a largish house at 82 Chorlton Road,
three-quarters of a mile from the church and the rectory; once
again, the helping hand of the Parkers can be discerned here. Jane's
family may well have objected to the possibility of her waiting on
the itinerant foreigners at Greenheys Hall. Her time was in any
case taken up with their baby daughter, Georgina, who had been
born on 2 May.

Garrett spent the next year helping his father – taking services,
marrying parishioners, burying them and teaching in the day
school. Evenings, however, were spent on his breathing apparatus.
The carbon dioxide 'scrubber' was now grafted onto a diving suit;
Garrett named the whole the 'Pneumatophore'.

The Pneumatophore startlingly anticipated the closed-cycle
breathing apparatus worn by British and Italian 'charioteers'
(human torpedo pilots) of the Second World War, though there
was no provision made for carrying compressed air or oxygen –
which, considering oxygen's toxicity at depths below thirty feet,
was just as well. As no compressed gas was carried, only a
knapsack reservoir of air, and the diver's exhalations were re-cycled
via the 'scrubber', the wearer would leave no tell-tale trail of
bubbles when wearing the suit under water. At the outset, however,
Garrett's primary interest, following his mentor Frankland, was
access to fume-filled mineshafts, but he was by no means unaware
of the Pneumatophore's potential maritime and military uses.

The military possibilities of such a suit when used in an

operation such as attaching mines are obvious now, and should have been so then, but Garrett had the greatest difficulty in drumming up interest at the Admiralty – or anywhere else. He made at least one approach to the Admiralty with the Pneumatophore, but the reply consisted of little beyond a blatant attempt to extract the secret of the 'scrubber' from him without payment, a rather amateur shot at piracy made possible by his curious failure to patent the device. Eventually, this lack of a patent would have precisely the opposite effect from the battalions of bootleg versions that usually greet the unpatented good idea: the Pneumatophore would be completely forgotten, and its principle left virtually unexplored, for more than a quarter of a century.

Garrett had been a curate only a matter of days when the world beyond the Church beckoned. In June 1877, reports of the Russo-Turkish War began to appear in the *Manchester Courier*. What Garrett read there set the pattern for the rest of his life. As his father recalled:

> Two incidents were reported which sent a thrill of deep interest through the public mind, and which combined may be taken as the originating cause of my son's design [for a submarine boat].
> I refer to the attack which was made by a Russian officer in command of a torpedo boat upon a Turkish ironclad, in which the Russian boat became entangled in certain chains which had been fixed as a barrier round the ship. When reading the account it occurred to my son's mind, 'Why could not the attack be made by going under the chains?'
> And, about the same time, we were all made intensely anxious by the appearance of a Russian ironclad, or other warship, outside the town of Victoria in Vancouver's Island, when for several hours it was felt that such a town and colony must lie almost at the mercy of such an enemy if he came to bombard it. This brought the thought of 'Why some means of defence could not meet such an enemy under water, and so render all bombardment of the land and all landing of hostile troops upon any of our coasts next to an impossibility'.[11]

The threat to Vancouver's Island, and therefore to the Diocese of Columbia, was, of course, of special interest to the Garretts, but the 'threat' does not appear to have been a serious one, and certainly never came to anything. On the other hand, the escapades of the Russian torpedo-boat commander bear closer examination, in view of the fact that both Russia and Turkey would eventually patronise Garrett's submarine enterprises.

On 12 June 1877, three ironclads of the Turkish Danube Flotilla

– *Idjalalieh, Feth-i-Bulend* and *Mukudim-i-Hair* – lay at anchor at Sulina, accompanied by a gunboat. The squadron was commanded by Hobart Pasha, a former British naval officer, who had recently returned to Turkey after a very bizarre assignation with a Devonshire duck-pond, of which more later. Hobart's main fear was of attack by Russian torpedo-boats, against which he designed a simple, but, as it turned out, effective defence.

The Turkish flotilla was surrounded, like so many covered wagons, by a ring of picket-boats, each connected to the next by a strong rope. Thus prepared, they awaited the arrival of Lieutenant (later Admiral) Makarov, aboard the *Grand Duke Constantine*, an armed merchant steamer, in company with her sister-ship *Vladimir*.

Considering future developments in naval warfare (the Second World War midget submarine-carrying cruisers of the Japanese Navy spring to mind), the main armament of these ships is of enormous interest. Each ship carried up to six torpedo-boats on davits: these would be lowered into the water to make separate attacks on the enemy while the parent vessel stood off – on this occasion, well off. These little boats conveniently summarise the state of torpedo warfare in 1877.

It should be explained at this stage that in 1877 the word 'torpedo' referred to virtually any explosive device detonated underwater: the famous 'Full speed ahead and damn the torpedoes!', uttered by Captain Farragut at a passionate moment in the American Civil War, actually referred to moored mines in Mobile Bay. Mines apart, 'torpedoes' came in three distinct versions in the 1870s: towed, spar and Whitehead (automotive, or 'fish').

The first division of three boats, lowered from the *Grand Duke Constantine*, was led by the *Tchesma*, commanded by Lieutenant Zatsarennyi. *Tchesma*'s armament consisted of a towed torpedo.

The towed torpedo, as the name implies, was simply a mine towed across the bows of the target by the attacking craft and detonated electrically. This entailed a particularly terrifying evolution for the attacking boat and a faith in the weapon's electrics and the strength of its tow-rope that was rarely justified. On the occasion in question, *Tchesma* merely fouled the Turkish barrier ropes, but managed to limp back to the mother ship more or less intact. Significantly, she was fitted with Whitehead torpedoes on her subsequent refit, an alteration entirely vindicated by her success in torpedoing a Turkish revenue cutter later in the war.

The two other (unnamed) boats of the first division, commanded, respectively, by Lieutenants Rozhdestvensky and Poutschine, were armed with spar torpedoes. The spar torpedo was a (not very) modern equivalent of a medieval lance, a bomb-on-a-stick protruding from the bows of the boat: this unfortunate vessel was expected to steer within ten yards of the target, at which point the bomb would be pushed against the enemy's hull and detonated. This placed a great deal of faith in the enemy being mesmerised by the torpedo-boat's attack, presumably watching in bemused fascination rather than lining up his own main armament on the boat – a rather more likely event, one suspects. On this occasion, Lieutenant Poutschine's boat was capsized by the barrier-rope, detonating the torpedo in the process and leaving six of the crew to the legendary hospitality of the Turkish Fleet.

Zinovi Rozhdestvensky was rather more fortunate. He managed to jump the barrier-rope, damaging his boat in the process, only to detonate his torpedo against the *Idjalalieh*'s torpedo-nets: he made his escape under heavy Turkish fire which missed his craft, but entirely wiped out the second division of torpedo-boats.

The *Idjalalieh*'s torpedo nets had been fitted on the orders of Hobart Pasha as a defence against the third type of torpedo – the Whitehead automotive (or 'fish') torpedo; the torpedo, in fact, broadly as it is known today. At this early stage of its development, however, the Whitehead torpedo, powered by compressed air, had two major disadvantages for most navies. One was its astronomic price: Robert Whitehead ran a ruthless monopoly from his Fiume works, taking particular care to keep secret the principles of the weapon's depth-keeping mechanism (widely known in the naval world, in fact, simply as The Secret). The other drawback was the automotive torpedo's unreliability beyond roughly a hundred yards' range. Although its deployment lacked the sombre implications for the attacking vessel that haunted the towed and spar torpedoes, the Whitehead was still not in general naval use for both of these reasons.

For once, the Royal Navy had taken an interest in a new weapon, and had negotiated an agreement with Whitehead (on the usual colossal terms) as early as 1870, but the Service was to take rather more convincing of the claims of the vessel best suited to its use – the submarine. It is strange to note that Admiral Fisher, later the champion of submarines in the Royal Navy, recommended the use of the dreaded towed torpedo over the high-cost, short-range, low-reliability Whitehead until the late 1880s, by which time submarines – and Garrett's submarines in particular – were making their first genuinely ominous moves.

In the meantime, Garrett's interest in submarines had been aroused, though he had no apparent interest in the Whitehead torpedo at this stage. The submarine torpedo boat, quite apart from its intrinsic military applications, was an application for his Pneumatophore: the possibilities, technical and financial, were enticing. His future in submarines was beginning to take shape. Elsewhere, others were also contemplating the future of submarine warfare.

In America, John Holland was negotiating with the Irish Republican Brotherhood for the funds to build the *Fenian Ram*: after his experiences in Ireland, it is highly unlikely that Garrett would have seen much to commend in either the cause or the name of the vessel. Also, his heroic Uncle Alexander had once been subjected to the unlikely indignity of a Fenian ambush during one of his missionary journeys, an earlier effort of American-backed Irish Republicanism that seems as strategically sensible as their attempted move into submarines. He would in any case take issue with the *Ram*'s means of propulsion (a petrol engine) – as, indeed, would Holland. Quite unknown to Garrett, however, the Turkish navy, in the shape of Hobart Pasha, had its own ideas about submarine warfare, while in Greece another, altogether less attractive personality was also beginning to contemplate the subject.

In 1875, following the Royal Navy's uncharacteristic show of enthusiasm for the Whitehead torpedo, Hobart Pasha visited the unlikely naval Mecca of Upottery, a village in Devonshire. Here, under conditions mixing intense secrecy and near-fantasy in equal measure, he set about experimenting with a model Whitehead torpedo, running it up and down the village duck-pond, paying a trustworthy local lad to help retrieve the thing. Examining his results at this most far-flung Ottoman Naval base, Hobart decided that the Whitehead torpedo was indeed the weapon of the future. While it would be some time before sufficient funds could be extracted from the Sultan for the Ottoman Navy to have Whiteheads of its own, Hobart saw the writing on the wall, and ordered his ironclads to be fitted with anti-Whitehead nets. When he saw Lieutenant Rozhdestvensky's near-success two years later, the same idea as the one that struck Garrett must have crossed his mind: if the Russians could have gone under the nets ...

Meanwhile, virtually on the day that Garrett pored over his *Courier*, Thorsten Nordenfelt, the Swedish inventor of the Nordenfelt quick-firing machine-gun and other advanced weapons, had appointed a new agent in Athens. Finding Greek business slack, Nordenfelt decided not to send a man from his London head office, but instead asked the retiring agent to name a local man as his successor. The agent looked no further than his hotel bar.

The job went to Basil Zaharoff, who at the time was combining more or less honest toil serving drinks in the Hôtel Grande Bretagne with a rather less respectable sideline showing visitors round the Athens Red Light District – in particular round one recreational establishment in which he had an interest. Life had been hard since he had (just) beaten a serious theft charge in London in 1874, following an ill-advised diversification into big-time pawnbroking. Although the Nordenfelt agency only paid £5 a week as salary, generous commission terms and Zaharoff's hitherto untapped talent for seeking out wars and arming both sides would soon lay the foundations of an awesome fortune. When (rare event) war was in short supply, Zaharoff would set about fomenting one, a Mephistophelean business technique that eventually became known the world over as the *Système Zaharoff*.

Apart from possessing a gift for arms-peddling, Zaharoff was also an inventive man, and soon filed apparently genuine patent applications for time-fuses and a new type of screw-breech. However, at a time when Nordenfelt had noticed the business potential of the Whitehead torpedo and was busy looking into refinements of the surface torpedo-boat, Zaharoff was later remembered as having been a submarine enthusiast from the earliest days of his time with the firm. Mr Lampsas, proprietor of the Hôtel Grande Bretagne and an early recipient of Zaharoff gratitude (doubtless in the customary used notes), remembered him well:

Basil Zaharoff was, as far as I know, the first man to have made specially for him a model submarine. It was part of his sales equipment to bring this out and to amuse businessmen by inviting them to watch it perform on some pond or lake. I remember when one of the Vickers family came to Athens there was an argument about submarine boats. Mr Vickers argued that the submarine was the ridiculous invention of two mad Frenchmen [Fathers Mersenne and Fournier, presumably].

'On the contrary', replied Zaharoff, 'it is an invention of your own country, Britain. As long ago as 1596 John Napier, a Scotsman, published a treatise on "devices for sailing under water". What is more, in James I's time an attempt was made to row a boat under water, and in 1774 a submarine boat was built at Plymouth.' I remember these details because I wrote them down at the time, for I was greatly impressed by Zaharoff's knowledge of his subject.[12]

This prince of scholars (and his Boswell) would have another British name to add to his catalogue soon enough – and, in his supposed boss Nordenfelt, a better listener.

The Manchester parson and the pimp from Odessa, Constantinople, Paris or Anatolia (depending on which of his large collection of birth-certificates one chooses to believe) would eventually unite to supply the Turkish Navy, completing a chain of events that began at a Devonian duck-pond.

Garrett's road to the East, however, was a complex affair – as, alas, was the road back. In the summer of 1877, his career in submarines began in the manner familiar to all who have sought to interest the Navy in new ideas: he was ignored.

CHAPTER TWO

The Curate's Egg

The 25-year-old George Garrett was hardly in an enviable position to begin work as a pioneer submariner, or indeed as anything else. Although he was entered on the diocesan payroll as his father's curate, his stipend was, so to speak, retroflexed into the family's coffers in the endless efforts to pay off Dr Garrett's legal bills, an attempt at creative accounting that would soon supply Dr Garrett's many detractors with further ammunition. In the meantime, however, the rector's finances slithered further into the mire following the sudden deaths of two of the Garretts' wealthier neighbours, one of whom was the eminent but rather dim physician Sir James Bardsley. Dr Garrett had had an uphill task cultivating this important but obtuse man, whose death seemed something of a personal insult. Property speculators swooped on the two gentlemen's land and threw up several streets of cottages, breaking the rector's housing monopoly and thus knocking a substantial hole in the earning power of Greenheys Hall.

Scientific interest apart, George Garrett entered the submarine business out of dire necessity: he had become the auxiliary motor for his father's now apparently permanent fiscal levitation act, and a rather under-powered motor at that. Meanwhile, Dr Garrett's talent for making enemies appeared undiminished: he used his seat on the Manchester Schools Board as a platform to denounce his critics, attracting further demands for rapid settlement of his huge debts – but still he ranted on. However, his enemies, an unlikely alliance of hard-line temperance fanatics and others who thought Garrett an unfortunate and devious influence on Church life, were a politically sophisticated group of men: they knew their target, and waited for him to hand them a suitably weighty stick for them to hit him with. He would not let them down. Under these circumstances, George and Jane may well have been looking for an escape route.

It is clear, then, that Garrett's road-to-Damascus experience in reading of the Russian torpedo boats' exploits had a harder financial edge than his father's account would have us believe. With the zeal of the semi-desperate, George set about acquiring, in his father's words, 'accurate knowledge of all previous attempts, especially in America' to build submarine vessels. For the most part, this was rather depressing reading.

America had seen the first operational use of a submersible craft, in the attack on Lord Howe's flagship HMS *Eagle* on 6 September 1776. The underwater machine concerned, the *Turtle*, was the invention of David Bushnell (subsequently – of course? – a minister), who had demonstrated what appears to have been the first, clockwork-triggered underwater mine while still a Yale undergraduate in 1774.

Turtle amounted to a drastically-revised barrel, made of oak staves. The solitary crewman submerged the boat by kicking a foot-valve, which flooded the ballast tank. The tank was emptied by ferocious application of a manual force-pump. Propulsion was also manual: the pilot turned one (or both) of two cranks, each connected to an oar-bladed propeller. One propeller drove the boat horizontally, while the other, trained upwards, controlled the boat's depth. Or such, at least, was the theory: this arrangement for controlling the boat's attitude under water, and the problems that went with it, would make a surprise comeback in Garrett's later creations. Another interesting anticipation of future designs was the provision for jettisoning a quarter of the boat's lead ballast in an emergency, allowing her to rise to the surface: reserves of buoyancy and emergency drop-keels were long to be features of early submarines.

When afloat, a six-inch conning tower protruded above the surface, through which the pilot could take his bearings before diving and pressing home his attack. Below the surface, life, apart from being busy, was very dark. Candles consumed too much oxygen: Bushnell hit upon the idea of daubing the compass-needle and the depth-marker with fox fire, a phosphorescent fungus. This gave off a useful (if eerie) glow until winter came along and killed the fungus. As a result, the attack had to be put off until spring, when *Turtle*'s instruments came back to life. Fox fire could only be obtained from decaying wood: Bushnell and his brother sat out the winter of 1775 in their highly secret submarine base (their barn) and anxiously watched the logs rot. From the earliest days, submarine navigation could be a very strange business indeed.

Turtle's armament consisted of one of Bushnell's clockwork mines, which was to be attached to the bottom of the target vessel:

the pilot was to bore into the bottom of the enemy's hull with an auger protruding from the top of the *Turtle*, attach the mine and retreat.

Bushnell was encouraged to develop the *Turtle* by no less a person than Benjamin Franklin, whose powers of scientific insight seem to have deserted him in his enthusiasm for the destruction of the British fleet, then blockading New York. In the event, 'Black Dick' Howe's ship was saved, according to Ezra Lee, *Turtle*'s pilot, by the fact that her hull was sheathed with copper, and thus impervious to the auger.

Alas, the facts suggest otherwise. *Eagle*'s hull, as it happens, was *not* copper-sheathed. In any case, it would have been quite impossible for Lee to gain a purchase with his auger, assuming that the *Turtle* was at neutral buoyancy or anything near it, and that Newton's law of action and reaction was not suspended for the occasion: the more he pushed, the more he would be pushed away. He could have thumped the *Turtle*, and thus the auger, against the side of the *Eagle*, but this would have been felt on board the target: *Eagle*'s log lists nothing amiss on the relevant evening.

It is far more likely that he never reached the ship at all. Although *Turtle* was provided with a schnorkel-like tube for taking in air while submerged, carbon dioxide would soon have built up in the tiny hull. Before long, Lee would scarcely have known what day it was, or (more urgently) which way was 'up'. But he had to tell Mr Franklin and General Washington *something*.

With his Pneumatophore, of course, Garrett felt he had at least solved the problem of carbon dioxide. The Pneumatophore, or at least its active constituent, was itself an echo of one of the earliest submariners. Cornelius van Drebbel, a Dutch physician, tested a submersible rowing-boat in the Thames in 1620 (supposedly, for the romantically-inclined, with James I as passenger – a likely story), keeping the air pure by the use of a 'chemical liquor'. This was a 'liquid that would speedily restore to the troubled air such a proportion of vital parts as would make it again for a good while fit for respiration'. It has long been usual to dismiss this statement as so much sixteenth-century wind, but, as Garrett must have realised, there may in fact have been something in it.

The Abbé de Hautefeuille, in his 1680 pamphlet on underwater respiration (yet another subaqueous cleric, by the way), rather unkindly suggested that van Drebbel used a system of pipes communicating with the surface to supply air – a schnorkel, in fact.

However, van Drebbel was supported in the most glowing terms by Robert Boyle (of Law fame), who might have been expected to notice such a device: add to this the fact that caustic potash, the Pneumatophore's 'scrubber' component, is water-soluble, and van Drebbel's 'chemical liquor' enters the realms of the possible. It would not be the first time that a scientific insight was forgotten, to be rediscovered later, particularly in maritime matters. For example, lemons were in use to ward off scurvy in the early middle ages, but Lieutenant Bligh had virtually to ram them down the crew of the *Bounty* in 1789. Science has often been ill received at sea.

It was the American Civil War, however, that finally brought the submersible boat into serious consideration as a weapon of war. The Confederacy, confronted with a vastly stronger Union Navy, was, perforce, ready to try just about anything to break the Union blockade of Southern ports, which was all too successful in strangling the cotton trade. The Manchester newspapers had taken a deep interest in the naval situation: after all, the interests of Cottonopolis were at stake. Richard Cobden, MP for nearby Stockport, took a fiercely pro-Confederacy stand on the slightly abstract grounds that the South supported free trade. As Cobden was one of Dr Garrett's many political heroes and acquaintances, the Garretts supported him, leading to understandable friction with anti-slavery parishioners and other clergy. Dr Garrett was nothing if not consistent; he had railed at the wicked when they burnt Cobden in effigy, and blamed them for Cobden's sudden death from bronchitis in 1865.

The first underwater products of the Union's economic strangulation of the South were the Confederate Navy's so-called *Davids*. These were 40-foot-long steam-powered semi-submersibles with cigar-shaped hulls, ballasted down so as to run awash: only the vessel's funnel and observation cupola showed above the water. An unusually keen Northern eye, watching a *David* approaching, would also have seen an eighteen-foot spar protruding from the boat's low bow: at the end of the spar was the prototype spar torpedo, at this stage simply a keg of gunpowder detonated by pulling on a lanyard. One of these unpromising vessels almost managed to despatch the Union monitor *New Ironsides*, causing in the process the first known casualty of a submarine attack – *New Ironsides'* ensign, Lieutenant Charles Howard, picked off by a lucky rifle shot from the *David*. Three of the *David*'s crew of five survived.

Although the *Davids* were hardly a great military success in themselves, the possibilities of the semi-submersible (or at least very low-freeboard) boat were subsequently investigated by other navies: the Russian torpedo-boats of the 1877 Turkish war had similar cigar-shaped hulls skulking behind the now all-electric spar torpedo. Even the British gave the idea a try, building two cigar-hulled gunboats, *Abyssinia* and *Magdala*, for the defence of Bombay Harbour.

The great submarine 'success' (with severe reservations) of the Civil War, however, was the attack on USS *Housatonic* by the gallant but almost ludicrously suicidal Confederate submersible *H.L. Hunley* – the first sinking to be achieved by a submarine. Lieutenant Horace Hunley had tried his hand at two earlier submarines, but had had to scuttle the first before the advancing Union fleet and had (ominously) lost the other under tow in Mobile Bay. His third attempt, bearing his own name, was an old boiler, widened with extra plating at top and bottom, powered by eight extraordinarily brave men turning a crank connected directly to the propeller. Powering apart, she further differed from the *Davids* in being fully submersible, if only for very brief 'dipchick' movements beneath the surface: the final attack run would be made awash, with only the two tiny conning towers at either end of the boat protruding above the surface. The weapons system consisted – yet again, and incredibly – of a spar torpedo. An attempt to use a towed torpedo was abandoned when it was found that the mine was prone to being swept back to Mother in anything other than a flat calm – as if life in the submarine were not dangerous enough already.

The tale of the trials of the *Hunley* is one of the classic horror-stories of early submarines: most of three entire crews (including Hunley himself) perished in an appalling series of accidents, at least one caused by water slopping down an open hatch when the boat was running awash. Some years later, Garrett would come close to re-enacting this particular catastrophe in the Sea of Marmara: he was never one to learn from mistakes (his own or anyone else's) – an unfortunate character trait in an inventor.

Hunley's moment of glory was also her last: when the torpedo exploded, spelling death for the *Housatonic*, the little boiler became stuck in the hole made by her own weapon and went down with her prey. This blackest of farces must have deterred many from further work on submarines, but the quest for mastery of the depths continued.

In 1872, Oliver Halstead, working from a design previously offered to and rejected by the French Government in 1866, built his

Intelligent Whale, which turned out to be similar to the *Hunley* in two significant ways: firstly, she was powered by a team of heroes turning a crank; secondly, the *Whale* munched her way through thirty-six crewmen in accidents before being hauled ashore to bask in an obscure corner of Brooklyn Navy Yard.

This, then, was the sombre substance of Garrett's background reading in the latter half of 1877. The only British exemplar to turn to (and Garrett could *not* turn to it, as it had been kept a close secret in the noble cause of worrying the Russians) had briefly seen the light in 1856. Wilhelm Bauer, the German submarine experimenter (and first submarine escaper when one experiment went awry) had been gently leaned on by John Garrett's friend the Prince Consort, in the hope of recruiting his help in the prosecution of the Crimean War. In what seems little less than a nautical brainstorm, John Scott Russell, father and high priest of Victorian naval architecture, had been induced to produce a submersible Frankenstein's monster, combining the borrowed ideas of a now justifiably paranoid Bauer with a conventional diving-bell, adding for good measure a hefty dash of *Turtle*. The resulting two-man, manually-cranked freak, although the first submersible to evacuate its ballast with compressed air, was an almost worthless failure that did much to poison Royal Navy thinking against submarines.

At this stage, Garrett was convinced that the key problem in submarine navigation was the shortage of air in a submerged boat. While he had his own solution to this problem, it was nothing like as great a stumbling-block as he imagined: one of *Hunley*'s crews had, after all, managed to sit on the bottom for two and a half hours in comparative comfort, without the aid of artificial atmospheric enhancement. If the hull of the boat was large enough, atmospheric survivability was surprisingly lengthy, as Garrett's later boats would show.

Garrett's key insight was into the problem of underwater propulsion: he would design the first submarine to be *mechanically* propelled below the surface. His first effort, however, was nothing like as ambitious as this.

On 8 May 1878, Garrett patented a 'Submarine Boat for Placing Torpedoes, &c', the patent being sealed on 29 October. This was a design for a modest little craft:

I generally construct the vessel of small dimensions, a handy size being about 14 feet long (when arranged to contain only one man), so as to be easily lifted by the davits of an ironclad or other ship, or from a pier or other structure.[1]

The Russian mother-ship arrangement had obviously made an impression.

The shape of the boat (described by Garrett as 'elliptical or somewhat resembling the shape of an egg') is interesting. One of the few successful features of Halstead's *Intelligent Whale* had been her hull-form, a full, rounded fish shape that was as different from *Hunley*'s cylinder as it was from the 'cigar' that would dominate early submarines, very much to their detriment. (This was how everybody thought a submarine should look, at least partly a result of the fact that Jules Verne's *Nautilus* was widely illustrated as a metallic cigar in the early editions of *Twenty Thousand Leagues Under the Sea*, first published in 1870). Though Garrett's little craft was never going to achieve speeds, depths or very much else that would benefit from such a hull, it is pleasing to see him starting out with the right idea, however much he apostasised later in his career.

At this stage – before the boat was built – Garrett intended to power the vessel with 'a small gas or vapour engine', exhausting the resultant gases into the water through a non-return valve – precisely the method that Holland would adopt in his *Fenian Ram*. However, back-pressure through the exhaust pipe would certainly have stopped the engine at depths below about 15 feet, as Holland would discover five years later. Garrett seems to have anticipated this (he had in fact dabbled briefly in petrol engines during his period at the Kensington Museum), and never returned to the internal combustion engine in his submarines. He never actually lost interest in this type of engine as such; his last marketed invention, months before his death, was an internal combustion motor steam-engine hybrid.

The boat was submerged by flooding ballast tanks in the bottom of the boat until near-negative buoyancy was reached and the boat was awash. Actual submergence was achieved by means of a simple enough contraption: a piston, connecting directly to sea, allowed in sufficient water to overcome the boat's remaining buoyancy, and down she went. To ascend, the pilot had only to push the piston back, expelling the water, and the boat would rise to her awash condition. The remaining water ballast could then be shed using a hand pump. The same pump was connected to a four-way cock, for distributing the water around the ballast tanks to regulate underwater trim. Varying the boat's weight with the piston was, to say the least, nothing new – this technique appears in Father Fournier's 1634 offering – but Garrett rather cheekily claims it for his own in the patent.

The experimental 'egg' was Garrett's one and only attempt at dealing with negative and neutral buoyancy. With the exception of *Resurgam*, which had a naturally very low water-line, all of his later submarines were ballasted down to an awash state and then driven under the surface mechanically, keeping a reserve of buoyancy to bring the boat back to the surface if an emergency arose. Obviously, Garrett was converted to this system, which he had earlier seen but rejected in the *Davids* and the *Hunley*, by unfortunate experiences in testing the 'egg'.

The boat was to be fitted with a Pneumatophore, but Garrett, following the example of Whitehead's Secret, kept his own counsel on this, settling for the rather gnomic 'I arrange apparatus or chemicals for purifying the air ...'.[2] Those benighted souls without the benefit of the Pneumatophore, however, could be supplied with oxygen, or 'I might supply air by pumps and pipes from a distance, as with divers'.[3]

This system would hardly combine well with the *avant-garde* military mission for which the submarine was ostensibly intended. Garrett was forthright in describing the intended function of his boat: 'I purpose employing these boats to go before ironclads searching for torpedoes, and when found, cutting the wires connecting them to the shore, or otherwise destroying them ...'[4] A submersible minesweeper, in fact.

He then suggests underwater mine-laying and limpet-attachment (dangerous but not impossible), before floating off into a regrettable flight of fantasy that mars an otherwise sane document: 'These boats could also be used for laying or placing torpedoes in various situations, or be used to cut through vessels' moorings, or a number of them could tow a vessel out of a roadstead by connecting powerful vessels to the keel or other part, first taking the precaution (if a steam vessel) to disable the propeller and rudder'.[5] One can only imagine the messy results if Rozhdestvensky and his colleagues had attempted this.

Garrett ends on a note more obviously drawn from the Russian adventures: 'The propellers of these boats should be protected by guards to preclude the possibility of chains or other obstructions fouling them.'[6]

The placing of 'torpedoes' (mines in this case) was to be achieved via arm-length greased leather gauntlets emerging from holes in the sides of the conning-tower. While this is a workable arrangement so far as it goes, close inspection of Garrett's drawing (and, indeed, the actual building of the boat) reveals that the petrol engine has in fact been superseded by muscle-power, to be applied via a crank and a flywheel. From this point of view, the boat is surprisingly reminiscent of the *Turtle* of a hundred years earlier, rather than any of the more recent craft.

Command of Garrett's 'egg' was to be an energetic job. The pilot would be expected to pump the ballast, manipulate the piston, turn the crank and grope about through the gauntlets dutifully placing mines, presumably while the enemy was dropping unfriendly devices into the water to add interest to the proceedings. One of the multi-armed gods of a Hindu priest might have been better suited to the task than a conventionally-limbed curate, but Garrett seems to have managed commendably in the trials.

Before anything was built, Garrett tried offering his design to the Admiralty as a package with the Pneumatophore, but was greeted with indifference. Not wholly unreasonably, they wanted to see a working model – at least – before taking much interest, let alone buying anything.

The Navy's procurement of new weapons and equipment in the 1870s was a ramshackle, disorganised affair, relying largely on the readiness of inventors to push their ideas; there was barely a semblance of Government-inspired defence research. If a potential enemy was seen to be in possession of something dangerous, steps would be taken to ensure that Britain caught up, as had happened when France built the *Gloire*, which resulted in the building of the first true ironclad, HMS *Warrior*. This amounted to progress through periodic panic. There was, however, very little that could be termed a weapons development policy. Admiral Fisher's Board of Invention and Research, founded as late as 1915, was the first attempt to deal with this state of affairs, but foundered due to internal bickering; then, as in the 1870s, the Navy seemed incapable of running a decent bureaucracy.

This rather stumbling set-up did in fact have the virtue of slowing down the arms race to some extent; the dangerous phenomenon of weapons that were solutions in search of problems coming to distort tactical or even strategic policy (like the ground-launched cruise missile in our own time) was virtually impossible when novelty itself was too much trouble to administer. On the other hand, capriciousness could play an exaggerated role: it is entirely typical of what passed for policy in this period that the Navy had originally been frightened into taking Whiteheads seriously by the 'Battle of Dorking', an engagement entirely restricted to the pages of *Blackwood's Magazine* in 1871, raising the spectre of (French) torpedoes wiping out the fleet.

Long before the Government attempted to set up a structure for dealing with new inventions, the ghost of a rational arrangement could be seen in the appearance of agents specialising in naval intentions, who would cultivate the relevant officers and civil servants on behalf of their clients, which at least fitfully concentrated minds on new developments from time to time. These men tended to be ex-patent agents, rather than inventors or ex-officers; they soon became a powerful breed of entrepreneur in their own right, essential for the inventor who was to succeed. While this increased the flow of ideas into the Admiralty, it left the small inventor, who at this stage included Garrett, out in the cold.

These were in any case bad times for submarines at the Admiralty. The *Intelligent Whale* had been discreetly spied upon in New York (between disasters) by the British Naval Attaché, Rear Admiral Inglefield: nobody seems to have been particularly impressed by his findings. Nor had there been any obvious developments to make the Navy sit up and listen now. While Garrett's design was sound enough so far as it went, it looked as though it was at best a sketch for a larger vessel – as, indeed, it was.

Consultations with the lodgers at the rectory led Garrett to the offices of J.T. Cochran, the new proprietor of the Britannia Iron Works in Birkenhead, who was just starting out on what would be a notably successful shipbuilding career. Cochran perused the drawings, and, seeing at least the possibility of Admiralty orders in the Navy's vague hints to Garrett about working models and prototypes, agreed to build the boat at cost.

The agreement with Cochran was, of course, a breakthrough for Garrett, but, in his parlous financial state, even the funding for the 'egg' was monstrously difficult. Garrett was, coincidentally, in particular favour with his wife's family at this time: on 23 May, Jane had given birth to their second child – a son, John William. The 'egg' may well have been a rather unusual present to the proud father, for Cochran did indeed build her in the July of 1878. Early in August, the 4½-ton iron boat was lowered into the Great

(Right) The young submariner, about the time of *Resurgam.*

(Below) The Garrett's church: Christ Church, Moss side.

The maritime curate and his wife (right) with brother Henry and wife (left): Georgina and John Garrett, the inventor's children, between them. Taken about the time of Garrett's departure for Sweden, 1882.

Float at Birkenhead, and trials began.

Garrett was careful to see that his new vessel was noticed by the press:

> The inventor, the Reverend G.W. Garrett of Manchester, remained under water for some hours and tested the efficiency of his invention for purifying the human breath ... and also the correctness of his calculation for floating the vessel at such a depth in the water as he might desire.[7]

He was rather less anxious to reveal the problems that the trials of his little boat revealed. Ship-hull hydrostatics was still at a very adumbral stage in 1878; knowledge of submarine hydrostatics, for want of experimental data, was little short of primeval. Garrett, whether he knew it or not, was at one of the least fashionable and most dangerous frontiers of science. It is much to be regretted that his own need for commercial secrecy about the performance of all his submarines prevented him from writing frankly on his findings. The industrial competition between the early submariners often only resulted in them repeating each other's mistakes, to the disadvantage of all concerned, as is still the case in companies trying to gain an edge in basic technical research. The lack of a coherent Admiralty policy hardly helped.

At the moment a submarine dips below the surface of the water, her centre of buoyancy moves, instantaneously, from the centre of the immersed section of the hull when afloat to the actual centre point of the hull, but her centre of gravity is fixed: this results in a sudden change in fore-and-aft trim, requiring, in a boat like Garrett's 'egg', prompt and efficient re-ballasting to prevent a sudden and potentially terminal crash to the bottom. The free surfaces in the 'egg''s ballast tanks can only have made things worse.

For all Garrett's trumpetings about the boat's ease of underwater manipulation, he must have decided early on that the ballast-and-piston system was not the way to proceed if he intended to stay alive long enough to build a bigger boat. This, if any one error is to be singled out, was the major mistake of his submarining career: others, notably Holland, would bite the bullet of neutral buoyancy – maintaining equilibrium between floating and sinking – while Garrett struggled with increasingly baroque methods of avoiding the problem.

The search for backers was now on: possible financial supporters were invited to watch the performance of the boat. This was not always without incident. Garrett's younger brother Thomas, then sixteen, joined him at the trials, acting as what seems suspiciously like a fairground barker while Garrett did his stuff in the Float. Occasionally, however, Thomas had more urgent work to do.

> I well remember the trial of the thing at Birkenhead. By accident or design [!] one of the rubber sleeves had been slit, and when my brother unscrewed the inside cap there was an inrush of water. He had to pump out his water ballast for dear life in order to rise to the surface, and I remember that in my excitement, as he got nearer the surface, I fished him up with a boathook. However, the damage was repaired, and the idea so impressed certain gentleman who saw it that financial backing to the extent of some thousands of pounds was obtained for a larger venture.[8]

The 'larger venture' was the world's first submarine construction company. The Garrett Submarine Navigation and Pneumatophore Company, Limited, was incorporated in September 1878, with a capital of £10,000. The board consisted of Edward Gabriel, an insurance agent, William Sadler, an accountant, Henry Clemesha, a financial agent, John Leyland, an actuary, and E.F. Monlin, a solicitor. The chairman of the company was Garrett's father, who held two thousand £1 shares, the money coming mostly from the mortgage of two plots of land earlier the same year.

Dr Garrett, while not actually bankrupt (yet), was financially a very dubious proposition at best, but he still held a position of considerable respect within Manchester society on the strength of his political and ecclesiastical prominence, which made his chairmanship of the company less surprising in his prestige-conscious age than it would be in ours. He could still call upon friends in high places.

The prospectus of the Submarine Navigation Company produces one of Dr Garrett's celebrities with irresistible panache. Rightly suspecting that some might be disturbed at the spectacle of clergymen going into the arms business, Dr Garrett extracted from Norman MacLeod, Queen Victoria's private chaplain, what would now be called a plug, offered by way of a benediction on the front page of the prospectus:

> As to the inventions being for the purpose of murdering people – that is all nonsense. Every contribution made by Science to improve instruments of war makes war shorter, and, in the end, less terrible to human life and to human progress.[9]

The company's aims were

> to work certain inventions, consisting of a breathing apparatus,
> submarine torpedo boat, diving dress and pneumatophore granted by
> Letters Patent No. 1,838 to George William Garrett for improvements
> in apparatus connected with submarine navigation.[10]

The firm's offices were set up at 56 Deansgate, agreeably close to
the cathedral.

George Garrett was not on the board of the company and held no
shares: he was its sole employee, the earnings from his inventions
threading back, of course, into the Christ Church financial
labyrinth. The Garretts, father and son, moved in a mysterious
way: strictly (and strangely) speaking, the Garrett of the
company's title was George's father.

It might be thought that combining a curacy with a career in
marine engineering would have absorbed most of Garrett's time,
but he was forced to take on a third job for most of 1879. He did,
after all, have his own family to support, as well as holes to plug in
his father's financial dyke. He became second master at Talbot
House School, Old Trafford, a position not unlike the one he had
held at Seighford after leaving school. This became a major
commitment; Reverend Heathley, the headmaster, became
seriously ill. Nearly twenty years later, when Garrett was a
pathetic, broken man in desperate need of work, Mr Heathley
testified to Garrett having worked staggering hours filling in for him
at the school, fulfilling his parish duties and getting his submarine
built. Through all of this, Garrett, an 'anxious, conscientious' man,
earned an understandable degree of affection and respect that he
rarely encountered elsewhere, though it must be admitted that Mr
Heathley rather exaggerates Garrett's parochial diligence. Heathley was one of the very few people who stood by Garrett when his
star fell.

With the company set up and rolling, negotiations began
immediately, both with Cochran for the construction of a full-size
submarine and with the Admiralty, the hoped-for future customer.
The all-important middle-man was another unlikely combination
of the military and the ecclesiastical: Hugh Birley, Dr Garrett's
colleague on the Manchester Schools Board.

Dr Garrett had lost much of his Metropolitan clout with the
death of the Prince Consort and the fallout from the libel action.
Birley was therefore the Submarine Navigation Company's vital

bridge to the London defence establishment. Although best known for his political and ecclesiastical activities in Manchester (he was a close friend of the bishop and an authority on Church history), Birley came from one of the North's foremost military families, and had plentiful connections in the military and the Government. Despite Dr Garrett's often bizarre behaviour on the Schools Board (walk-outs, diatribes and worse), Birley formed a close association with the rector that spilled over into industrial co-operation when the Submarine Navigation Company came into being. Birley, who knew the First Lord and the Secretary of the Admiralty socially, agreed to act for the company in dealings with the Admiralty. By the time work actually began on the construction of the new boat, discussions were well in hand.

Meanwhile, life went on at Christ Church as normally as it ever did. Garrett's health, however, was showing signs of deterioration. Also, as news of his extra-ecclesiastical activities reached the parishioners, his popularity, such as it was, began to slide. A fascinating glimpse of life in the parish is given by a letter from Mrs Royle, a Moss Side doctor's wife, to her daughter:

15 December 1878

Your Father and Charlie have just come in from church. George Garrett overtook them. Charlie thought him looking very thin and ill and had a poor look. The boat that he has been building or having built is likely to turn out well, but the Admiralty are giving him great trouble in their way of asking for plans and trying to get as much information as they can about the breathing apparatus, which of course he won't give, and your father told him tonight not to do so. I believe the gentleman who has been finding the money for him to carry on the work is already paying him £400 a year, with the promise of an increase when the experiments are complete. I sincerely wish him every success, although as you know he is no favourite of ours. We never see anything of him but in church, and that only once or twice a month.[11]

No boat was actually under construction at the time in question; Garrett's public relations would always contain an element of over-selling. Mrs Royle's letter, however, is interesting from many points of view.

Garrett's health was never robust. He suffered all his life from recurring lung trouble, which can only have been exacerbated by his Pneumatophore experiments and subsequent underwater adventures. The fumes from caustic potash, the active ingredient of the Pneumatophore, are emphatically not to be recommended over long periods: also, like the Charioteer's breathing apparatus that it foreshadowed, the Pneumatophore's scrubber would have produced a lethal chlorine soufflé on contact with seawater. Garrett was certainly chemist enough to have predicted this; whether he (or anybody else) was quite certain of what this sort of work might do to him is a different matter – to some extent, this is still the case, as undersea respiration systems develop to achieve ever greater depths. It is probable, however, that his experiments did him no physical good whatever: the long-term effects of tinkering with his own lungs one way and another must have contributed significantly to his early death from pulmonary disease.

Mrs Royle's letter also gives a hint ('he is no favourite of ours') of the curate's dubious popularity in the parish. The Garretts were, to say the very least, an eccentric family. Dr Garrett's fitfully convincing amalgam of high principle, bombast, self-promotion and (sometimes) outright fraud was reflected to an unfortunate extent in George: while the manic glare and even the curled lip of his photographs may be a result of illness and the difficulties of early photography, it has to be said that, just occasionally, a very bizarre personality indeed peeps through the surviving documents. While, mercifully, he does not seem to have inherited his mother's epilepsy, Garrett, even at his calmest, seems to have been an unusually quirky character. Fred Jane (he of the *Fighting Ships*, and another clergyman's son) once described Garrett as 'an enthusiastic and somewhat excitable inventor', which, in the stilted journalistic dialect of the period, was half-way to describing him as a maniac.

There is an unavoidable suspicion that the Garretts were subject to a hereditary mental condition. At least three of George's brothers (Oliver, Henry and William) became drinkers on a frightening scale, in Henry's case sufficiently in public to jeopardise his position on the Board of Guardians. George at least avoided that particular vice, doubtless helped by the social rigours that ruled a clergyman. Premature senility and (in one case) clinical incarceration bedevilled the subsequent generation. It is striking that the family's problems in this regard stop dead in the next generation, when the habit or necessity of marrying within a small community (the small-town rural Ascendancy) had ceased to affect the family. While the Ascendancy was hardly an isolated community in the Amish sense, blood ties between families were strong, especially in rural areas, giving a dangerous predisposition to congenital chorea and other inherited problems – extra toes and the like were once common in the more remote outposts of Protestant Southern Ireland, which would definitely include the Garrett family stronghold of Ballymote. There was certainly a strong suspicion within the later American branches of the family that some taint had been bred out; it is possible that George's mother suffered from the florid version of a condition which only touched him.

On a less sinister note, Garrett was taken for an Irishman by at least some of Cochran's boilermakers. His family, wife and recent education were Irish; he had been surrounded by Irish people most of his life. It is quite possible that he had at least a faint Irish accent: there are certainly occasional dim flickers of Irish English in his letters.

Personalities aside, open mutiny was visible in the congregation at Christ Church from the earliest days of the Submarine Navigation Company. The furious arguments over Dr Garrett's support of the Confederacy and the festering sore of the libel case made another eruption inevitable when such an obvious *casus belli* appeared. Apart from the many who doubted the Christian propriety of a clergyman building engines of war, Dr Garrett's enemies could hardly be expected to forego such an opportunity for criticism. As usual, however, they would await the very worst moment before actually attacking.

The identity of the gentleman paying Garrett the very generous £400 per annum is of great interest, offering a glimpse of an *eminence grise* behind the whole Garrett enterprise at the very earliest stage of his career. The money did not come from the company.

While planning the full-size submarine, Garrett made several trips to Portsmouth to consult with naval officials under the aegis of Hugh Birley, who seems to have introduced him to another of his acquaintances, the Swedish arms tycoon Thorsten Nordenfelt, Garrett's future partner.

The primary function of Garrett's own company (internal Garrett financial wizardry apart) was to raise funds for the building of the full-size submarine, on the model of the 'egg'. If this were successful, Garrett would be looking for an outlet to the wider world of the defence industry: Thorsten Nordenfelt, influenced by his faithful submarine buff Zaharoff, was precisely such an outlet. There was no public, overt agreement between Garrett and

Nordenfelt at this stage, but they certainly met in London early in 1879: the link between them – Birley – played an important role throughout the building and trials of the new boat.

No records survive to establish whether Garrett followed his father into Freemasonry, but it is very likely that he did so. Nordenfelt certainly was a Mason, however; it is not impossible that Masonic influence brought them together in the way that it had often helped Dr Garrett. There would certainly be nothing particularly sinister in them meeting in this way, especially if one compares Nordenfelt with Holland's backers. Given this possible link, and the certain link via Birley, Nordenfelt emerges as the most likely face behind the £400 mask.

Early in the planning for the new boat, Garrett made the crucial decision to power the submarine using an orthodox marine steam plant, linked to a highly specialised, supposedly smokeless boiler arrangement. This was by no means the wildly eccentric concept that it may first appear: Garrett's idea seems bizarre now, but was at the time a convincing solution to the pressing problem of underwater powering and power storage.

Man-power, despite or (more realistically) because of its 'success' in the *Turtle, Hunley* and *Intelligent Whale*, was a dead end if speed, manoeuvrability and endurance were ever to be achieved below the surface. But, as things stood in 1878, the alternatives were not promising.

When the 'egg' came to be built, Garrett, on entirely sound technical grounds, had considered and rejected the use of an internal combustion engine. In this early electrical age, electrical propulsion – ultimately the universally-adopted means of underwater propulsion – might have seemed a worthwhile option. After all, Captain Nemo had been equipped with an all-electric submarine as early as 1870. Not everybody, however, had access to Jules Verne's technological resources, which became somewhat elusive outside his admittedly farsighted pages.

The first electric motors had been constructed in the 1830s, taking to the water for the first time in 1834, when Jacobi demonstrated his electric boat, fuming electric cells and all, in the Neva at St Petersburg. Taking the same cells below the surface in a sealed hull was out of the question.

Planté more or less tripped over the lead-acid cell (as opposed to inventing it, not that he laboured the distinction) in the mid-1860s, but in 1879 the development of the lead-acid storage cell was at too primitive a stage for electricity to be a realistic choice for submarine propulsion.

Faure's 1881 improvements to Planté's cell would result in a sudden profusion of electrically-powered submarines, but by then Garrett had more or less proved his steam concept and, for better or worse (for better *and* worse) was committed to it.

The obvious difficulty in using steam underwater lay in producing and storing sufficient heat and steam without the attendant smoke and fumes resulting from the use of an ordinary boiler. In the face of there being, in 1879, no credible mechanical alternative to steam, Garrett turned to the steam equivalent of the storage battery – the Lamm fireless steam generator, patented in 1872.

Eugene Lamm's system, a product of the nineteenth century's rapidly improving boiler-making and insulation techniques, was based upon the simple idea of superheating water in a boiler until a temperature was reached corresponding to some 200 pounds pressure (Garrett's necessarily smaller boiler managed 150): at this point the furnace was extinguished. The water was then forced into reservoir tanks, taking its surplus heat with it. Assuming good insulation in the reservoir, when the throttle valve was opened, roughly 15% of the water would flash to steam at a pressure of about 100 pounds per square inch, capable of driving a conventional steam engine. This system was originally devised for the San Francisco streetcars, in which it was successful for many years. Because of its obvious advantages from the point of view of preventing smoke-pollution, it was also used on the Central Line of the London Underground, and in the Royal Dockyard, where the system's avoidance of naked flames and sparks made it a sensible measure in the presence of explosives.

As Garrett saw it, the fact that the furnace was extinguished relatively early in the procedure made it suitable for propelling a submarine, assuming adequate heat insulation and that the combustion products of the boiler could be reliably sealed in when the furnace was shut down. Excessive faith in boiler seals and lagging apart, it is, objectively, difficult to fault his logic. Steam, albeit with a rather exotic boiler, is, after all, the means of propelling modern nuclear submarines – as was pointed out by Garrett's then ageing son John at the launch of the second nuclear submarine, USS *Seawolf*, in 1955.

In 1879, the problems facing Garrett were limitations in the available technology – furnace seals, thermal insulation and the complex business of shutting off the whole complex from the outside world before diving. Lamm's system was only 'smokeless' relative to the muck-belching boilers that it replaced on the Underground; it turned out to be somewhat less so when one was sharing a submarine with it. To Garrett, it looked like the answer – on paper. But, like a bridegroom with bad feet, unexpected fumes rather spoilt the performance.

By March 1879, Garrett's new, full-size design was almost complete. On 31 March, Garrett wrote to Cochran:

> 82, Chorlton Road,
> Hulme,
> Manchester
>
> Dear Sir,
>
> I leave for Portsmouth this afternoon and if you desire to communicate with me during this week, please address me c/o A.J. Durston, HM Dockyard, Portsmouth. I send with this a sketch of the general outline that I propose for the boat and also a short description of the various parts.
>
> You will observe that the boat, as sketched by me, is forty feet long and seven feet in diameter, with a twenty-foot cylinder, and two ten-foot points. I wish that you will make your calculations upon this scale, as I am satisfied that these proportions are the best for my purpose. I think you will see in the sketch and description, a mention of all the parts that you would have to make, but there would be the fitting up of my apparatus, gauges, etc etc, which must come after the bulk estimate.
>
> I hope you will put as low a price as you can feel upon the bulk estimate, as you know there will be many expenses over and above the bulk estimate and I do not want the immediate price to be such as will frighten and perhaps stop the proper carrying out of my plans. I will call upon you on Monday next and have a chat with you as to the result of your week's consideration before we open the matter of cost to other people. It is almost as necessary for yourself as for me that a good article should be produced.
>
> Yours very faithfully,
>
> George W. Garrett[12]

It is in the specifications for the new boat, technically far removed from the 'egg', that the 26-year-old curate shows that his technical education was as sound as anyone's. While Garrett's description of the 'egg' had shown signs of inexperience that might almost be taken for crankdom (such as fleets of 4½-ton iron eggs helping to tow away illegally parked ironclads), the instructions to Cochran show that he had learnt quickly and knew precisely what he wanted. The workers in Cochran's yard, who disagreed only between those who took him for an Irishman (the boilermakers) and those who opted for 'a Southerner' (the clerks), would soon learn to take him seriously:

> The boiler should be 45″ in diameter and 144″ long, and capable of standing, with perfect safety, a pressure of 130 pounds per square inch.
>
> The fire grate should be as small as possible for sufficiently working a six horse-power engine (as, if it were required to get up steam quickly, a stronger blast would effectively do so, even on a small grate).
>
> The furnace should be of such construction that although a pressure was kept up inside, yet it should be possible to supply fuel.
>
> The engine should be situated as near the screw as possible and should be such as would do six horse-power work at a pressure of from 30 to 40 pounds per square inch on the piston. A blower should be situated as near the engine as possible and might possibly be worked by a band round the fly-wheel, which could be stripped off if desired. The conning tower should be three feet high and should be two feet broad by three feet long. It should have a manhole in the top which could be fastened from the inside. The manhole should be 16″ in diameter and round. There should be four lookouts at each of the four cardinal points and a dead light in the top. There should be one pair of sleeves on each side.
>
> The rudders are four. Two situated about the stern of the boat, as near the screw as possible, which direct the boat either to port or starboard. Two large balance rudders at the centre of the boat, which would raise or lower the level at which the boat would float within certain limits.
>
> In addition to the above, there remains a reservoir for compressed gas, which must stand the pressure of 1000 pounds, which can be got from Birmingham in the shape of steel tubes which could conveniently be stowed in the boat. These I would provide myself, as also the float, which has for its object the minute and rigid variation of the specific gravity of the boat.[13]

The 'float' (i.e. ballast piston) and the sleeves were remnants from the 'egg' that would be dropped before the boat was completed.

Once Garrett had deposited this more-or-less final specification with Cochran, matters moved with a swiftness that modern commerce could scarcely match. Garrett returned from Portsmouth and visited the Britannia Iron Works on 7 April: at this meeting,

Cochran produced an estimate totalling £1,357, which Garrett took back to Manchester for consultations with the Submarine Navigation Company.

The board of the company clearly felt that Cochran could be persuaded to drop his price, as Garrett returned to Birkenhead with Birley for another bargaining session with Cochran on 10 April. Although they emphasised the benefits that success with the submarine might bring to Cochran's company, and offered an exclusive right to the manufacture of subsequent Garrett submarines if he could be persuaded to lower his price for the prototype, the final price was in fact slightly higher.

On 11 April, Britain's first submarine construction contract was despatched to the rectory:

Dear Mr Garrett,

Referring to our interview with Mr Birley and yourself of yesterday. We have now pleasure in submitting for your approval our tenders for constructing the Garrett Submarine Torpedo Boat, which is detailed as completely as possible, including everything which you have communicated to us verbally and in writing, and also other details which our knowledge of your requirements show to be necessary.

We undertake on our part to construct a boat in a complete manner, according to the true intent and meaning of the specifications, whether enumerated there or not. Also that the whole of the materials will be the best and most suitable for the respective requirement, free from flaw and defect and that the whole will be fitted and finished in the highest class and style of workmanship. The whole of the design we also undertake to perfect and complete in so far as lies in our power and in conjunction with your view or requirements. But if after the construction of any portion it should be found on trial unsuitable for the purpose (provided the failure is not due to defective material or workmanship) and a new design is required, our tenders do not provide for such new design or construction, which should be the subject of fresh agreement. In addition, the trials and tests enumerated in tender we undertake to try by steam in our premises, the whole of the machinery and fitments, in order to prove that it is efficient and satisfactory in every respect.

We also guarantee that the propelling machinery will, when in the water, do its work in an efficient and satisfactory manner. We also undertake to complete the several parts in 12 weeks from date of order and in consideration of our tenders, as follows, being accepted:

Hull etc.	£520
Side Rudders	25
Boiler etc	355

Automatic Valve	50
Propelling Machinery	348
Blower etc	72
Hand Pump	27

TOTAL SUM £1,397

Payable in twelve equal instalments, weekly. The work generally being pushed forward by us vigorously. In the dereliction of which payment may be stopped and in the event of the instalments failing to be remitted regularly, the work may be stopped.

In addition to the foregoing, the additional items of putting the boat into the water, ballasting and assistance in your preliminary experiments, we will undertake again tenders for [the work] at a schedule of rates as may be eventually agreed upon, which after will be rendered as payable weekly under the same conditions as the rest of the work.

In conclusion, we remark that we will do everything in our power to assist you, to carry out your plans and inventions, having based our estimate at as low a cost as we reasonably can, on the understanding that in the event of success following our joint effort, we are to have the sole right of manufacture for a term of years to compensate for the great amount of personal time and attention which such an undertaking requires.[14]

Garrett's rather rough drawings, which included a sketch of the boat's boiler and engine quite literally on the back of an envelope, were handed over to Cochran's chief draughtsman, Jack Aitkin, who executed the working drawings from which the boat was to be constructed. Mr Hodgson, the firm's foreman boilermaker and shipwright, was to superintend the building of the vessel.

Back at Chorlton Road, Garrett's wife joined in her husband's productive fervour; their third child, Jane, was born on 5 October. By then, however, Garrett was an absentee father; Jane's launch had been a little behind that of her father's other project.

On Friday, 21 November 1879, the new submarine was declared complete by Garrett, the supervising engineer George Price and shipwright Hodgson. The following day, the citizens of Birkenhead were treated to the spectacle of the boat being pulled by thirty Shire horses to the Great Float, a distance of about 300 yards. While this magnificent performance was drawing the crowds, Mr Hodgson's family received a strange visitor:

During the removal of the submarine from Mr Cochran's yard, a stranger called at our house and asked for a coat, saying that my father had come into contact with the new paint on [the boat] and must have another. Just as we were getting it, my father appeared and the stranger bolted.[15]

This curious little incident apart, all went well. The boat reached the Float unscathed: the assembled gentlemen, doubtless with Garrett's encouragement, then retired for the Sabbath.

On Monday, the new submarine was photographed. One photograph shows Garrett on the conning-tower with Cochran, Jack Aitkin and Captain W.E. Jackson, who was to assist in the vessel's trials. A second shot shows the boat's future crew – Garrett, Jackson and George Price. Garrett is shown leaning over the edge of the conning-tower, proudly holding two-year-old Georgina toward the camera.

The boat was declared ready for launching on Tuesday after a final inspection by the project's principals. The honour of launching the submarine fell to George Price, who took the controls of the Great Float's celebrated 60-ton steam crane for the occasion.

At 2.30 p.m. on 26 November 1879, before a small crowd of journalists, shipyard workers and assorted Garretts, the world's first mechanically-propelled submarine was lowered into the Great Float. In a moment of genius, combining his Rossall Latin, his clerical calling and his invention's purpose in a single triumphant word, Garrett christened her *Resurgam* – 'I shall arise'.

CHAPTER THREE

Resurgam – I Shall Arise

A week after the ceremonial launching of *Resurgam*, Garrett, now once again father to both a healthy infant and a new submarine, climbed aboard the new boat with Captain Jackson and George Price. The trials, held entirely within the Great Float, attracted great local interest:

> A new submarine vessel, the invention of the Reverend George W. Garrett, of Manchester, was exhibited on Tuesday in the Wallasey Dock, before a large number of scientific and other gentlemen. The object of the boat is to get near to ships of war without being observed. The vessel is pointed at both ends. On the top there is a tower provided with windows, and there is a manhole by which the operator gets in or out of the vessel with ease. The Reverend Mr Garrett, who was accompanied by some gentlemen in a steam-launch, began to test his apparatus at one o'clock, and in his first trial, at a depth of 25 feet, he remained under water for an hour and a half, during which time conversation was kept up with him by the telephone. In the second trial the reverend gentleman was under water an hour and ten minutes. The tests appeared to give great satisfaction to the spectators, and no doubt for the purpose intended the vessel will prove valuable in times of war, when ships are liable to be destroyed by torpedoes. We understand that the inventor is in communication with the Government with a view to their purchase of the invention.[1]

This was quite certainly the reporter's first submarine trial. As such, it is interesting to note how he describes what he saw. It took several hours to get steam up: when the time came to dive, the furnace door was sealed and faith asserted in the automatic valve on the boiler's chimney. Lamm's arrangements then took over.

Resurgam had no ballast tanks. Her natural floating condition left only the conning tower standing above the surface on a ton or so of buoyancy which was overcome on diving by water-flow over the boat's hydroplanes. Following Garrett's experiences with the 'egg', *Resurgam* was not only designed without the ability to perform a statical, vertical dive on an even keel: she was specifically designed to avoid the buoyancy condition that such a dive would require.

Even diving in the manner intended will have been a rather sluggish affair, as the position of the hydroplanes – amidships, where they could obtain little leverage on the hull – rendered them highly inefficient. When the engine stopped, the boat would rise to the surface.

The Lamm steam plant gave the submarine a submerged endurance, according to Garrett, of about twelve miles or four hours. While it is not impossible that the boat was run up and down the dock for the time described, it is rather more likely that, after a quick dip to 25 feet, she was brought back to the surface and left floating awash, with only the conning-tower above the surface, for ninety minutes. It hardly seems likely that Garrett would have hauled a telephone cable up and down the dock. At the time, it was widely thought to be almost as amazing to be cooped up in the confined space of the boat for this length of time as actually to dive in her.

There were, of course, submerged trial runs, as reported by a sailor who watched the proceedings from a tug at the Victoria Wharf:

> Her favourite run was from the grain warehouses to the entrance of the Egerton Dock. Her movements were slow, but on the trials I saw her being submerged. By the ripple under the surface you could always tell where she was, and now and then you would see her diver's-shaped helmet come to the surface. I suppose that was to fix her position.[2]

It was: there was no periscope. The Polish submariner Stefan Drzewiecki, working in Russia, had fitted a crude periscope to a pedal-powered boat, not unlike Garrett's 'egg', earlier in 1879, but the instrument's second submarine appearance was delayed until 1898, when Goubet fitted a periscope to one of the submarines that he built for Brazil. The periscope only became widespread after Lake's 'omniscope', fitted to his submarine *Protector* in 1902.

It was not long before Garrett began to experience difficulties with the boat's propulsion system. The temperature inside the boat, revealed to the press as 90 degrees (Fahrenheit), was liable to creep well beyond this after half an hour closed up or submerged. Fumes leaked from the boiler, giving Garrett his first taste of what would be his recurrent bouts of what might be called 'steam submariner's lung'. His fellow crewmen, lacking his pre-existing weak lungs, merely became very uncomfortable.

Back in Manchester, the parishioners grumbled. At this new

high-point in the Submarine Navigation Company's activities, with trials and negotiations with the Navy to attend to, neither the rector nor his curate was much in evidence at the church. George's twice a month shrivelled virtually to permanent absenteeism. The fact that he was away building instruments of death hardly helped his image with the congregation.

On 5 December 1879, in an attempt both to raise funds and to repair George's reputation with the parish (something of a forlorn hope by now), Dr Garrett held a special, submarine-promoting parish sale of work at Christ Church. Young Thomas was again recruited to extol his brother's achievements and to explain *Resurgam* to the parishioners and the press. At a time when the rector's finances and the church's were virtually inextricable, the sale of work was a crass public relations gaffe, even by Dr Garrett's standards.

The sale of work and its press coverage started a small war in the parish between the Garretts' supporters and the persistent temperance lobby, who had always at least partially sympathised with Dr Garrett's creditors and were now joined by those who felt that submarining was no business for the Anglican clergy. The *Manchester Courier*'s society reporter seems to have been blissfully unaware of the local tensions surrounding the event, but the remarkable degree of accuracy in the coverage of the boat's technical particulars says a great deal for young Thomas's powers of scientific understanding and explanation (like his brothers Oliver and Henry, he eventually became a highly respected doctor, though without their regrettable fondness for the bottle):

> At a sale of work and entertainment held at Christ Church, Moss Side for church and school expenses, photographic views of 'The new 33-ton submarine boat and its crew', invented by the Rev. G.W. Garrett, son of the Rev. Dr Garrett, Rector of Christ Church, were exhibited. The name given to the boat is 'The Garrett Submarine Torpedo Boat *Resurgam*'.
>
> It is a cylinder, six-and-a-half feet in diameter in the centre part, and tapers off at each end, the central part being encased in timber for the purposes of protection. The aim of the inventor is to convey torpedoes under water, and to approach a large ironclad invisibly, and within a certain distance to discharge a torpedo by means of the usual telescope and springs which are used by the Admiralty.[3]

Garrett's contact with Nordenfelt was beginning to bear fruit: he was now thinking in terms of discharging Whitehead torpedoes from *Resurgam*, launched from mountings on the sides of the boat.

An idea has prevailed that the natural position of the boat is under water, but the real fact is that its proper position is what the inventor calls on the surface with the tower just out of water. When the boat has to go under water, it is made to do so by means of side rudders, which depress the body of the boat under the surface, and it remains there as long as the navigator desires.[4]

This is, in fact, rather more honest than several of Garrett's own statements, which often tend to suggest that the boat was capable of remaining fully submerged for long periods – actually, disaster apart, physically impossible in *Resurgam*. Prompted by young Thomas, the *Courier* proceeds to one of the earliest unambiguous statements of classical submarine doctrine:

It is meditated that in action such a boat should attack an enemy under water, so as to be safe from attack itself, and that it should discharge torpedoes when within about fifty yards of its object [a clear and positive allusion to Whitehead torpedoes], afterwards removing invisibly out of the way. Its natural state is to remain submerged with a buoyancy of about three tons, and it is a vessel of 30 tons displacement.

The boat has been under trial in the past week in the Great Float at Birkenhead, and has exceeded the inventor's expectations in its floating powers and in its steering capacities. Yesterday the Rev. G.W. Garrett was shut up in the boat for 12 hours with his crew of two men, Captain Jackson and Mr George Price, the engineer, whose photographs are shown in the views exhibited.

The inventor is just about to start on his way to Portsmouth to prove that the boat is no toy. The admiral superintendent of the dockyard at Portsmouth has been instructed by the Admiralty to receive the Inventor with every attention, with the view of his demonstrating the usefulness of his invention, and subsequently a purchase of it by the Admiralty. The main point of the boat is its power by which it can move under the water at the rate of from eight to ten knots per hour without giving off any smoke or other evidence of its presence.

While on the surface the boat has a current of air through it, and when under the water the air is kept pure by means of the inventor's novel breathing apparatus. The features of the boat were explained by Mr. T.J.G. Garrett, and the views were examined with great interest. A large number of ladies and gentlemen were present.[5]

This provincial newspaper report of a parish fête is by far the clearest and best-informed popular press account of an early submarine of the entire period, pleasantly free of the exaggerations and evasions to which Garrett and his competitors were prone. Whether they liked the submarine or not (and most of them definitely did not), none of them could plead ignorance after this.

The figure missing from the parish jollifications was, of course, the inventor himself. Garrett was too busy in the Great Float for this sort of trifle, as was doubtless remarked at Christ Church.

Preparations were well advanced for *Resurgam*'s Naval examination and trials. Birley had done his work well. Thorsten Nordenfelt had been kept informed of the progress of the potterings in the Great Float, and had added his weight to Birley's petition to the Admiralty. He himself would be attending the Portsmouth trials. The problem remained, however, of getting the boat to Portsmouth for the Navy.

A disagreement arose between Garrett and Cochran over how *Resurgam* should be conveyed south. Cochran recommended conveying the vessel to Portsmouth by road. Not rail, oddly enough: perhaps he knew something about the railways of 1880 that has escaped commentators ever since – passing the boat in one piece through tunnels seems the most likely cause of difficulty. As it had taken an hour for a large team of heavy horses to pull the boat barely more than round the corner, land haulage was neither an attractive nor realistic proposition. Loading the submarine as freight onto a ship would have been a credible solution, but Garrett decided to sail *Resurgam* round the coast under her own power, taking the trip in easy stages and carrying out experiments as he went. Quite apart from seeking the indubitable cachet of sailing her round to Portsmouth, he was, after all, anxious to convince the Navy and Nordenfelt of *Resurgam*'s capabilities: assessing her performance for himself *en route* would give him a considerable advantage in advance of the official trials, not to mention notice of any faults needing repair or (frankly) suppression.

Resurgam was lifted out of the water and inspected, in preparation for her maiden voyage. No damage was found: she was swung back into the Great Float on Wednesday, 10 December and moved to the Alfred Dock to be made ready for sea.

The first-ever submarine voyage of any length began at nine o'clock that evening, under the bemused eye of the piermaster, Joseph Garner. The night was moonless, misty and very cold as Garrett, Captain Jackson and George Price began the great adventure. Meanwhile, like a character from a Silas Hocking tear-jerker, a lone figure stood apart from Cochran and his men and shivered in the fog, watching *Resurgam*'s lights disappear. Dr Garrett, who thought he saw something like an industrial bishopric beckoning, was in fact watching a great deal of money steaming into oblivion.

While his son was puffing up the Mersey, Dr Garrett wrote a long, long letter to the *Manchester Courier*, defending his son's doings in an attempt to heal some of the rifts that had opened up at Christ Church:

Sir,

As you have published some notices of the works upon which my second son, the Rev. G.W. Garrett, has thought it well to spend his leisure time for several months past, I hope you will allow me to explain the matter with sufficient detail to enable your readers to understand the points which render it peculiar and somewhat strange to the mind of the general public ...

I know quite well, and I fully appreciate, the underlying opinion that 'clergymen ought to have nothing to do with war, or its destructive appliances', and I also feel the force of the idea that 'clergymen, as a class, are very unfitted to taking part in the ordinary works of human life', but I have no doubt that the sound influence of our national religion, and all the labours of life in our country, would derive increased stability and energy if clergymen, as a body, could earn public confidence in their skill and power to develop as healthy examples of all that is good in the practical life of Englishmen ...[6]

Three column *feet* later, Dr Garrett, having sung (and *sung*) the praises of his son's radical interpretation of Muscular Christianity, ends on a strangely prophetic veiled threat: 'We feel sure that such a man as my son, and such a work as he has produced, need not be and never ought to be the officer and the property of any other nation but our own'.[7] In other words, the boat would be sold abroad if necessary, whatever the Russians were up to off Vancouver. That other defender of the submarine, Basil Zaharoff, would have recognised the sentiments, and quite possibly the circumlocution.

Meanwhile, *Resurgam* was slowly making her way up the Mersey. Garrett wrote up the voyage for promotional purposes and sent it to Cochran for onward distribution. Making careful allowance for commercially-inspired hyperbole, and applying the necessary Garrett Coefficient of Veracic Expansion (i.e. filtering out the nonsense) we are fortunate that the log of this historic (if occasionally mildly farcical) voyage has survived;

... We reached the Rock Lighthouse without accident of any sort, and entered the Rock Channel about ten o'clock. When we started, Captain Jackson remained outside on the look-out, whilst I took the helm in the conning-tower; but as soon as we were in the Rock Channel Captain Jackson came inside, when we shut ourselves up, and fairly started on our way.

We passed down the Rock Channel, and, safely making Spencer's Spit, we turned into the Horse Channel, which we cleared in due course, and were then out at sea. We laid our course for the North-west Lightship, and went very slow, intending to make some experiments in Victoria Deep as soon as daylight should come.[8]

The deep water in which Garrett had chosen to test his boat is still in use as a submarine training area. He had calculated *Resurgam*'s crushing depth to be about 150 feet (where the hydrostatic pressure is about 71 pounds per square inch), but the submarine's failsafe design would prevent an uncontrolled plummet to destruction. He settled on a trial dive to 35 feet.

However, the problems which had been hinted at in the Great Float emerged fully-formed out at sea, and were joined by the miseries inflicted by leaking compressed air. George Price, the engineer, unlike Garrett, was not trying to sell anything with his account:

> ... the heat from the boiler was intense, varying from 110 to 115 degrees, and we experienced great discomfort from the air pressure on the ear-drums. We had, owing to the very limited accommodation, to stand all the time, and when we returned to the surface we were all exhausted.[9]

Price was obviously a grumbler: it was perfectly possible to sleep, one at a time, on top of the boiler's wooden cladding – the ultimate in 1879 submarine luxury, Garrett-style. Tension appears to have been rising with the temperature. The boat's engine, a conventional return connecting-rod affair, though specially bored out for the occasion, found life under the Lamm régime almost as difficult as the crew: the forced-draught machinery, a rotary vane blower for the boiler made very necessary if the pre-heating for the Lamm system was to take less than a month, was an added complication that would have turned any marine engineer into a potential Mr Christian. A man can only take so much innovation, especially when his own internal water system is undergoing Lamm superheating.

Price might also have cared to contemplate the implications of the boat springing a leak. While Garrett confidently (and correctly) calculated the hull's crushing depth, he did not take the same trouble with the automatic non-return valves on the boiler flue and the air suction pipe, whose tolerance to external water pressure was (and is) a matter of faith and mystery. If water *had* found its way into the hull in any quantity, the boat was somewhat under-equipped for dealing with it. *Resurgam*'s one and only pump was a hand-cranked force pump for clearing the bilges: as the boat dispensed with ballast tanks, no others were deemed necessary. The machinery was already heavy and bulky enough without such frills.

Garrett, of course, mentions none of this. There is an amusing contrast between his account of the following morning and Price's. Garrett:

> When the morning of Thursday came there was a very thick fog, which prevented our making all the experiments we wished, and necessitated our proceeding very carefully. The fog did not lift all that day, so we moved about, testing various parts of our internal machinery, till the Friday morning, when the sun rose beautiful and clear.[10]

Price:

> The navigator had lost his bearings, and we came up alongside a full-rigged ship, homeward bound for Liverpool. When Mr Garrett threw open the top and shouted 'Ship Ahoy!' and inquired where we were, the captain of the ship was terribly surprised, and inquired who we were. We informed him that we were a submarine torpedo boat, and had been under his ship for two or three hours [very unlikely]. The captain almost collapsed at this news, and asked where we had come from, and where we were bound for. Mr Garrett informed him that we were from Liverpool, and were going to Portsmouth. The captain asked how many there were in our crew, and when Mr Garrett told him three, he answered: 'Well, you are the three biggest fools I have ever met'.[11]

Captain Jackson, a Master Mariner, has understandably been criticised for losing his way in Liverpool Bay – hardly the Irrawaddy. However, it must be remembered that much of the journey thus far had been carried out with the boat closed up and awash as part of Garrett's experiments: it is asking a lot of a man to carry out successful navigation when he can barely see where his ship is going, and is himself being slowly steamed in a pressurised carbon monoxide bath. The limitations of the Lamm system and the seals on the furnace were making themselves felt.

Price only broke what had by then been a 45-year silence over

Resurgam's voyage in 1925. His story of the ship's captain closely resembles a similar story that was current (but unauthorised, as it were) in 1880:

> The *Resurgam* once came up alongside an American, and the following conversation took place: 'Ship, ahoy!' 'What's your name? Where did you come from and where bound?' 'The *Mary Ann* from Baltimore. What's your name?' 'The *Resurgam*, submarine boat.' 'Submarine, be blowed!' And then down went the *Resurgam* for another exploration below.[12]

Conditions on board worsened: eventually, even Garrett complained, if rather more discreetly:

> We had now been at sea about thirty-six hours, a great part of which time we were under water, and we felt desirous of making some port, as sleeping on board was not attended with as much comfort as we wished.[!]
>
> At this time we found the North-west Lightship close at hand, bearing about North, so we determined to put into the River Voryd, as there is a good anchorage there, and she will dry every tide, which is very convenient, as we are going to make a series of further experiments.
>
> The boat answered splendidly in the seaway. The seas pass easily over her, and cause hardly any motion, nor do they interfere in any important degree with her way of steering.[13]

As the boat had no buoyancy at either end, this last is no surprise: the boat would not be lifted by a wave, but would, by and large, pass more or less undisturbed through the water, a feature of the hull-form familiar from the wondrous but unsuccessful cigar-ships of the 1860s.

Mr Price informs us that *Resurgam* was less than rapturously received as she edged towards Rhyl:

> The weather was still very thick as we shaped our course for Rhyl, where we arrived at daybreak. There we gave the submarine in charge of a pilot who took her to the jetty. When the customs and coastguard came out, they refused to go below, being frightened by the steam rising from the boiler. When we went ashore, we were so dirty and untidy that at first the proprietor of the hotel would not take us in. When Mr Garrett produced his card, however, we were soon enjoying a good meal after a refreshing bath.[14]

Garrett, for all the tribulations of the *Resurgam*'s journey, was elated:

> Our comfort completely restored, we could congratulate ourselves on having passed successfully through so novel and interesting a trip as any sailors could wish to experience.[15]

Ever the dutiful husband and son, Garrett's first action on landing, even before the confrontation with the recalcitrant hotelier (who could have been forgiven for thinking Garrett and his friends were Martians) was to send a telegram to assure everybody of his safety. Mindful as ever of publicity, he also sent one to the *Manchester Courier*, who had done so much to promote his efforts thus far:

> THE GARRETT SUBMARINE TORPEDO BOAT *RESURGAM*: The inventor has telegraphed that he has successfully navigated this vessel from Birkenhead to Rhyl on her first trip. Crew all well.[16]

Submarine not so well, however. A few minor parts had failed – no real problem – but the propeller had turned out to be too large for the plant, and needed to be replaced. Meanwhile, the natives had noticed something strange in the harbour:

> A visitor of an unusual character is now in Rhyl. A torpedo boat came ashore yesterday (Friday) afternoon, opposite the West Parade, where it was lying high and dry on the sands. It is to be taken into the Voryd at the flood tide, where it will remain a short time.[17]

A short distance up the river was the answer to Garrett's immediate mechanical problems: there was a very adequate foundry at Rhuddlan, where Garrett proceeded to spend a great deal of Submarine Navigation Company money after the boat had been moved, under the supervision of her now clean and respectable crew.

He pursued his business with the Rhuddlan Foundry in great secrecy: the necessary parts for the submarine were made under Garrett's careful and suspicious supervision, then fitted, at his insistence, by himself and his two crewmen. This must have been quite a sight in the case of the propeller.

Garrett seems to have laboured under the delusion that the Welsh were a race of spies. A guard was placed on *Resurgam* when the crew were ashore, holding the nosey Celts at bay. Although large numbers came to stare, nobody was allowed near. A very few exceptions were made, notably for an English engineer whom Garrett met in the crew's hotel, which was now functioning as the nerve centre of Rhyl Submarine Base. This gentleman (who had the suspiciously Welsh name of Owen, but presumably passed the accent test) and his two friends were treated to a magnificent po-faced Garrettism concerning the procedure on *Resurgam* for disposing of what the Navy now knows as 'gash' (and, presumably, the contents of the heads – in *Resurgam*'s case, as far as one can tell, a bucket):

> An exceedingly short space of time only at the surface will suffice to discharge incombustible matter [as it were] as well as some of the results of chemical combustion from the boiler.[18]

The engineer and his friends were impressed:

> [We] found the boat, its machinery and appliances substantially built and well planned. I have come to the conclusion that Mr Garrett has a grand invention in his hands, and he is quite capable of bringing out that which he says he has already perfected.[19]

'Perfected' seems a little strong, but Garrett agreed: 'Every day's experience has added to the confidence of the inventor and his crew that perfect success has been secured for all he has proposed to do'.[20]

In the meantime, Garrett had to prepare his perfect machine for the next stage of her journey. *Resurgam* had been expected at Portsmouth within a month of departure, but the boat's mechanical problems and the December weather saw to it that the submarine's one and only Christmas was spent in Wales. Garrett was at least spared embarrassing press coverage: at the turn of the year, the nation's newspapers were almost entirely taken up with the news of the Tay Bridge disaster.

January came, blew very hard, and went: the pressure on Garrett mounted. As he and his crew had obviously been very much the worse for wear after only thirty-six hours at sea in *Resurgam*, Garrett may well have wished by now that he had either listened to Cochran or thought of a less harrowing way of getting the submarine to Portsmouth.

After consultation with his board, Garrett arrived at a reasonable if expensive compromise. Rather than subject himself

(Right) J.T. Cochran, builder of
Resurgam.

(Below) John Garrett, Chairman of the
Garrett Submarine Navigation and
Pneumatophore Company, Ltd.

Thorsten Nordenfelt.

(Below) Garrett share certificate − one of the many issued after the loss of *Resurgam.*

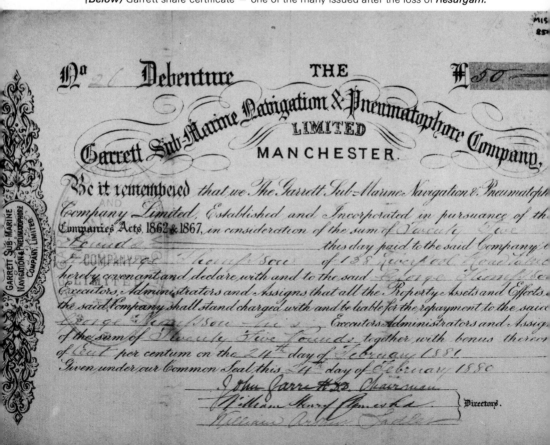

and the two others to more nights of heat, steam and gas, Price tells us, 'Mr Garrett decided to go to Birkenhead to buy a yacht to accompany the *Resurgam*'.[21] The yacht would be used to tow the submarine between experiments, and would provide decent bunks for the three heroes: 'He purchased one called the *Elphin*, and about a week later I proceeded to Birkenhead to bring her to Rhyl'.[22]

In an inky blackness reminiscent of *Resurgam*'s departure from Birkenhead, the little convoy proceeded to sea at 10 p.m. on Tuesday, 24 February 1889, watched by the all-seeing (but ever so slightly sarcastic) local media:

> The strange and mysterious-looking torpedo boat was successfully towed out to sea. The queer little craft looked like a huge hippopotamus as it floated down the river.[23]

The huge hippopotamus and her keepers slowly made their strange and mysterious way westwards along the Welsh coast. During the night and morning, the weather slid through descending grades of filthiness until the beginnings of a *bona-fide* west-north-west gale made themselves felt late on Wednesday night. While *Resurgam*'s hull rendered the rising seas less frightening than might have been expected, chaos broke out on the *Elphin*. Soon, engineer Price was needed:

> While off the Great Orme's Head, the captain of the yacht signalled to the *Resurgam* that they were in difficulties, being unable to feed their boilers. They sent a boat across, and we all three went over to the yacht, taking the submarine in tow. Garrett and Jackson went below whilst I went to the engine-room to repair the pumps.[24]

The crew all took their kit to the yacht with them. In Captain Jackson's case, this included the submarine's pennant, a cheerful little affair bearing the single word '*Resurgam*', stowed away ready for the boat's triumphal arrival at Portsmouth. It was just as well that he had this memento to give to his sister, who still had it forty years later.

> During that time a gale sprang up, and prevented us from returning to the submarine. We towed her until ten o'clock the following morning, when she broke her hawser, and consequently we lost her.[25]

Resurgam's conning-tower hatch (like that of a modern submarine) could not be sealed from the outside. With no one on board to close the boat up, the heavy seas broke over the tower and swept down the hatch, increasing the boat's weight until the hawser parted, and she sank. But even this was not the end of the nightmare:

> We were compelled to run the *Elphin* up the Dee for shelter, and dropped anchor off Mostyn. Next morning, the wind changed, and another gale came on. The *Elphin* parted her chains and went adrift, and we had to signal for assistance. A boat called the *Iron King* came to our rescue, but, unfortunately, she rammed us, making the *Elphin* a total wreck.[26]

One of the few bright aspects of this sorry tale was that all eight men – the submariners and the crew of the yacht – were saved, a considerable achievement in the dreadful weather and at the hands of rescuers whose level of competence must have confirmed Garrett's opinion of the Welsh. The distraught curate sought help from the (English) experts:

> Mr Garrett proceeded to Liverpool by train for assistance in search of the submarine. The weather was still very bad, and no vessel was able to venture out, so, unfortunately for us, we lost the *Resurgam*.[27]

Despite the boat's departure having been seen and reported, strange tales soon began circulating about the loss of the submarine. The crew had gone ashore for dinner, and had returned to find the submarine gone. She had slipped her moorings and drifted out to sea in the gale. Russian spies had spirited her away.

It is not impossible that Garrett himself was behind some of these fairy-tales: he himself was always very vague about the precise details of the loss, a fact which has led in recent times to the mildly hilarious suggestion that *Resurgam* was scuttled. A casual inspection of Garrett's subsequent financial adventures shows this to be not so much unlikely as laughable; whatever the risks he took with his life, he was never consciously the fiscal suicidal type. Eccentric, sometimes inept, arguably slightly mad and certainly mendacious on occasions, he was never actually anything so banal as *stupid*, which he would have needed to be to expect to obtain much of a return from scuttling his pride and joy. The loss of *Resurgam* was an accident, with an unfortunate dash of pig-headedness.

That aside, however, why the stories? Garrett would certainly not have enjoyed admitting that putting to sea under such circumstances with a highly marginal vessel of unproven abilities may have been somewhere between ill-advised and insane. Also, a modest withholding of distressing facts may have made it easier to ask local fishermen if they had noticed anything large, black and vaguely submarine torpedo boat-shaped while going about their business.

If the journalist who watched *Resurgam* leave is to be believed, the Submarine Navigation Company's losses were not merely appalling, but apocalyptic: 'It is said that Mr Garrett has been offered £60,000 by the Admiralty, and £144,000 by the Russian government, for his boat'.

There is no other evidence for either of these figures, and the second is preposterous. The Admiralty had certainly not made any firm offer in advance of the trials. Perhaps Garrett had indulged in a little hyperbole while discussing matters with the Fourth Estate. What is absolutely certain, however, is that Garrett was now in deep trouble.

Whether through meanness, bravado or sheer foolishness, *Resurgam* had not been insured; the Submarine Navigation Company bore the loss. How the news was received at the rectory can only be imagined: Dr Garrett may have felt that his Friend was exceptionally invisible that winter. He must, however, have counted his blessings in that *Resurgam*, by any standards, had been built on the cheap, and had been paid for in instalments as she was constructed: the loss could have been a very great deal worse.

With what seemed to be its one and only visible asset gone to the bottom, the Submarine Navigation Company might have been expected to call it a day. Far from it. Shares and indentures, all bearing Dr Garrett's signature, were still on sale months after the loss, a practice which, under the circumstances, teetered on the edge of fraud. But young Garrett was far from finished.

He fell back on the Pneumatophore. It is reasonable to assume that his name might have raised something of a wry smile with the British Admiralty in the months following *Resurgam*'s loss: faced with a dip (as it were) in the home market, Garrett went on an export drive.

April 1880 found him in Paris, apparently recovered from his winter trauma:

A very interesting experiment took place on the Seine at Lévallois, in the presence of a committee appointed by the Minister of Marine to assist at the trial of Mr G.W. Garrett's submarine apparatus. The apparatus exhibited was an ordinary diving-dress, to which the inventor had adapted his system for maintaining air at its normal composition, thereby enabling the diver to dispense with all communication with the surface ...

Mr Garrett descended into the water and remained there for 37 minutes, and when coming to the surface again was in perfect health and spirits, although the dress employed, being one bought in Paris for the purpose, did not fit him comfortably.

The inventor has constructed a torpedo boat ... with which he has remained 36 hours at sea, going from Birkenhead to Rhyl, most of the time completely under water. Mr Garrett attaches the greatest importance to the fact that he has discovered a method by which he is able to keep working an ordinary steam engine without the necessity of giving off the products of combustion.[29]

Delightful as it is to see the shipwrecked curate back in business, this report gives a glimpse of a less-than-saintly aspect of Garrett's character. While Garrett's work is of immense historical interest and importance (more than he knew, in fact), commercial pressures (and, it must be said, sheer ego) tended to bring out a streak of charlatanry that would eventually boomerang with a vengeance.

Here, not content with extolling the (genuine) virtues of the Pneumatophore, Garrett claims for himself the Lamm boiler system. Yet again, he over-sells the submarine: *Resurgam* was quite incapable of remaining *completely* under water for longer than her closed-up endurance, but Garrett, here and elsewhere, deliberately fudges this distinction, as though *Resurgam* were *Nautilus* come true, which she was not. Rather worse, and with devastating cheek, he neglects to point out that his torpedo boat was not only completely, but *permanently* under water as he was speaking.

Somehow, the loss of *Resurgam* had been kept out of the newspapers. Even Gardner Colton, Garrett's erstwhile patent agent, knew nothing about it as late as September, only finding out about it from a letter in *Design and Work*, a popular science weekly. Obviously, Garrett worked on a 'need-to-know' basis.

Despite positive response from French Government scientists who took samples from his air reservoir at the end of the demonstration and declared them healthy, there do not appear to have been any sales resulting from Garrett's trip. This may have been because of misgivings over the safety of caustic potash, which Garrett's cadaverous appearance would have reinforced. As to his demeanour after the demonstration, he was *always* in – as they put it – 'perfect spirits'; in a sense, that was his problem.

Doubtless because of the caustic potash's unpleasant and potentially lethal reaction with sea-water, Garrett never tested or demonstrated the Pneumatophore except in fresh water. It is possible that this restriction on the device's operation discouraged commercial or military interest – not that the same problem caused any such qualms in World War Two. However, this seems to have been, to coin a phrase, the Pneumatophore's last gasp. There was another, less scientific reason for the invention being shelved: while the forces of nature and the indifference of ordinary mortals could be withstood, the juggernaut of John Garrett's financial doom flattened all before it.

Meanwhile, Garrett, apparently undaunted by *Resurgam*'s fate – which, after all, was in no way due to faulty design – set about designing another submarine, larger again than *Resurgam*, hoping to offer it to Nordenfelt, with whom he kept in touch. With the Submarine Navigation Company at the edge of the abyss, this was very much a paper submarine, with no prospect of being built. For the moment, Armageddon was on its way at Christ Church; such speculative projects would have to wait.

Dr Garrett had of course caught the same cold as the other directors of the company when *Resurgam* went down, but he could least afford it. The repayments on his various loans and mortgages became sporadic: he was forced to sell his life insurance policies. In a magnificent gesture to his Temperance-fanatic tormentors, Dr Garrett sold them to a Rochdale wine and spirit merchant. But by Christmas 1880, when he had taken to his sick-bed after a fall from the pulpit, the critical point had been reached. In the middle of Christmas Week, the rector was finally forced to petition for bankruptcy.

Even before this calamity could sink in, one of the parishioners, a leader in the anti-Garrett faction, pointed out that the rector could elude meeting his debts, even as a bankrupt, simply by resigning the living. Cutting this trick off (and it *had* occurred to the rector), the bishop sequestered the living: every penny from the parish was siphoned through the bishop's office to the various creditors. The rector was left with no income whatever, while the Receiver got to work on his assets.

There were two major casualties of the bankruptcy. Dr Garrett's shares in the company were put up for sale: hardly surprisingly, once potential investors had investigated the background of this mysterious company, there were no takers. The company was wound up: Hugh Birley, sniffing scandal, melted away. The second victim, in his case more directly of the sequestration, was George, whose stipend was withdrawn. Both the rector and the curate faced the New Year effectively unemployed, though they were still expected to hold services and administer the parish: during the festivities, the Garretts could be forgiven for wondering precisely what the parishioners were celebrating.

Even the family themselves could see a funny side, however, which emerged after one of the blackest moments of all – the loss of their home. Soon after the Garretts had sold Greenheys Hall and moved into a far more modest house in Moss Lane East, Dr Garrett returned one evening from a meeting with the Receiver to find that his wife had papered his study walls with his depressingly large collection of worthless Submarine Navigation Company share certificates. This was a rare glimmer of Garrett humour in the midst of crisis.

Faced with the family's appalling plight, George hunted frantically for a job: he would have to support his parents and younger brothers until his father's affairs were finally unravelled. His two older brothers, for whatever reason, seem to have done very little to help. After what must have been persistent protestations from the Garretts, father and son, the Unseen Friend made a mercifully rapid return to his station following his inexplicable Christmas absence: inside a month, George had found himself a position as a consulting engineer on the Milford Haven Docks project. In the event, however, he found the financial atmosphere at Milford Haven curiously familiar.

Garrett's boss, the engineer Samuel Lake, had taken over the project in 1879, when his predecessors, Appleby and Lawton, had gone down in a blaze of legal acrimony after the auditors discovered that the firm was borrowing sums as small as £30 to stay afloat week-to-week. Lake had promised to complete the docks in nine months – an outright impossibility: he soon ran into money troubles. As Garrett joined the firm, Lake was in the process of setting up an elaborate but very dangerous scheme to raise £350,000 from leases on the company's property, including the docks themselves. This arrangement became a popular ruse with British local authorities in the 1980s: property is sold, then leased back, though in this case the company that owned the property had lethally incestuous links with the leasing concern. Negative feedback soon built up. Garrett, by now something of an expert on deficit financing, probably knew that his job was temporary.

Garrett, in fact, had just over a year with a steady salary before Lake's creation finally strangled itself. The docks were built around a truly fantastic template – Brunel's *Great Eastern*, then in her declining years, originally moved to Milford Haven in 1876 for a refit that more or less turned into retirement. Unfortunately, she seems to have brought along her awesome power to drive men bankrupt. Although a business disaster by any standards, the *Great Eastern* represented the peak of Victorian shipbuilding and an inspiration for Garrett, whose vessels, although a very great deal smaller, were in their own way just as revolutionary. With this example before him daily, it is hardly surprising that Garrett's new design flourished in his spare time, for all that he had no immediate prospect of seeing it built.

Garrett's family did not accompany him to Milford Haven; this was his first taste of working away from his wife and children, which would be the pattern of much of his later working life. However, as his curacy was over in all but name (and probably to escape some of the post-bankruptcy opprobrium), Jane and the children moved from Moss Side to the bracing seaside town of Morecambe. George came home as often as work allowed. Their fourth child, Mary, was born in October, but was far from strong. Expecting his new daughter to die almost at any moment, Garrett baptised her himself in the family's surprisingly substantial home, in Brighton Terrace. Fortunately, Mary rallied; Garrett could return to Milford Haven with an easy mind, at least for the time being.

Soon after Christmas 1881, a rather more cheerful affair than the previous Yuletide, Garrett was sent to London to discuss the possibility of lighting the new docks with electric arc lighting. While he was there, Samuel Lake's paper world finally caved in, after a farcical attempt by Lake to have the company secretary arrested for forgery when the firm's accounts were questioned. Not surprisingly, the company secretary fell out with Lake, who was declared bankrupt. Garrett was unemployed again.

Fortunately, Garrett had business of his own in London which eclipsed the Milford Haven débâcle. Taking his new submarine design with him, he went to see Thorsten Nordenfelt at his home in Parliament Street.

Nordenfelt's business was booming after a recent British court decision in his favour. Nordenfelt had claimed that the Gardner Gun, then in widespread use by the British Army, infringed on one of his patents. The decision meant that the Army was compelled to replace all of its Gardner Guns with Nordenfelts, bringing a very welcome windfall to Nordenfelt, who was therefore well placed to expand into a new and potentially very profitable field.

Thorsten Vilhelm Nordenfelt was born in Sweden in 1842, fractionally below the aristocracy; his family had been honoured by the king in 1719, and included such Scandinavian exotics as the first, last and only Duke Larsson of Mongolia. Trained as an engineer in Stockholm and Lund, Nordenfelt had moved to London in 1869, founding the Nordenfelt Ammunition Company in 1874. He had rapidly become a fixture of the British and European defence establishment, using an extensive network of personal contacts to compensate for his lack of the sheer industrial muscle that powered his major European rivals, the mighty Krupps. Basing his initial efforts on the fairly large amount of family capital that he had brought with him in 1869, Nordenfelt amassed a large personal fortune from his rapid-firing guns and other innovative ordnance.

Nordenfelt's interest in the Whitehead torpedo had led him to suggest several developments and improvements for torpedo-boats, but it was only with Zaharoff's prompting that he had turned to submarines. He had taken a somewhat arm's-length interest in Garrett, all the more so following the loss of *Resurgam*, but Garrett, with his tentative plan for a large submarine – as large as some surface craft and potentially more lethal (and therefore more lucrative) than any – convinced him that now was the time to act.

Events had moved on in the submarine world since Garrett's first approach to Nordenfelt. News was beginning to leak from Russia of Drzewiecki's first submarines – surprisingly advanced, electrically-propelled craft that had originally been built for pedal-propulsion, but had now been fitted with electric motors driven from the new lead-acid cells. None of the technical details had exactly been advertised; nor had the disappointing (though not, for once, particularly tragic) results of the trials. Rumours were spreading, however, of large numbers of these things being built. Then as now, a Russian war scare was always good for business in the armaments trade, a fact that cannot have been lost on Nordenfelt.

Meanwhile, Garrett's future chief competitor and ultimate nemesis, John Philip Holland, had launched his first submarine of any size, the *Fenian Ram*. Even given the industrial espionage that was rife at this time (and Holland's rather Chestertonian security), it seems unlikely that Garrett knew much about the *Ram*. Unless, of course, Nordenfelt's network of industrial whisperers – who most certainly existed, especially after Zaharoff joined the firm – reached into the Irish Republican Brotherhood. Unlikely, perhaps, but not impossible.

Regardless of recent developments and whether or not he knew much about them, Garrett remained faithful to steam propulsion. Even with electrical power appearing over the horizon, there were still sound reasons for taking this stand. One was the fact that any competent marine engineer of the time could take charge of a Garrett steam unit without much training: electrical engineering was a long way from being considered a nautical profession at this stage, a difficulty that became clear when electrical submarines became widespread.

In one important aspect, steam propulsion was in fact a marketing advantage when it came to trying to sell submarines to the world's navies, not least the Royal Navy. In the early 1880s, there was still a considerable gulf between executive and engineering naval officers. Put bluntly, engineers were 'trade', and (regardless of the number of rings on their sleeves) were seen as being several rungs lower on the social scale than the executive officers who actually fought the ship while these blackened Nibelungs toiled in their oily caverns below. There were clear political differences that could take astonishingly clear geographical forms: one could pass from Etonian Conservatism to leftish Liberalism (or, in some European navies, very much further Left) by descending a single deck.

The first navy to confront this problem face-to-face was, interestingly enough, that of Imperial Japan, which united the engineering and executive branches in 1907, though to no great effect. The USA, inverting the conventional view of Japanese relations with the West, observed and imitated.

In the Royal Navy, things remained much as before. The entire Submarine Service, once formed, soon came to call itself 'the Trade' in the face of naked snobbery from the surface fleet. The old division of executive and engineer, now just beginning to crumble in the surface fleet, had shifted to the gulf between submarines and surface vessels.

While navies would be reluctant to hand over entire vessels to socially suspect engineers in the 1880s, they were at least becoming familiar with steam technicians after thirty years of practice. To expect them to take on electrical engineers, then a class of men with the same social aura as the modern City computer analyst (vaguely snooty behind his frightening wall of jargon), was asking a great deal of what were, after all, very conservative institutions. Whatever the technical arguments against underwater steam propulsion, it had a decided psychological advantage over electricity that is now difficult to grasp.

The real difficulty – and Nordenfelt knew as much – was underwater stability. Everybody's idea of a submarine – a vessel that could descend like a lift, in a stately vertical line – was by far the most difficult and dangerous object to achieve: it had certainly been beyond the capabilities of *Resurgam*, which had only managed the perpendicular trip in one direction. Nordenfelt would never, in fact, be fully convinced of the need for underwater endurance, seeing complete submergence as a necessary and dangerous evil to be used as sparingly as possible. In the meantime, however, he took Garrett on.

The Nordenfelt Submarine Torpedo Boat Company emerged separate from the Gun and Ammunition Company. Nordenfelt, entering into a full partnership with Garrett, agreed to finance the construction of submarines that were to be built to Garrett's designs but sold as 'Nordenfelt boats'. Profits from the sale of the boats were to be shared equally between the two partners. After a few months in which the two inventors would discuss Garrett's new design and make any changes that might be necessary (in other words, iron out the aspects of the design that did not conform to Nordenfelt's ideas), the first boat would be built in Sweden, necessitating another domestic upheaval for Garrett and his family.

Garrett's professional life had gone through a considerable change of fortunes – from unemployment to partnership in an international company in a matter of days. Although he had attained considerable seniority in the Milford Docks Company very quickly – helped, it must be admitted, by other engineers scrambling for higher ground as the tide came in – civil engineering had been an unwelcome stop-gap, forced upon him by circumstances at Christ Church. After a weekend briefing in Morecambe, Garrett made his way to the now rather small rectory with his news.

CHAPTER FOUR

Dykeri Pråm En

When he entered into the new arrangement with Nordenfelt, Garrett probably felt that his troubles, if not exactly over, were at least very substantially mitigated. The creditors – his father's and those of the Submarine Navigation Company – could at last be paid off with his substantial advance from Nordenfelt. The social status of his family – always an obsession – would be enhanced in direct proportion to the vast income he expected to receive from the new submarines. Jane and the children would return to polite society after an uncomfortable couple of years in the lower middle classes, propping up the bankrupt rector and the rest of the family.

The fact was, however, that Garrett's decline (or rather return) into obscurity began with this period of apparent success. Britain's foremost pioneer submariner would effectively become Thorsten Nordenfelt's ghost-writer, a spectral figure dimly perceptible over the Swede's shoulder, only entering the limelight when physical risks had to be taken – and when things went wrong. The 'Nordenfelt boats' would be Garrett's inventions, pursued by problems largely of Nordenfelt's making; Garrett would have little opportunity to enhance his own reputation as an inventor, but would soon encounter copious opportunities for getting himself killed, an unpleasant career package leavened only by his frequent (but apparently unconscious) flights into the ludicrous.

It was about the time of Garrett's departure – the summer of 1882 – that Garrett's relations with his father, which had acquired unpleasant overtones of unwilling benefactor and grumbling dependant, appear to have crumbled to some extent. The move to Morecambe had been a fairly obvious blow to family solidarity, but the difficulties between George and his father went deeper than this. Dr Garrett was a ferociously proud man whose social standing – an asset on a par with virginity in the Victorian pantheon – was severely damaged by the bankruptcy and the Submarine Navigation Company's demise.

The parishioners of Christ Church had made their feelings clear: God's judgement had fallen upon young Garrett for meddling with the things of Satan, and had He not smitten Dr Garrett, chairman of this devilish company?

Subtle references to Dr Garrett's dubious probity began to spice the usually anodine proceedings of the Schools Board: the fire-breathing rector could no longer stalk out of meetings on a wave of high principle, once his favourite tactic. He became, at gunpoint, precisely the type of committee-man that he had spent his life opposing. This definitive Victorian patriarch had begun a ten-year slide that would take him from a position of genteel authority to a death that had more than its share of the ridiculous.

Dr Garrett's son had been an absentee curate at best, and all the more so while working in Milford Haven and London, but when George left for Sweden in August 1882, this now very tenuous link with his father's church was finally broken.

An unknown hand firmly strikes George Garrett's name from the bishop of Manchester's clerical register for 1882, never to appear again. Garrett never renounced his vows, but neither did he ever seek another pastoral appointment. For the rest of his life, he remained in a limbo between laity and clergy – a perpetual curate, never raised to the priesthood. It must be said that evidence for piety beyond a rather superficial moral uprightness is embarrassingly scarce in his life – quite the contrary. Indeed, a tendency toward what would later be fashionably known as moral pragmatism was all too obvious, especially when it came to his remarkably elastic concept of patriotism.

When Garrett left for Sweden, Jane and three of the children accompanied him, leaving little Mary in the care of Dr and Mrs Garrett. It was never intended that the whole family should live in Sweden; Jane and the children returned to Morecambe after a couple of months in Scandinavia. George wrote to his wife frequently, often enclosing notes for his older children. Another family crisis erupted at Christmas 1882, when Mary, who appears to have suffered from the less subtle incarnation of the family's nervous complaint, again appeared near death. She was re-baptised, this time by Dr Garrett, but recovered again. Her father, now supervising preparations for the building of the new boat, only heard of all this in his wife's letters. Garrett would often complain about the huge distances that working with Nordenfelt would place between him and his family.

Garrett's relationship with Nordenfelt would always be a tense affair, personally and (more obviously) technically. Although it had been agreed that Garrett would design the submarines and Nordenfelt would take the helm in every sense bar the obvious one, Nordenfelt and Garrett disagreed over important technical features of the boat's design, very much to its detriment.

Nordenfelt, it should be emphasised, was not primarily interested in submarines or their operation as such: after nearly ten years' experience in the arming and equipping of torpedo-boats, precisely the same developments in anti-torpedo warfare that had attracted Garrett to the submarine had rattled him. He was looking for a more reliable delivery system for the Whitehead torpedo, but a submersible only if absolutely necessary. Garrett, the quintessential early submariner, approached the technical challenges of submarine navigation from precisely the opposite direction: he wanted to design submarine boats to deliver torpedoes. Because of this contradiction, it is often surprisingly easy to distinguish the contributions of the two men to the Nordenfelt submarines: while Garrett designed the boat to carry the weapon, Nordenfelt attempted to stretch the concept of the weapon almost to the point of turning the boat into a huge, manned torpedo. It is no surprise whatever that when the idea of the manned torpedo was realised – literally – by the Japanese in suicide weapons toward the end of the Second World War, their handling problems seem eerily familiar to a Garrett aficionado, with the signal difference that Garrett's machines came back, if occasionally a little reluctantly.

The precise paternity of the Nordenfelt boats was always rather vague during Garrett's lifetime, despite their being almost entirely of his design. Nordenfelt's long career of self-promotion, entrenching himself within the European defence establishment, had not encouraged him to be generous; while Nordenfelt's life continued to shuttle between the patent office and the bank, money pouring in regardless from his very profitable gun company, Garrett slowly degenerated into a highly-paid Bob Cratchit, a status that would become horribly clear when Nordenfelt dropped out. To outward appearances, the submarines were as much Nordenfelt's inventions as the guns had been, with the strange Mancunian clergyman making technical suggestions.

It would be a mistake, however, to cast Nordenfelt entirely as a villain in this. His military and social contacts were extraordinarily wide, including most of the crowned heads of Europe and the rapidly-expanding European plutocracy, quite apart from comprehensive links with the worldwide military: Garrett certainly hoped (by no means unreasonably) to profit from this market. When it came to marketing the submarines, it cannot be denied that the Swedish millionaire's name had considerably more cachet than the Manchester curate's.

A different question arises, however, if one considers not so much the practicality as the morality (or even the sanity) of Nordenfelt's business – the late nineteenth-century arms trade. This unquestionably centred on the Balkans, the 'Third World' of the period – a powder-keg that would ultimately detonate in 1914. The first Nordenfelt boat would be sold to the Greeks, the second and third to the Turks and the last to the Russians, all protagonists – and mutual opponents – in the continuing Balkan ferment: Nordenfelt was prepared to arm any or all of them if the money was right, and does not seem to have been particularly troubled (or even amused) by the prospect of his maritime deterrents deterring each other. The risible fact that this particular military balance eventually resolved itself into three rusting hulks glowering at each other across the Aegean is irrelevant: the fact remains that the Nordenfelt-Garrett submarine bazaar was a dangerous place. In Garrett's case, business acumen would give foolhardiness a powerful nudge more than once. In his time with Nordenfelt, his earlier tendency to exaggerate the achievements of his submarines would sometimes give way to unadorned charlatanry, a tendency that extended to his accounts of his personal adventures: if his own account is to be believed, the adventures of the first boat even brought him within surfacing distance of the gallows, a strange source of pride for an erstwhile clergyman.

In deciding to build in Sweden, Nordenfelt was taking advantage of Swedish Government financial encouragements – tax concessions and even a limited amount of direct financing – to the shipping industry. Sweden became an industrial nation far more quickly and much later than Britain, and brought what now seem remarkably modern politico-economic ideas to bear on the process: in the early 1880s, Swedish industry and communications were in a phase of dynamic expansion that directly suited Nordenfelt's new needs. In Britain, there was no submarine-building tradition to build upon, and there would have been difficulty in persuading such a conservative body as British shipbuilders to take an interest without direct and clearly stated Government interest, especially among those who knew of the *Resurgam* débâcle. In Sweden, there were no such disadvantages: Nordenfelt obviously decided that he could virtually start the submarine-building industry there, more or less as such, from scratch.

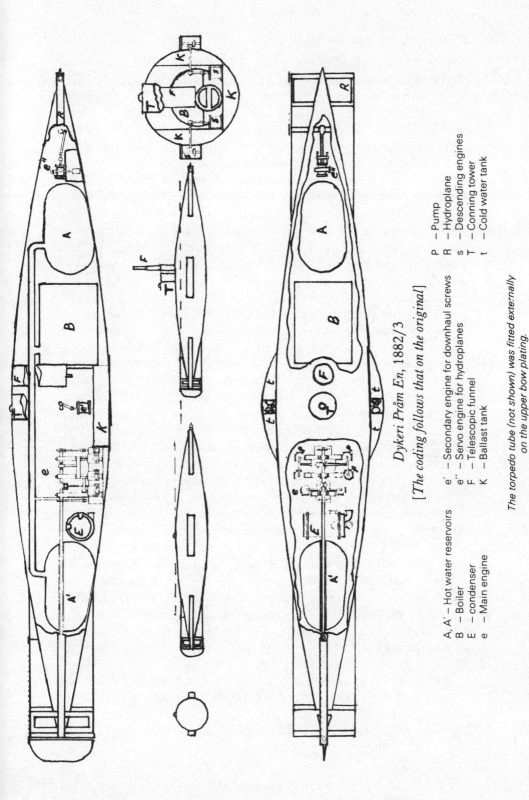

Dykeri Pråm En, 1882/3

[*The coding follows that on the original*]

A, A' – Hot water reservoirs   e' – Secondary engine for downhaul screws   P – Pump
B – Boiler   e'' – Servo engine for hydroplanes   R – Hydroplane
E – condenser   F – Telescopic funnel   s – Descending engines
e – Main engine   K – Ballast tank   T – Conning tower
   t – Cold water tank

*The torpedo tube (not shown) was fitted externally
on the upper bow plating.*

The first Nordenfelt boat was laid down at the Palmcrantz Company's semi-rural yard at Ekensberg, near Stockholm, late in 1882, presenting the slightly odd spectacle of this new weapon of war taking shape against a picturesque background of mountains and conifers, a far cry indeed from Cochran's Birkenhead vistas. The construction was supervised by a Swedish engineer named Enroth, later a submarine pioneer in his own right.

The shape taken by the new boat was very different from that of *Resurgam*. The new boat had the cigar-shaped lines of the *Davids* and the Russian torpedo-boats: the cylindrical mid-section of *Resurgam* was now faired down at either end in an elegant but mistaken imitation of *Nautilus*. Verne's fans would have been impressed and convinced. At 64 feet, she was half as long again as *Resurgam*, and displaced 60 tons.

From the point of view of submerged stability and the toleration of underwater pressure, by far the best shape for a submarine hull is a sphere, closely followed by the 'teardrop' and 'porpoise' shapes favoured by modern submarine architects – and by Garrett, in his 'egg'. Next best is the cylinder. The cigar hull, however, has little to recommend it once submerged: the very uneven distribution of the new boat's bulk over her length (technically, a poor prismatic coefficient for this purpose) would actually hinder the boat beneath the surface. The shape, derived for submarine purposes by false analogy from the 'wave-form' hulls then beginning to be used in surface vessels – a genuinely helpful shape on the surface in heavy seas – was Nordenfelt's choice. This was the clearest manifestation of Nordenfelt's basic desire to submerge a torpedo-boat rather than design a submarine. It would take Garrett five years and several trips to the edge of doom to convince Nordenfelt of his error.

The error in the design of the hull could only be demonstrated the hard way; it would not have occurred to anyone to test the hull before building it. William Froude, the founding father of mathematical hull-design, had persuaded the British Admiralty to set up a test-tank in 1870 (thus marking the advent of scientific naval hydrostatics), but the use of models to determine stability and performance was still widely distrusted in the marine industry at large.

As late at 1911, model tests proving Captain Smith's culpability for the collision between the liner *Olympic* and HMS *Hawke* were greeted with derision as 'gentlemen playing with bathtub toys in pleasant remembrance of younger days', an opinion clearly shared by the White Star Line, who proceeded to give Captain Smith the *Titanic*.

In spite of the efforts of Scott Russell (no submariner himself, as we have seen) and many others, naval architecture was still very much in the no-man's-land between art and science; there are those who maintain this is still the case. At a time when engineering science was surging ahead on all fronts, ship design had a particularly conservative market to contend with, a fact which tended to discourage the application of scientific methods until something went badly wrong.

The mathematical theory of floating and immersed stability is hardly romantic at first sight, but it is no exaggeration to say that much of its history has been written in blood, and never more so than in the field of submarines. It is a great tribute to Garrett's competence – for all the faults of his boats – that his submarines never killed anybody.

The new boat's power plant was, like that of *Resurgam*, a steam engine with a Lamm boiler system, but now the plant would be expected to drive not one propeller, but three: there were two horizontal propellers, mounted amidships in sponsons on either side of the hull, to drive the boat up and down when submerged. Ballast tanks fore and aft were flooded to take the boat down to an awash condition, at which point the horizontal screws took over, submerging the submarine in precisely the vertical plane that *Resurgam* had avoided. Wisely, as it transpired.

Much of the boat's weight was, of course, accounted for by the machinery, which was far more complex than *Resurgam*'s. Apart from driving the three propeller shafts, the engine also powered the blower for the furnace: the boiler had a forced draught, sucking air through the conning-tower when the boat was on the surface. Vacuum was supplied from the main engine to the two independent motors that drove the downhaul screws: these could be automatically shut off by depth-sensors in the hull.

An early casualty from Garrett's original design was a primitive schnorkel system that would have allowed the submarine to run awash using the steam plant in the ordinary manner: Garrett seems to have run into problems with the design of the valve, thus saving himself the burst eardrums experienced by the early efforts with schnorkels in World War Two. It would, however, have overcome what was perhaps the main military disadvantage of the whole system: the very considerable length of time required to raise steam and heat enough for a submerged patrol – nearly twelve hours. This fact alone points to a technical problem: it would have been very unlike Garrett (and even less like Nordenfelt) to compromise sales potential in the interests of crew comfort.

The steam machinery also drove powerful vacuum pumps for the ballast tanks and bilges. Crowning the whole system was a tele-scopic funnel, which had to be retracted and capped off before diving.

The boat's four-bladed propeller was five feet in diameter, with a pitch of 7 feet 6 inches – rather too large for the engine, as things emerged.

Like *Resurgam*, the new boat was designed with a reserve of buoyancy to bring the boat back to the surface automatically in the event of engine failure. The obvious potential for military disaster possessed by this system was outweighed by an understandable dread of an unscheduled crash-dive. Davy Jones did not take prisoners.

Nordenfelt held strong views on submergence which were largely the product of justifiable timidity in the face of history. The system of horizontal screws, perhaps the strangest feature of the design to us, a hundred years later, was entirely of his design:

> All previous boats [have] had most unreliable means of descending and ascending. The descent by steering downwards in the American boats, twenty years ago, was quite as dangerous as the attempts before and after that time to lower and raise the boats, and to keep them steady at any desired depth, by means of increasing and decreasing the weight of the boats by more or less water-ballast, or by altering their displacement.
>   None of these boats used the principle which I have applied to pull the boat down by mechanical means, while relying upon its always retained buoyancy for rising; so that if the mechanical apparatus fail, the boat rises again to the surface. Nor did they have the tendency to steadiness given by the two forces of constant pulling down, by my horizontal screws, acting all the time, whether still or moving, against the pulling upwards caused by the buoyancy.[1]

When Nordenfelt uttered these apparently fervent words, six months after the trials of the boat, he already knew that this system did not work: Garrett was not alone in wishing to avoid boring the audience with details. Free surfaces in the boat's water tanks would not allow the apparently common-sense balancing act he describes here. Submerging in the new boat was in fact a terrifying business that verged on the heroic.

By far the most novel aspect of the boat's machinery was its depth-keeping mechanism, which depended on the two horizontal propellers and a very remarkable system of automatically-operated hydroplanes. From a modern perspective, there is something vaguely laughable about this set-up, but the fear of sinking in a submarine was real enough – especially Nordenfelt's, all the stronger in a man who never personally went down in one. It is in this system that Nordenfelt's torpedo-oriented mentality makes itself most apparent:

> The greatest difficulty in constructing a safe submarine boat is to ensure its maintaining the horizontal position ... for should the bow of the boat point downwards ... it is clear that the boat would in a moment strike the bottom or be wrecked.
> In the bow of the boat and on either side are balanced rudders on one and the same axle.
> These rudders are always maintained in the horizontal position by a weight attached to an arm fixed at right angles to the rudder axle.
> This weight will always maintain its arm in a vertical position, and since the rudders are at right angles to it they will always be kept in a horizontal position ... if the boat should take any position pointing downwards, the boat will be at an angle to the rudders, which will then tend to force the boat up again into a horizontal position.[2]

This system, like its hydrostatically-controlled shutoffs to the downhaul screws, was borrowed directly from the depth-keeping system on the Whitehead torpedo: it is not too far from the truth to describe the whole boat as a somewhat suspect compromise between *Resurgam* and a very large torpedo. A cynic might also point out that this balance system was not only patented at the time but (in Britain at least) a military secret. On the positive side, the hydroplanes were in potentially effective positions fore and aft, rather than amidships, one of the worst features of *Resurgam*'s design.

It was the boat's other safety (!) device, however, which contained a hefty handful of the seeds of doom: '[Longitudinal balance] can be adjusted by having more or less water in the two cisterns fore and aft.'[3]

This was no more than the dreadful truth, and the most obvious proof of the ignorance of the laws of flotation at that time. Free-surface effect is now the small change of naval architecture; the dire effect on stability of liquid, however little, slopping about in tanks aboard ships was still little understood at this stage, though

Garrett, having glimpsed it in the 'egg', would discover it soon enough.

Nor can we afford to smile at this from our bastion of technological omniscience. In March 1987, the worst English Channel shipping disaster to date, the capsize and loss of the *Herald of Free Enterprise*, was directly attributable to the free-surface effect of water that had breached the ship's car deck. What can sometimes seem like the antics of the early submariners resulted in important contributions to the theory of shipbuilding; all too often, it has been forgotten that rational application of the theory can require a high degree of single-mindedness and vigilance.

Having dealt, if only to Nordenfelt's satisfaction, with the problems of submerged stability, it only remained to consider the problems of actually living on board the new boat. The boat's trials would reveal dire problems of atmospheric hygiene far worse than those of *Resurgam*.

Nordenfelt dispensed with the use of air purifiers. Although it was obviously impractical to have the boat's crew encumbered by Pneumatophores, this was nonetheless a tremendous blow to Garrett. Nearly ten years (off and on) of work had gone into perfecting what was, after all, a revolutionary breathing apparatus: he could not pursue its development while working for the Nordenfelt Company, least of all in Sweden. The Pneumatophore, already doomed by the death of the Garrett Company, slid into limbo, never to return. Nordenfelt expressly damned the idea of chemical assistance in the Nordenfelt Submarine Company's brochure:

> No compressed air need be, nor has it ever been carried, nor any chemical method of maintaining the air at its normal composition, as the boat contains such efficient air space as to render such arrangements unnecessary.[4]

This, as Nordenfelt and Garrett both knew (in the latter's case from dire experience), was only true if one assumed perfection in the firebox seals and adopted a wilfully optimistic estimate of the temperature in the boat while under way submerged. The public trials would be carefully presented so as to mask these difficulties. Carefully omitting any embarrassing provisos, Nordenfelt went so far as to distribute an affidavit on the matter, sworn by Eskil Lindblad, the Managing Engineer at the Palmcrantz yard:

I am ... able to confirm that four full grown people [one more than the boat's operating complement] ... were at one time for a period of six hours hermetically shut up in the said boat; that these persons did not carry with them any apparatus or ingredients for the purifying of the air, or any similar apparatus, and that after the lapse of the said six hours they appeared to be in fully good health; and further, that the temperature of the air, which, when I entered the boat immediately after the experiment was finished, was between 20° and 30° C and did not seem to me worse than that the persons in the boat could still have performed, for some time, the work that might have been required for the management of the boat.[5]

This is promotional sleight of hand, pure and simple. Putting to one side the fact that Lindblad, who was not a medical man, was hardly qualified to testify on the men's health, he neglects to point out that the machinery, once operating, would have *at least* doubled the ambient temperature in the boat. The fact that lighting within the boat came from candles could only have made things worse, though Nordenfelt, in a moment of high comedy, once declared these a safety measure – the crew knew it was time to surface when the flames took the last of the oxygen and went out. Garrett would be the one to suffer from this advanced concept of safety engineering while Nordenfelt literally downed the champagne up top in his yacht.

Similarly, while Nordenfelt luxuriated in his mansion during the early trials of the boat, Garrett would have to rough it on board. In what seems almost like a joke at Garrett's expense, sleeping arrangements were only slightly more comfortable than those of *Resurgam*: while two of the three crewmen could (just) swing hammocks, someone (Garrett, for reasons that defy divination) had to sleep on top of a pile of empty coal-sacks.

The manufacturer's recommended depth for the new boat, according to the early brochure, was 100 feet, a figure later adjusted in the face of experience and prudence to 50 feet, which if anything slightly underestimated the strength of the hull, whose riveted construction appears to have been sound enough. Our paramedical friend Lindblad was only prepared to confirm having been to an operating depth of *16* feet. This was probably in an accident.

The submarine's *raison d'être*, the Whitehead torpedo, was carried in an external tube at the bow, making her the first submarine ever to be mounted with a torpedo-tube. The torpedo could not be launched while the boat was submerged, a feature that would place the crew in hair-raising danger if the tube were ever used in anger.

The crew was expected to bring the boat within Whitehead range of the enemy, either fully submerged or awash, the latter if they wished to see where they were going; the boat would then surface and the crew would swarm out to launch the torpedo. To have any chance of hitting the target, the boat needed to surface within 100 yards of the enemy. The embarrassing fact that the wash resulting from the torpedo's launch would have thrown everybody overboard was not insisted upon in the brochures: the trials were carefully (not to say brazenly) designed not to include actual use of the torpedo by filling the tube *after* the trials.

The first gun to be mounted on a submarine, a Nordenfelt 1½-inch quick-firing gun, was fitted in a removable mounting forward of the conning-tower: like the torpedo tube, this could only have been used while the boat was surfaced, an unappealing proposition when one considers the extremely low freeboard of the boat floating at rest, let alone the frankly terrifying idea of trying to use the gun while the boat was actually on the move in a seaway. There are no records of this being attempted. The brochure's stipulation that the gun should be fired by the Captain can hardly have been well received by the already overworked Garrett.

The completed boat was launched in July 1883. There was no ceremonial. In keeping with the boat's secret-weapon status, the launch was a clandestine affair. The boat was launched more or less fully fitted out, and was promptly fitted with the rudimentary mast and rigging needed for the surface trials.

These took the form of a jaunt (no other word seems suitable) from Stockholm to Gothenburg in the August of 1883, to bring her round to the naval yard at Karlskrona for final fitting-out. This entailed taking a delightful route through the lakes and canals of Sweden's Lake District. While this would certainly have helped to keep her from the prying eyes of Nordenfelt's rivals (real or imagined), it is difficult not to imagine Cap'n Garrett commanding the submarine in a straw boater. Taking the record from *Resurgam*, this relatively unpretentious trip became the longest voyage by a submarine up to that time, albeit entirely on the surface. The tale of the trials begins as an idyll of submarining folk:

> On Saturday the 18th of August 1883 the Nordenfelt Submarine Boat left the quay of Aetelbolaget Palmcrantz and Co at Carlsvik, near Stockholm, about 4 o'clock in the afternoon, having on board as crew G.W. Garrett (Captain), L. Nordström (1st Engineer) and Mr Jansson

(2nd Engineer). We had in bunkers and in sacks altogether about 150 cubic feet of coal, and, since our average consumption was about 6 [cubic] feet per hour when making from 6 to 7 knots, we could undertake a journey of 24 hours' duration, which if the weather would permit us to proceed so fast would mean a distance of about 150 miles.

Since I had a new bearing on the high pressure connecting rod, I deemed it best to go at no greater speed than 5 knots [nautical miles] per hour. I steamed therefore down Lake Malar to Södertalje, where I arrived about 8 o'clock, having made 21 knots. As I had a long stretch the next day, I deemed it best to fill up again with coal, so I took in as much as I could conveniently stow. I arranged with the Lock Master to let me through the gates at 4 o'clock on the Sunday morning and then went to the hotel to get some supper and somewhere to lie down for an hour or two, as although the two engineers had hammocks and places to hang them up there was no possibility of stretching the third hammock. I found it impossible to get a bed, and should have been obliged to lay down on the coal sacks but for the kindness of Captain Pettersson of the Steamship *Södertalje*, who allowed me to use a sofa in his cabin.

At 1.30 on Sunday morning, I got up and went on board, roused up the crew and got steam up and coffee drunk by about 3.30. A Pilot came on board about 4 o'clock, and we passed by means of a lock from Lake Malar to the Baltic. We had fine weather all the morning with a westerly breeze. I kept well in under the land and therefore had almost no sea to contend with until late in the afternoon, when, abreast of Braviken, the wind increased to half a gale and shifted to the south-west. This was the first time I had been on the boat in a sea which made a clean breach over her and I was a little anxious. However, I went slow and after rounding Oxelö I kept her more to the westward, which brought the sea better ahead. She went through well, with the sea falling off her seeming to have no effect whatever on her to make her either pitch or roll. [...]

Having cleared my papers at the Custom Office [at Mem] and paid the canal dues, I entered the canal which joins Lake Roxen with the Baltic. There being many locks and it being dark, I did not reach Söderköping till after 11 o'clock. Having seen the engine wiped down and the men to their hammocks, I laid down on the coal sacks and did not open my eyes till about 7 o'clock. Having seen the fires lighted, I went into the town to send telegrams and buy coal etc. I could buy no coal in Söderköping but by favour I got some slack, which having taken on board I left Söderköping about 12 o'clock on Monday the 20th of August. I proceeded by the canal to Norsholm on Lake Roxen, where I arrived about 6 o'clock. The canal was most troublesome. The boat, having no keel, steered wretchedly in the very little water we had in the canal, and there being no protection whatever to the propeller made the shooting the bridges and entering the locks an extremely difficult job, as they fine you heavily for every time you run against the gates.

> Leaving Norsholm about 7 o'clock, where we had some little delay in
> clearing the Canal Office on account of their never having heard of a
> boat described as 'en dykeri pråm' and having no name. However, I to
> please them christened her *Dykeri Pråm En* and so went free.[6]

The boat had been launched without a name, presumably in the
expectation of her being given one by whichever lucky government
won in the inevitable scramble to buy her. The canal's rules were
simple: no name, no passage. Garrett presumably thought that his
typically laboured semi-joke would go no further. However, then as
now, nothing escaped the all-seeing eye of Swedish bureaucracy:
the boat was officially registered as *Dykeri Pråm En* (*Diving Barge
One*), a bathetic name in every sense imaginable. Nordenfelt's
reaction, perhaps mercifully, is not recorded.

Garrett's account of the sea-keeping of the boat has the ring of
truth: it would not in fact have taken much of a sea to 'make a clean
breach over her', as in the case of *Resurgam* and, indeed, most
modern submarines.

Garrett's complaint about the lack of a keel causing difficulties is
interesting. The canals in the Swedish lakes were not intended for
large craft, but were mostly used by small vessels and barges (hence
'Pråm'). The submarine was large enough to be subject to a
phenomenon, familiar to house-boat owners, known as 'sniffing the
ground'. This is an interaction between the hull and the canal wall
very similar to the tendency of two ships to collide sideways when
under way in close proximity, a serious problem for naval vessels
when replenishing at sea. There was also insufficient water under
the boat's rudder for it to have had much steering effect (an
alarming feature in supertankers when close inshore).

Steaming across inland lakes in a submarine also has its
drawbacks, especially when the boat has the deliberately low
profile of *Dykeri Pråm En*. Even now, it would be less than
reasonable to expect the average Lake Windermere steamer
captain to make allowances for maverick 60-ton cigars in the lake.
In the provincial Sweden of 1883, such a presumption was barely
sane. Garrett, however, saw things differently:

> Leaving Norsholm, I laid my course for Berg, about 16 miles distant on
> the other side of Lake Roxen, where we arrived shortly after 10 o'clock.
> About 9 o'clock, it being very dark, I heard a steamer's whistle not far
> off. The steamer carried no lights. After whistling, she increased her
> speed, and since she was high pressure I could make out her position by

(Right) Garrett's sketch for the engine of **Resurgam,** literally on the back of an envelope.

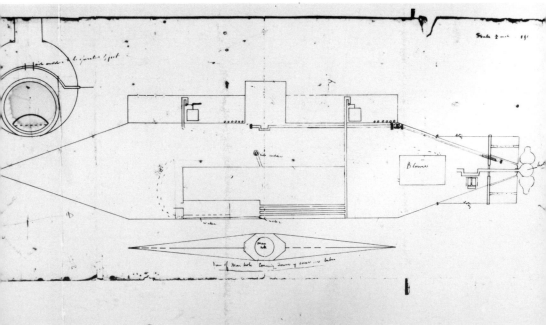

Jack Aitkin's re-drawn builder's draught of **Resurgam.**

Resurgam, 24 November, 1879. Right to left: J.T. Cochran, Captain Jackson, Garrett, George Price and Jack Aitken.

means of the sparks from her funnel. We had all our lights on in order, both masthead and sidelights. Seeing that she was right ahead and coming down on us, I blew my whistle and ported my helm. The Captain of the steamer put his helm to starboard and increased his speed, seeing which I deemed a collision unavoidable. I gave the order 'full speed astern' and then called the engineers out of the engine-room. I put my helm hard-a-starboard so that I should come steam on to her side. We just cleared her stem. Had we touched her, we should certainly have sunk her without damage to ourselves.[7]

It may be kindest to describe this last remark, or at least its final observation, as the expression of a pious hope. Garrett's precaution of summoning his crew up from below shows a firmer grip of the situation than his exaggerated faith in the integrity of the submarine's hull.

Garrett, who held no formal seaman's qualifications whatever (and never would hold any), appears to have overlooked at least the local rule of the road. From the point of view of the denizens of *Dykeri Pråm En*, Garrett may have handled a genuine emergency well, if the boat's actual manoeuvres were not analysed too closely. The steamer captain almost certainly thought otherwise; Garrett, who never mastered Swedish, would at least have been spared understanding the inevitable torrent of abuse from the bridge of the other craft. Typically, he did not trouble to record the aftermath of what was, after all, the product of his own folly. To put out at night in a craft with such a low silhouette was a dubious policy at best, but taking her out into traffic in pitch blackness was another example of the hubris that sank *Resurgam*. Throughout his life, Garrett showed a tendency to repeat his mistakes as though he were testing them for experimental error.

Having sniffed and swung his way through the Göta Kanal, much of it at 1 knot through dense fog, Garrett finally reached Lake Boren at 4 p.m. the next day. The lake offered no problems beyond a little rain: at the entrance of the Motala Kanal, where Garrett 'knew that crowds would be down to look at the remarkable craft I was in charge of' (so much for secrecy), the weather cleared in time for Garrett's talent for the ridiculous to put in an appearance.

In a scene worthy of Edward Lear, Garrett and his intrepid pioneers sat down to an ostentatious high tea on the after end of the hull. Not surprisingly, this attracted attention:

Whilst eating, I was astonished to see quite a number of boats put off, chiefly rowed by women. These came, and on daring to come close rowed round and round us. I invited them to take coffee and cognac with us, but they dared not come on board. Having finished our evening meal I proceeded through the Motala Canal to Lake Vättern, and having laid her up to the quay I succeeded in getting a bed at the Hotel there, and slept well till about 7 o'clock the next morning (Wednesday the 22nd).[8]

The two other crewmen stayed in their hammocks. Their relationship with Garrett must have been a complex affair.

After a day cleaning the boiler, blackened by the slack that Garrett had been forced to burn, Garrett allowed himself another night of luxury before setting off again. August 23 began with an intimation of mortality from the Spirit of Naval Architecture and ended in the grand Garrett manner, with his boat defying the elements and *just* getting away with it:

The barometer had been falling steadily for the past 24 hours and this morning opened with a thick mist and rain, with the wind from the South East. I noticed that the boat lay lower in the water than before, the cause being [the lower salinity in] Lake Vättern: we never tasted better or sweeter drinking water.

We started about 10 o'clock and all went well until we were clear of the Skägärd off Motala: when we got out into the open water, the wind suddenly increased to a gale from the S to SW and in an incredibly short time a nasty choppy cross sea got up, which rose so high that at times the broken tops of the waves went over my head as I stood on the boat, and a little water went down the tower and found its way into the boat. I began to be a little doubtful as to the result, so having made Fjukö, which is as nearly as possible in the middle of Vättern, I determined to lay to under its lea till the weather moderated, which I quite expected it would, as by this time it was raining very hard. I rounded the north end of Fjukö, and having brought the land dead to windward I shot a line ashore and went below to get a little food and warmth, as I was completely wet through, in spite of oilskins. I had just got a plate of cold ham and hot potatoes on my knees when bump! I felt we were aground. I sprang on deck and found that although I had not been below 10 minutes the wind had gone round to the west and the boat had swung broadside on to the land. As the wind had only just begun to blow on that side of the island, no sea was running, so no damage was done, and after a little backing and filling I got her afloat again and took her round to the eastern side of the island. I did not go below again, but had my ham and potatoes brought up to me, but it was impossible to eat anything, as the plate filled with rain the moment it came from under cover.

By this time it was 4 o'clock and I could wait no longer, as the

No hotel this time, and *wet* coal sacks to boot. After this night of

navigation from Vanäsudde to Forswik is more intricate than our journey hitherto, and was more dangerous, as I had no pilot on board. The sea was still coming from the south-west, though the wind was in the west, so I was obliged to go to the southward of my course in order that she might be head on. However, as soon as I got near the land the sea began to moderate, and so I bore up again to the Northward and rounded Vanäsudde about half past seven o'clock and arrived at Forswik between 9 and 10. Leaving Forswik, I proceeded about a knot and then, the night being dark and we being almost worn out, I took the boat out of the Farleden and, having anchored, we went to rest.[9]
soggy martyrdom, the boat began her descent through the canal system, reaching Sjötorp on Lake Vänern the following evening after 'a most laborious day'.

Two days of laborious but uneventful flogging through the canals brought them to Trollhatten, where the expedition's leader 'got a good meal for myself and the crew and a bed for myself' in preparation for the final leg of the journey, a last slog down the ditch to Gothenburg:

On Monday morning – the 27th – we were under way before 11 o'clock, and after a most laborious day – for it was blowing a full gale right in our teeth and raining hard all the day – we arrived at Gothenburg about 5 o'clock, and, proceeding up the Hamnkanal, I made fast opposite the Bourse and went ashore to recuperate.

In conclusion, it is only justice to the men who were my companions that I say that a harder week's work seldom has to be gone through by 3 men, but after a night's rest and some good food we none of us felt the worse for our exertions.[10]

The journey had established that the boat was at least a worthy surface vessel, which surprised nobody. Submerged trials, however, would prove a different matter. In the meantime, the boat was taken on a slow, careful crossing of the Øresund to Copenhagen, where the king of Denmark had his first glimpse of a submarine boat. Wisely, no attempt was made at this stage to press her underwater claims.

No records of the boat's secret submerged trials (off Landskrona, in southern Sweden) have survived beyond the deeply suspect claims in the brochure. There is, however, an affidavit from Garrett's shipmate Lars Norström:

I have several times been under water with the boat, and observed that the master [Garrett], who was in charge of the heightening and lowering apparatus, was able to lower the boat to any depth he wished, and to let the boat remain at such depth so long as he wished, and that he, when it pleased him, was able to heighten the boat to the surface of the sea without lightening the boat in any way. I have observed that the temperature when we commenced working with 150lbs pressure on each square inch in the hot water tank is about 45° Celsius, and that after having been at work the temperature has gradually gone down to 35° Celsius. I place in general full confidence in the Nordenfelt Submarine Boat system and am willing at any time to accompany my present master under water whenever he wishes.[11]

Making due allowance for the fact that Norström was a Nordenfelt employee, and therefore unlikely to criticise the boat or its management, the last personal reference to Garrett is an interesting testimonial. The phrase 'so long as nobody moves a muscle' could be inserted almost anywhere in the paean to the boat's depth-keeping qualities, but it is just possible that an engineer with Garrett's talent might have been able to manipulate the boat broadly as described for short periods and at a very conservative depth, an interpretation borne out in the subsequent public trials.

Norström's comments on the temperature inside the boat require closer examination, however. It is fairly astounding to find a working environment of 45°C being offered as a selling point, but even this sultry statistic wilts under careful inspection of what is actually said. When work *started* with the hot water pressure as given, the boat would have just been closed up, either for diving or running awash: the process of stoking up the boiler to raise sufficient heat and steam would easily have generated 45° by this time. When the boat was closed up, it is quite certain that the temperature would have risen even further, conceivably to 60° and beyond: as the engine cooled, the temperature may indeed have dropped to the advertised 35°. How long would this take?

I have subsequently observed the boat to have gone a distance of 14 knots [nautical miles] propelled by steam stored up in the boat when the shutting had taken place.[12]

On the surface, about three hours; submerged, nearly six – a long time to spend breathing carbon monoxide in an underwater autoclave, breathing out (and in) copious quantities of carbon dioxide while performing one of the most dangerous tasks in nautical history. The affidavit is careful not to spell this out, any more than it spells out the time taken to raise sufficient steam for this respiratory adventure.

The engine room of USS *Monitor* is known to have reached a

(literally) breathtaking *87°C* in the summer of 1862, *before* being closed up for battle, a situation directly comparable with the Nordenfelt boat. There is quite simply no reason to believe that the submarine could have done any better – on the contrary. The persistent illness of Garrett and his assistants and the careful wording of the affidavit can only add to one's suspicions.

It was during the early underwater trials, carried out in secret in the spring of 1884, that the first serious danger signs appeared. Garrett, newly returned from spending Easter with his family, reported that the crew were complaining of drowsiness after being shut up in the boat even for short periods. The trials continued regardless until July, when Garrett himself collapsed on board during an underwater run: without Garrett's guidance, the boat was only brought safely to the surface with the greatest difficulty.

Garrett was out of action for three weeks. While no medical records survive, it is fairly certain that this was a recurrence of the respiratory condition that had repeatedly struck him down in Manchester, exacerbated by the atrocious conditions inside the submarine. The trials were halted until Garrett recovered: they were impossible without him. When Garrett returned to Morecambe at Christmas, just in time for the birth of his son George on Christmas Day, he was visibly unwell. Nor was all well at home: in a noticeably shaky hand, Garrett rules off the entries chronicling his family on the fly-leaf of the family Bible, and writes '*finis* – no more allowed'.

Regardless of the implications of the effects of the boat on the crew and the fact that only one man seemed capable of handling her with any degree of safety, preparations went ahead for a full programme of trials, both dived and on the surface, to be held off Landskrona in the summer of 1885.

The tensions between Garrett and Nordenfelt surfaced early in 1885, when Nordenfelt patented his own alternative to the Whitehead torpedo. This was a wire-guided electric torpedo, revolutionary in that its electric power-source was internal: other early guided torpedoes, such as the Sims-Edison, supplied power down the command cable. The new torpedo, however, could only be launched from a surface vessel: Nordenfelt, still unconvinced of the practicality of the submarine as a delivery system, was trying to find another, less problematic way to solve the problem of the Whitehead's lack of long-range accuracy. Fortunately for Garrett's work, Nordenfelt's torpedo was an utter failure at its early trials.

Had it been otherwise, it is more than likely that Nordenfelt would have cancelled the whole submarine enterprise, in which (at this stage at least) he had little faith.

Modifications were made to the submarine in an attempt to deal with her more tractable defects. Early awash trials of the boat had revealed a tendency for the boat to take in water through the hatch when under way in even the calmest sea; the cigar hull was disgracing itself. Coamings not unlike those round the conning-tower of *Resurgam* were fitted to deflect the boat's bow-wave, an ironic vindication of Garrett's original design.

While Garrett slaved over what he knew to be the impossible task of rendering the boat sea-worthy below the surface, Nordenfelt issued invitations to the trials, which would be the world's first public trials of a submarine (and very nearly the last – we are unlikely to see the trials of the Trident boats on television).

Nordenfelt's good friends the Prince and Princess of Wales headed the list; the King and Queen of Denmark were also invited, as was the Tsarina. Political tensions never seem to have spoilt the conviviality of an international royal armaments jamboree in this period. For European royalty, of course, such events were simply family gatherings, but the mood seems to have extended to the remarkable array of 39 naval and military potentates summoned to the Oresund that year.

Senior officers came from Britain, Germany, France, Holland, Belgium, Greece, Turkey and Russia, all in varying degrees preparing for war with each other,conceivably employing Nordenfelt's new boat. Three other powers were represented: Japan, a genie beginning to tire of the confines of his bottle; Brazil, in many ways the least likely of all, – and Turkey, then as usual in a state of semi-war with Greece. The Sick Man of Europe was roused from his bed in the person of the Minister of Marine by this note from Nordenfelt (we can assume that the other invitations were similar):

53, Richmond Street SW

London 29 June 1885

I have the honour to enclose a statement with reference to my Submarine Boat. It is my intention to make a series of official experiments with this submarine boat this summer in the Sound near Copenhagen.

If your Excellency is good enough to let me know whether you would like to send an officer to attend at these trials, I will give notice in good time for him to reach Copenhagen. If I can get ready, it is my intention to carry out the experiments during the first and second week in August.

I have the honour to be Your Excellency's Most Obedient Servant

T. Nordenfelt[13]

Nordenfelt, ensconced in his London home, played no part in the physical preparation of the boat; this was entirely Garrett's responsibility. Nordenfelt did not in fact return to Scandinavia until the week before the trials. Given the state of international communications at that time, this is evidence of a remote style of management at best, even making allowance for his promotional and other activities. Apart from his very limited confidence in the submarine ('if I can get ready' hardly glows with pride), the fact was that Nordenfelt considered the Submarine Torpedo Boat Company to be very much a sideline, at least until the hardware proved itself. The mid-1880s were the peak years of the Nordenfelt Gun and Ammunition Company, with Nordenfelt patenting and marketing worldwide a daunting succession of improved guns and other ordnance. All of this kept him too busy to take adequate direct interest in the submarine, leading to a huge work-load devolving onto Garrett, whose wellbeing suffered accordingly. The prime beneficiary of this state of affairs was Zaharoff. An armaments salesman was unlikely to starve in the Balkans: for a man of Zaharoff's abilities and very attenuated morals, the opportunities, and therefore the returns, were immense. Nor was business confined to the Balkans. Zaharoff would later remember the mid-1880s as the time when he read in the newspaper of a small war in West Africa: he chartered six ships, filled them to the gunwales with arms, and sent three to each side. Whether the anecdote is true or not, it is entirely characteristic. Although a Nordenfelt employee, Zaharoff's complex of kick-backs, bribes, commissions and back-door pay-offs ensured that in the long run his income greatly exceeded his employer's.

Meanwhile, the fact that Garrett's task – rendering the new boat reliable under water – was all but impossible cannot have contributed much to industrial relations. Although Lars Norström's personal faith in Garrett and the submarine (in that order) appears to have been genuine, the Nordenfelt boats would always be subject to desertions from the crew. Given the danger of the task and Nordenfelt's Dickensian management, it is impossible to criticise anyone for this. Being a pioneer is often directly at odds with common sense: working within the cotton-mill hierarchy of the Nordenfelt company, it must have been difficult to see a convincing reason for risking one's life. Except for the usually absentee ownership of Nordenfelt, Garrett himself would be the only common factor among the four Garrett-Nordenfelt boats: he was, after all, the only man with a motive for being so.

The sheer logistics of bringing so many celebrities together forced the date of the trials back to the end of September, by which time the weather in the Øresund (the Sound between Sweden and Denmark) was far less reliable than it would have been in early August, though it was nothing like as bad as Nordenfelt would later claim. By way of making excuses for the boat's performance, he declared that 'the wind blew like furies', a grotesque exaggeration: a chill wind did indeed blow, however, for the commercial prospects of the boat.

The Swedish Admiralty laid on a gunboat, the *Edda*, for the use and convenience of the visitors during the trials. The *Edda*, herself only built in 1884, was largely a showcase for Nordenfelt's other wares (hardly a coincidence), and attracted rather more compliments than the submarine once the trials had started, on a very cold (but calm) 22 September 1885.

The submarine, commanded, as always, by Garrett, was towed out from Landskrona by a steam launch: two miles out, the boat was being cast loose when the forward hydroplanes were fouled by the tow-rope, necessitating the urgent attentions of a Swedish rating from the launch, who ran along the submarine's hull and cleared the rope, to warm applause from the *Edda*. Unfortunately, the hydroplanes were damaged; the boat could dive, but could not manoeuvre under water.

The first day's trials were therefore confined to circling the *Edda* at five knots: the twelve knots proclaimed in the published specification was quite simply beyond the machinery's capabilities. However, the day's great achievement was a three-hour run with the boat closed up. When the boat was re-opened, Nordenfelt proudly announced that the temperature on board was a mere 33°C; the temperature in the middle of the run, easily determined from the boat's own thermometer, was neither offered nor – amazingly – requested. This must have been a great deal higher, quite possibly in the *Monitor* league. Presumably to head off such unkind criticism, Nordenfelt was fond of citing the 45° supposedly reached in the stokeholds of (unnamed, and suspiciously chilly) monitors when comparing his boat with her putative rivals.

Underwater operations were limited to a series of rather apologetic dives to an unconvincing 5 feet, surfacing almost immediately. After the twenty-minute rigmarole of telescoping the funnel and closing up, the boat took an eternity to dive, a matter of flooding the tanks fore and aft and then gently pulling her under with the vertical propellers, standing stock still as the free surfaces in the tanks did their worst.

In spite of supposedly frantic overnight repairs, the second day's operations were even less exciting, including no underwater activities at all. The boat merely steamed ten miles on the surface towards Helsingør, again at a dreary five knots, demonstrating a surface capability that was not in fact in doubt. The visiting celebrities expressed little more than polite interest.

The boat's underwater capabilities finally came under the public gaze on the third day. Operating in a glassy sea, the submarine's best performance was a submerged run of 300 yards, which took her $4\frac{1}{2}$ minutes – a submerged speed barely exceeding two knots.

The *Times* anonymous correspondent (actually Lord Sydenham of Combe), who had previously described the conning-tower coamings, rather uncharitably, as 'coffin-shaped', described the underwater trials in commendably even-handed detail:

Riding light on a gray [*sic*], and almost motionless, sea, the hull of the torpedo boat was scarcely visible at 1,000 yards. In spite of her light gray colour, however, the vertical combings [*sic*] supporting the cupola showed out dark on account of the abrupt changes in the angle of reflection. Thus, viewed broadside on, the appearance was that of a short dark log lying on the surface of the water. In this position, and in a calm sea, the wash of the screw was visible, and in broad daylight could hardly fail to attract attention. It was generally felt, however, that such a boat advancing head on at speed would offer a particularly unsatisfactory mark to fire at even with machine guns; while in a bad light it would be almost impossible to shoot with any chance of effect. [...]

There was no smoke or escaping steam to proclaim her presence at a distance of many miles, and up to 1,500 yards range at least she could probably advance with absolute impunity. The process of sealing up and sinking to deep draught occupied about 20 minutes, and in this position the top of the combings was just awash, and only the cupola was visible above the surface. Thus trimmed the available target becomes insignificant and the possibility of hitting it extremely remote. Submerged to a depth of 5ft in a calm sea, the boat was visible as a shadow on the surface of the water, and from the tops of the *Edda* she could be distinctly made out at a distance of about 600 yards. The observer, however, knew, exactly the spot at which she had sunk, and, failing this advantage, would probably have been quite unable to detect her position. While moving under the water no trace of the boat was visible, and it was impossible to foresee the position at which she would rise. The impression produced on the mind by seeing the boat thus disappear was decidedly uncomfortable, and it was generally acknowledged that the sense of insecurity which the mere presence of such a boat would cause on board ship would be no small factor in war.[14]

The fact remained, however, that the boat could not be said to have proved herself as a submarine. It was widely felt that the best use of the boat would be as a semi-submersible torpedo boat, like the Confederate *Davids* of the American Civil War, making her final attacking run in an awash condition, at maximum speed. Sydenham thought the Nordenfelt boat would be ideal in this mode, if her awash speed could be brought up to twenty knots. This figure, however, was monstrously in excess of the submarine's capabilities, especially when running closed up. Even the twelve knots specified in Nordenfelt's brochure was expecting too much. Sydenham offered a checklist of faults:

> Certain defects are obvious. The speed is insufficient: the period of 12 hours necessary to get up pressure is too long: the vertical combings must be abolished: there is no means of getting in or out of the boat when it is submerged; the perfecting of the vertical steering arrangements is perhaps doubtful.[14]

Unfortunately, the 'combings' could not be abolished without abolishing the crew when the boat foundered as a result. Whether he knew it or not, Sydenham had touched upon the submarine's main fault in criticising the 'vertical steering arrangements'. They were not merely unperfected: they barely worked at all.

Examination of the accounts of the submerged trials reveals what was wrong: the problem turns out to be a vicious circle of technical shortcomings. The boat's underwater speed was far too slow for the hydroplanes (the 'vertical steering arrangements') to have any effect, with or without the pendulums – the flow of water over them, which should have held the boat on an even keel, was simply inadequate at the speeds reached. This, added to the unchecked free surfaces in the tanks, would have rendered the boat lethally unstable below the surface: quite simply, nobody dared move, for fear of upsetting the boat's balance, especially in the absence of the supposed steadying power of the hydroplanes. Garrett could therefore only operate at a very conservative depth.

For a submarine to escape the surface wave turbulence of her own hull, she must dive to a depth equal to at least half her own length – in this case 32 feet, over six times the depth actually achieved: the Nordenfelt boat's speed, unimpressive to begin with, would be cut even further by her own turbulence. The low speed in turn rendered the hydroplanes ineffective, and so on.

While the assembled VIPs would not have grasped the problem in these terms, it was soon apparent that the impression made had been a poor one. Lord Sydenham was not entirely damning, however. The sheer novelty of the submarine concept remained fresh in his mind:

> These first public trials of a submarine boat will, however, undoubtedly produce results far beyond a mere criticism of the existing craft. Many shrewd heads have been set thinking, and the great possibilities of this mode of attack have been brought home with a force which no mere description, however graphic, could have exerted. It is one thing to read of vaguely described exploits in the American war, or indefinite rumours of Russian experiments. It is quite another matter to be brought face to face with a boat which disappears before one's eyes to reappear in an unexpected position. The present boat is admittedly imperfect, but its performances have served to show clearly the possibilities which lie before us. Some of the difficulties which beset the construction of a submarine boat have been overcome more or less completely. The rest appear to be scarcely insurmountable, and it may be taken as certain that the perfection of this most dangerous weapon of attack is only a matter of time and brains.[16]

Inspired by a vision of submarine warfare glimpsed, however dimly, at Landskrona, he shared Garrett's original dream of a Götterdämmerung for ironclads:

> If [submarine boats] were to end the day of the great ironclads, few would perhaps be found to regret the change; and it would be a strange instance of the irony of progress if these costly monsters became obsolete before they had ever really justified their existence. On the whole, small and non-aggressive Powers would perhaps gain most by this new and comparatively cheap weapon ...[17]

Standing with Lord Sydenham on the quarter-deck of the *Edda* had been the official British Government representative, Sir Andrew Clarke, the Inspector-General of Fortifications, embodying the British view, promoted by a grudging Royal Navy with ironclads of its own, that submarine boats would be primarily a weapon of coastal defence. Unknown to Garrett and Nordenfelt, however, Sir Andrew was far more than a casual observer. That April, when the 1885 Anglo-Russian war scare looked more like turning into the real thing than usual diplomatic snarl-out, he had presented a secret memorandum to the British Government, urging them to set aside £20,000 for a submarine boat, which he considered vital for the defence of the realm. Sydenham, in supporting him, was writing for a more influential audience than the country's breakfast-tables:

> For purposes of defence, such boats could on the approach of a fleet take up their stations near the position from which bombardment was practicable and await the enemy in placid security. Open and otherwise almost indefensible towns, such as Brighton, would possess a means of defence ready to their hand. Submarine boats could be launched on any coast, and their mere presence would probably suffice to deter the approach of hostile ships. Coast defence, already very formidable, would be rendered less expensive and its sphere would be extended.[18]

If Sir Andrew still had doubts about the submarine now on offer (and he must have done), Lord Sydenham's patriotic peroration may have tipped the balance:

> Every change in the art of war has raised people who loudly proclaim it as fatal to the supremacy of England; but there will be some who will take a different view, and will argue that it implies increased strength of a Power, which has much to defend, and seeks no territorial aggrandisement at the expense of its rivals – a Power, moreover, to which conscious defensive strength means wealth and prosperity.
>
> It is certain that the Nordenfelt boat as at present existing will effect no revolution, but it seems to be equally clear that we shall shortly have to face possibilities which we have been hitherto able to neglect. Scientific experiments, in other words money judiciously applied, will enable us to hold our own in any future development of submarine warfare, and to omit to employ every effort to be first in a race in which the start is even would be to court disaster.[19]

While not recommending *Dykeri Pråm En* as such, this is a clear hint to use her as the basis of further research: Lord Sydenham's account is also one of the most far-sighted prophecies of the realities of submarine warfare of its entire period.

As Garrett emerged from the boat with just enough strength to crawl to his bed for another week of submarine-inspired pulmonary torment, Nordenfelt, encouraged by a Goldwynesque 'definite maybe' from Sir Andrew, announced a further week of trials, to be held on Southampton Water in November. It is by no means impossible that Vice-Admiral HRH the Prince of Wales put in a word for his friend's contraption. Preparations were made for the boat's voyage to Southampton, as freight aboard a Swedish steamer. Nordenfelt seems to have learned this much from the loss of *Resurgam*.

Meanwhile, in an unseemly exchange of diatribes with the torpedo designer General Berdan (hardly an objective commentator in the circumstances), Nordenfelt had taken to claiming that the boat had reached eight knots at Landskrona, fudging the advertised maximum down to ten knots while he was about it. Even this was roughly double the actual speed reached at the trials, a fact not lost on the Naval observers awaiting the boat at Southampton.

General Berdan fixed upon the embarrassing problem of the heat generated inside the boat when closed up. Unabashed, Nordenfelt replied: '[After a three-hour run] the thermometer only registered 87° Fahrenheit [30.5°C], or much less than the summer heat in hot climates ...'[20] – another subtle adjustment of the truth achieved by only offering half of the facts, as seen in the brochure.

Nordenfelt's overall attitude is best summed up in one preposterous multiple untruth; 'The Swedish trials showed that I [!] control absolutely the depth at which the boat runs'.[21]

No detailed records survive of the Southampton tests, but it is clear that this ludicrous flourish was not borne out. Persistent problems with the seals on the firebox door resulted in Garrett's health deteriorating even further as the atmosphere in the boat became all but sculptable: the boat's crew became easily recognisable by their wraith-like complexions and racking coughs. Worst of all for the boat's prospects, the phrase 'smoke sickness', the crew's own euphemism for their condition, made the transition from Swedish to English, to be thrown in Nordenfelt's face at the crucial meeting with the Admiralty.

Sir Andrew Clarke persisted in his interest, to the extent of recommending that the Government should actually buy the boat for the £9,000 that Nordenfelt demanded (a huge saving on his original £20,000), but he was heavily defeated by Naval opinion, ostensibly on the grounds that the Navy were investigating the new electrical means of submerged propulsion. No action was taken, and Sir Andrew's idea was quietly forgotten.

Dykeri Pråm En's career, however, was far from over. Zaharoff, the submarine missionary, would soon find a new convert. By the summer of 1885, the Eastern Rumelian Question, one of the many Balkan 'Questions' that occasionally erupted into full-blown crisis, had begun to bubble over: Greece and Turkey were openly preparing for outright war. Greece mobilised on 25 September; the region tensed, waiting for the explosion.

It was at this point that the ever-reliable Zaharoff spotted a gap in the market, and wrote to the Greek Minister of Marine, then understandably a worried man. A secret weapon would not go amiss in times like these. Zaharoff's letter is a superb example of the *Système Zaharoff* in full bloom: 'I am first a Greek, a patriot like yourself, and only secondly a salesman.'[22]

He may well have been a Greek; nobody is quite certain, but the most likely of his many supposed birthplaces appears to have been the Greek quarter of Constantinople. At any rate, the Minister of Marine believed him (or said he did).

Zaharoff offered the Nordenfelt boat to the Minister as a sure means of putting paid to the Turkish menace. He threw in a map of Turkey, with all the ports vulnerable to the submarine lovingly picked out. The Minister wavered, protesting that the Landskrona trials had been less than a complete success – the Greek Navy had been represented at the trials, and had hardly raved. What was he to say to the Prime Minister, the hard-pressed Mr Delyannis?

Zaharoff's response was to invite the Minister to the Hôtel Grande Bretagne, where, in one of the more absurd moments of a tale hardly lacking in them, he demonstrated a model of the *Dykeri Pråm* in his splendid bath. Beginning to crumble, the Minister asked how a poor country like Greece could afford such a thing, an eccentric question in what had become the El Dorado of the arms world – 80% of the previous year's national budget had gone on guns. Zaharoff assured him that the Nordenfelt boat was of such awesome power that only one would be needed – and he, Zaharoff, Greek patriot, would persuade Nordenfelt to lower his price. The Minister, overwhelmed by this display of nationalist zeal, agreed, on condition that further trials be held in Greece. Perhaps, even in this emotional moment, he could hear (or smell) something scampering in the bilges.

The boat was later declared by Nordenfelt to have been sold for the £9,000 that had originally been demanded. Zaharoff actually persuaded him to let the boat go for 225,000 French Francs, somehow convincing the Greek Minister that this represented a substantial saving. In fact, the discount amounted to all of £36, but Zaharoff offered Nordenfelt an excellent rationale for sustaining this loss. The glimpse behind the mask is terrifying:

> Let this first sale go through cheaply. Once we have sold one, we can sell others. And once we have sold to two countries we can force up the price.[23]

Meanwhile, Gladstone's government, fearing a European conflagration once the Turco-Greek squabble had worked its way through the cat's cradle of European alliances, threatened to send a fleet to Greece unless the Greeks demobilised. In the face of Greek defiance (including a personal message to Gladstone from the Demarche of Athens, entreating him not to hinder Britain's oldest friend in the Balkans), the Royal Navy was indeed sent in on 28 January. An armada of 23 ships under the command of Admiral John Hay, carrying a total of 140 guns and 5,147 men, was sent to blockade the Bay of Salamis and physically prevent an attack on Turkey – a particularly flamboyant enforcement of the Pax Britannica.

While there was understandable jubilation in the Nordenfelt Submarine Company, there remained the problem of delivering the boat to Greece. Britain was not at war with Greece: she was fulfilling her peacekeeping obligations to Turkey under the 1856 Convention of Paris, an impressive document, signed by all the major powers (including Turkey), designed to prevent the spread of any sudden flare-up in the Balkans. The fact remained, however, that Garrett, if he was going to deliver the submarine to the Greeks by sea, would have to run the blockade, as the new weapon was precisely the sort of traffic that the blockade was set up to interdict. This would set him militarily at odds with his own country's navy: on a strict interpretation of the law, he was in danger of being deemed guilty of treason if caught, especially if shots were exchanged. But off he went.

By the time Garrett arrived at Salamis, Admiral Seymour had taken over command of the blockading force from Hay. The fleet was gradually being joined by units representing most of the other European powers – except France and Russia, who had their own argument with Turkey and supported the Greek stand.

Garrett found himself confronted by three heavy ironclads and a squadron of torpedo boats, all equipped with powerful searchlights. He decided to attempt to enter the Bay at night, running awash with the top of the cupola just above the surface. As he edged along, navigating by peering into the gloom through the bull's-eyes, the boat passed close enough to HMS *Polyphemus* for him to hear voices on the ironclad's quarter-deck. The submarine passed through unmolested: Garrett had achieved the first successful submarine passage through a surface blockade.

Unknown to Garrett, soon surfaced and making his best speed for Piraeus, he had not in fact managed to pass unnoticed. Admiral Seymour had not attacked because a lookout had mistakenly reported seeing the submarine sinking, a message which was telegraphed to London. However, fortunately for Nordenfelt's peace of mind – to say nothing of Jane and the children – Garrett's report of his safe arrival reached London first. The first operational modern submarine had reported for orders, and was immediately commissioned.

This stirring tale, based on Garrett's own recollections and those of his son John, is entirely untrue. While the truth had sometimes been stretched in the *Resurgam* sales-talk, it has snapped completely here. The story has long been believed as the Genesis of submarine warfare, but, in the light of modern archaeology, it turns out to be more of a Piltdown Man. On this occasion, the Garrett Coefficient of Veracic Expansion is very large indeed.

The submarine was in fact cut into sections and loaded aboard an American vessel, the SS *Toledo*. The ship arrived at Piraeus on 13 January 1886 – fifteen days before the blockade was imposed. The submarine parts were off-loaded and taken to the nearby John McDowal factory (probably an American concern) for re-assembly.

Trials took place on 14 March, before a committee of Greek naval officers and a large crowd, followed by a second session on 26 March. With the blockade very much in force (it would only be raised in May, when the regional temperature had finally cooled after the usual diplomatic thuggery), there must have been considerable satisfaction in Athens at the appearance of a brief, rather embarrassed and carefully misinformed report in *The Times*, under the account of the mighty blockade:

> Athens, March 26: A trial was made this afternoon in the Bay of Salamis with the Nordenfelt Submarine torpedo-vessel in the presence of the Minister of Marine. The vessel was submerged for two hours, and the trial was esteemed a great success.[24]

It was nothing of the sort. As at Landskrona, no attempt was made to launch the torpedo, on this occasion for explicit safety reasons. The Greek naval committee expressed profound doubts about the war-worthiness of the vessel and vetoed any thought of her commission. She was towed back to Piraeus and laid up in secret. But this was not the end of her propaganda value: via the European press (including *The Times*), the Turks were informed that the Greeks had a new and fearsome weapon. Holding the trials under the noses of the European blockade was a delicious extra.

This ingenious use of misinformation was successful enough for Garrett to be able to weave his carefully-constructed tale of naval derring-do and get away with it for a century, though it did not fully emerge in public until long after his death, via his son John, who believed every word of it. While the truth would have been commercially embarrassing for the Nordenfelt Company, Greek political needs saw to it that Garrett's submarine career could continue. Garrett himself swathed the whole story of the fate of *Dykeri Pråm En* in a mixture of fog, lies and waffle that together reveal the darkest side of his character: it is debatable whether it was worse to spread the story in the first place, or to take such pride in an adventure that was a hanging matter under the 1848 Treason Act.

The Greeks must have known the military limitations of the submarine when they bought her. Their object in buying the boat was probably an assertion of national pride in the face of bullying from the Powers, with aggressive intentions toward Turkey an unlikely and technically inadvisable second. Not that the Powers were completely convinced by the Greek propaganda.

Among the blockading fleet was HMS *Temeraire*, flying the flag of Prince Alfred, Duke of Edinburgh. This second son of Queen Victoria (and the King of Greece's brother-in-law) had in fact been elected King of Greece by a vast majority in 1862, but had not been acceptable to the politicians. The man whom a generation of Greeks had known as 'Alfredakis' must have felt rather uncomfortable on the picket-line.

Alfredakis sent a young officer, the future Rear Admiral Sir Sydney Eardley-Wilmot, to take a look at the submarine in Piraeus. Eardley-Wilmot, who had missed the Landskrona trials, told the Duke what the Prince of Wales must have told him already: 'She has some ingenious qualities, one being a greater difficulty to submerge than to come to the surface, reversing the procedure in early submarine boats'.[25] Sly humour (and perception of the awful truth) aside, this report is most interesting in its explicit assumption that the early days of submarines were over.

The mystery surrounding the submarine's Greek period is by no means confined to her delivery, however. Surrounded by a swirling mist worthy of Zaharoff, there exists a report, undated but from late in the crisis. The Delyannis Government fell on 21 May, taking with it the Minister of Marine. Naval skirmishes broke out between Greece and Turkey between 25 May and 7 June when the new Greek Prime Minister, Trikoupis, capitulated to the Powers and stood down the armed forces. If (*if*) the incident concerned actually took place, it must have taken place during these two weeks.

The report describes an attempt to use the submarine in action with a Turkish cruiser at the entrance to the Dardanelles. As the cruiser approached, the boat submerged, intending not to surface for an attack until the last moment, as per the maker's instructions. Unfortunately, the pumps were not working properly (that much rings true); it took twenty minutes to get them going. When the submarine finally surfaced, the cruiser was disappearing over the horizon. No names, no dates. It may be true. In the interests of cold fact, it must be pointed out that unless Garrett was aboard (an intriguing thought in view of his other adventures), the Greek crew would have been trained astonishingly quickly. The report is almost certainly another facet of the campaign to turn the submarine, now beginning her long career as a pile of rust, into an effective verbal deterrent.

Rather better documented is Garrett's last Greek exploit. After further negotiations via the omnipresent Zaharoff, Garrett shipped two consignments of Nordenfelt guns into Greece under the French flag, an unashamed exercise in gun-running that tallies far worse with his clerical status than anything to do with his submarines, which always had at least the element of technological progress to explain his interest. Because of the French involvement, it was by no means impossible that the ramifications of his being caught might have stretched as far as the triggering of a European war –

precisely the danger that the blockade was trying to avert.

While the propriety of a curate devising weapons and participating in war is debatable, starting World War One 28 years ahead of schedule would have stretched the patience of any parish. It is a revealing insight into Garrett's personality that he would frequently boast of this escapade to his son in later years: occasionally, behind the panache and semi-comedy of this wildly paradoxical man, one glimpses something rather less edifying.

In Stockholm, a proud Thorsten Nordenfelt was summoned to court to be honoured by the King of Sweden and Norway. In recognition of the submarine's technical achievements and the Nordenfelt Submarine Torpedo Boat Company's contribution to Swedish industry and exports, he was made a Royal Chamberlain of the Swedish Court. The submarine, both (apparently) as a weapon of war and (genuinely) a product of mainstream industry, had arrived. Acclaimed as the man who had brought the submarine from the realms of fantasy into the very real world of international affairs and heavy industry, Nordenfelt polished his medal and kept his mouth shut. The Greeks, who had after all bought a fair amount of genuine Turkish worry, were not going to burst the bubble.

Meanwhile, even as the Balkans were simmering down to the local variation on normality, another complex man, the future self-styled Mystery Man of Europe, was striking ever further afield in the name of the Nordenfelt Submarine Company. Basil Zaharoff, only weeks after being fêted all over Athens as a treasure of the Greek nation, was corresponding with another Minister of Marine. Hassan Pasha, of the Imperial Ottoman Government, had been reading the papers.

Zaharoff's opening sentence is oddly familiar: 'I am first a Turkish patriot like yourself ...'[26]

CHAPTER FIVE

The Two *Abduls*

The government of Sultan Abdul Hamid II (known to his teeming admirers throughout the Levant as 'Abdul the Damned') had in fact been interested in the doings of Garrett and Nordenfelt from the beginning. Throughout the sale, delivery and trials of the *Dykeri Pråm*, Zaharoff had been negotiating fiercely with the Turkish Government, doubtless waving his Constantinople birth-certificate in ecstasies of Ottoman fervour. Quite simply, there was a war brewing between Greece and Turkey soon after the Landskrona trials: Nordenfelt, Garrett and Zaharoff made the best of a tempting market. They were helped all the way by the seething mistrust between Greece and Turkey: either side, it seemed, would believe virtually anything about the other's secret weapons and warlike intentions.

From the outset of their relationship with the Turkish Government, Garrett and Nordenfelt shared a patronising attitude to the Turks that was becoming widespread in Europe as the Ottoman Empire declined. Mishaps were airily blamed on Turkish incompetence and ignorance: the most blatant untruths concerning the two boats that Garrett and Nordenfelt built for the Turks were swallowed whole by the British press and written up with Ottoman-bashing relish. At best, the Ottoman Empire was seen as a rather shaky geopolitical bulwark against the Russians. This Occidental smugness would eventually boomerang horribly, at Gallipoli. There is plentiful damning evidence that Garrett, Nordenfelt and Europe at large badly underestimated the Turks: one of the most highly organised bureaucracies that the world has ever seen produced lavish quantities of Government papers telling a very different story from the one that reached the European capitals. Behind the exquisite Arabic script (in which the Ottoman language – the Arabic-Persian-Turkish hybrid that preceded modern Turkish – was written until 1928) there is usually a cool objectivity that visionaries like Lord Sydenham of Combe (and Garrett) would have done well to emulate.

Turkey had, in fact, seen one of the world's earliest submarines. In 1719, a Turkish naval architect, Ibrahim Effendi, built and tested a submarine. This boat, known as the *Timsah (Crocodile)*, was rowed by its crew of five, who breathed when submerged through a primitive schnorkel: this was a pipe protruding through the surface of the water, which led one of the Sultan's courtiers to describe the boat as looking like 'a kitchen under the sea'. The crew entered the *Crocodile* through its 'mouth'. The boat sank off Seraglio Point while being demonstrated to the Sultan, Ahmed III (a great naval reformer), during the celebrations for his son's circumcision. Fortunately, the *Crocodile* was not in a carnivorous mood: all the crew escaped.

Sultan Abdul Hamid II ascended the throne in 1876 in a comparatively bloodless (by Ottoman standards) palace *coup*: his predecessor (and elder brother) Murad was merely bundled off to the Çiragan palace, where he rotted and howled his way through a fearsome mixture of booze and schizophrenia until his death in 1904. Meanwhile, Abdul Hamid, not a liberal man, set about tightening up and extending the Ottoman police state and applying the instruments to anyone foolish enough to oppose him. However, he also embarked on an impressive scheme of modernisation: railways (using German money), roads and a telegraph network sprang up, much to the horror of Greece and Russia, who knew exactly where the railway lines led. Even less to their liking was the modernisation of the armed services, pursued all the harder after the Russo-Turkish War of 1877-8.

The Turks had been all too impressed by the performance of the Russian torpedo-vessels in the 1877-8 war. Following their experiences in that war – and Hobart Pasha's earlier doings in the duck-pond – the Turks were at least open to suggestions concerning innovations in torpedo warfare by the time of the Landskrona trials. Their first concrete response to the torpedo boats was as imaginative as it was impressive: a rocket factory was built at Constantinople, and tests carried out with explosive missiles against target vessels in harbour. These tests were deemed very successful, and a credible counter-measure to the Russian boats – and, indeed, to any Greek warship. But not to a submarine.

As early as 1881, the Turkish naval attaché from the Washington embassy had visited the Delamater yard in New York to investigate the doings of John Holland. At that stage, Holland's flagship had been the *Fenian Ram*, which was thought by the Turks to be sufficiently marginal as a warship for them to ignore her either as a threat or a possible investment for themselves. The same conclusion had been reached at Landskrona.

But if the new reports were correct, Garrett and Nordenfelt must have improved the submarine since the Landskrona trials: the Greek submarine boat must be a serious and dangerous war-machine. What was worse, Hassan Pasha had received reports that the Russians had built *fifty* submarine boats, which even then were being exercised around the Baltic naval base of Kronstadt. These were in fact tiny one-man, pedal-powered eggs, designed by Stefan Drze-wiecki – not at all unlike Garrett's first effort, though somewhat more elongated. They were *just* capable of three knots in deathly calm water, when crewed by particularly brawny Cossacks. They were little more than naval toys, but mere rumours of their existence were enough to send shudders through Russia's enemies. The submarine began its career as a hidden, lurking menace long before it actually went to sea in any meaningful form.

The Minister of Marine, Hassan Pasha, had responded to Nord-enfelt's invitation by despatching the London Embassy's Naval Attaché, Commander[1] Ibrahim Halil, to Landskrona. Halil reported his having been to a lecture on the powers of the boat, given by Nordenfelt to an audience of forty at the Hotel England in Copenhagen. This was followed by a lavish junket, at which Halil met more royalty than he had ever seen in London; he was particu-larly impressed by the Czarina's foresight in bringing her own orchestra with her – so very useful in the long periods of waiting while the submarine was coaxed into life and/or repaired. He was also rather taken with the *Osborne*, one of the four British Royal Yachts, which had brought the Prince and Princess of Wales to the trials.

While he clearly had a splendid time socially, Halil was not at all impressed by the submarine: he was in fact more anxious to recom-mend the purchase of boats like the *Edda*. The submarine was too slow, her diving powers were very dubious, and (he seems to have been the only observer to spot this) 'She would not be able to stand a strong current'. Indeed not.

Hassan Pasha seems to have taken his London attaché's word for it, but the submarine was thrust rudely back to his attention by Halil's Intelligence report of 25 November 1885,[2] declaring that the boat was to be sold to Greece. This, combined with the ever-growing likelihood of war with Greece, inspired a drastic re-think. Hassan Pasha consulted the brochure that had accompanied

Nordenfelt's original letter, and found that larger, more powerful submarines were on offer: '... it is probable that the next Nordenfelt Submarine Boat will be 84 feet long in lieu of 64 feet'.[3]

Nordenfelt was prepared to build the 84-foot submarine for £9,500. Hassan wanted more than length, however: he wanted stronger armament. As it happened, Garrett and Nordenfelt, he was told, had recently designed a 100-foot boat capable of carrying two torpedoes: this appeared to be the answer. Turkey must have two of these new war-machines, leaping at a single bound to the forefront of modern naval weaponry. Negotiations were immediately begun, via the inevitable Zaharoff. Hassan stated his country's position to Nordenfelt. If his conditions could be met, Turkey would pay £11,000 for each boat, an inflated price (Zaharoff's memo to Nordenfelt was being borne out) partly justified by an astonishingly short delivery-time: $2\frac{1}{2}$ months was demanded. Hassan seems to have thought he would be buying ready-built submarines off-the-shelf, an illusion that would soon – or rather, eventually – be dissipated. New intelligence reports coming in to the Sublime Porte (the Sultan's Council of State) had suggested that the British were actively encouraging the Greeks to attack Turkey, so time, for the Turks, was short. The blockade of the Bay of Salamis would end this particular fantasy, but that was still two months away. In late November 1885, Turkish nerves were very ragged: war was in the air.

While the order was, of course, good news for Nordenfelt and Garrett, the two undersea actor-managers were faced with a problem: just when they were about to bring submarine construction to Britain in a form that would set the pattern for the modern warship industry, they found themselves having to build in a rural yard that made Ekensberg look like the Isle of Dogs.

Nordenfelt's munitions business, largely through the efforts of Zaharoff, was booming. The guns and their carriages were made at the Nordenfelt factory at Carlsvik, near the Palmcrantz yard at Stockholm: Nordenfelt administered the sales and distribution network from London. However, his prime customer, the British Government, had expressed the wish that arms bought for the British armed forces should be of British manufacture: Nordenfelt responded by preparing to establish a second factory in Britain. The hitherto private Nordenfelt concern went public in 1886 as the Nordenfelt Gun and Ammunition Company: the first chairman was Admiral Sir Astley Cooper-Key, the recently-retired First Sea

Lord and a gunnery specialist. This is an interesting early example of the stately progress from quarter-deck to board-room which is now virtually expected of retiring senior officers. For Nordenfelt, however, the move from private business to Stock Exchange quotation, shareholder scrutiny and all, was a complex and traumatic affair that goes some way towards explaining his often ludicrous behaviour in his subsequent relations with the Turkish Government.

Nordenfelt's first move in the restructuring of his company, however, was to make arrangements to transfer the construction of the Nordenfelt submarines to Britain. Combined with his burgeoning gun trade, especially once he was making the guns in Britain, this would allow him to streamline and co-ordinate his (and Garrett's) efforts in a way which would have been impossible as long as the boats were built in Sweden. This combined armaments-and-shipbuilding enterprise anticipated the Vickers combine at Barrow by nearly twelve years, and Krupp's Germaniawerft, cradle of the early U-boats, by eleven. It was in fact the Barrow Shipbuilding Company – the same yard – which Nordenfelt, in close consultation with Garrett, chose for the construction of the Turkish boats. Forces which would bring Nordenfelt and Albert Vickers together were already in operation, and would drastically affect the careers of both Nordenfelt and Garrett, but late in 1885, for the moment sensing nothing larger in the offing, Nordenfelt entered into a formal arrangement with the Barrow Shipbuilding Company. Barrow had been going through a lean period, and were glad of the work: this was in fact Nordenfelt's first step on the path to the Barrow boardroom. Another two and a half years would see him there. For the first time, the hulls, fittings and armament of warships would be the products of what amounted to a single company: this genuine and important Nordenfelt and Garrett innovation is another of their many serious achievements to have been forgotten and attributed to (later) others.

Unfortunately, despite Nordenfelt's new corporate arrangements, the Turks had their own surprisingly specific and all too original idea of the best yard to build their submarines – the des Vignes yard at Chertsey. This was a small company specialising in the design and construction of steam-yachts, and was very much the private property of Mr G.F.G. des Vignes, the heart, soul and umpire of many Thames regattas of the period. Des Vignes, man

Dykeri Pram En ('Nordenfelt I') on the stocks at the Palmcrantz yard, near Stockholm, 1883.

Dykeri Pram En at the Landskrona trials, 1885. Note the absence of the torpedo tube, fitted later at Southampton.

An *Abdul* (probably *Hamid)* under re-assembly at Tashkizak, 1886/7. The gentleman in the fez is probably Commander Ismail Hakki.

Launching ceremony of the *Abdul Hamid,* 18 September 1886. Note the Swedish and Turkish flags (and the ham-fisted 1886 re-touching).

and yard, had come to the attention of the Turkish Government in 1885, when, as a rush job, they had converted a 30-ton steam yacht, already on the stocks, into a torpedo-boat. She was commissioned, interestingly enough (in view of her eighteenth-century ancestor) as the *Timsah* (*Crocodile*). One of Mr des Vignes' more lavish designs, built at Teddington, was the steam-yacht *Donola*, now one of the treasures of the National Maritime Museum at Greenwich. Steam-yachts, however, were more or less the limit of des Vignes' own yard: the specialised engineering skills and techniques (in effect, large-scale boiler-making) required to build the submarines simply were not available. The inevitable tensions that built up between Garrett and the des Vignes engineers combined with Nordenfelt's highly personal business practices to cause considerable strife in the production of the two Turkish submarines.

The formal agreement to build the boats was finally signed on 23 January 1886, with Nordenfelt agreeing to the $2\frac{1}{2}$-month clause. It was agreed that the boats would be built at Chertsey, then delivered to Constantinople in sections for re-assembly at the Tashkizak yard, a shipbuilding concern which (unlike des Vignes) is still in operation.

It is possible that Garrett had already begun work on a new submarine at Barrow before leaving for Greece; tentative plans for an 84-foot submarine (as mentioned in the Nordenfelt brochure) exist. This boat may have been scaled up on the stocks to become the first Turkish submarine (a very dubious procedure which would help to explain the boat's subsequent atrocious performance). It is certain that the first Turkish boat was built at Barrow: if she was laid down soon after the signing of the contract, she was built fantastically quickly. It seems rather more likely that it was having a boat already under construction which allowed Nordenfelt to countenance the $2\frac{1}{2}$-month clause. The Turks were led to believe that *both* boats would be ready in this time, but this was impossible from the outset, as Garrett and Nordenfelt both knew. But with Garrett away in Greece, Nordenfelt (and Zaharoff, who drew up the contract) dispensed with the usual consultative formalities. Barrow's Job No 143 became the first boat: the second boat was built at Chertsey.

Garrett, of course, was completely tied up with the Greek boat. Work continued at Barrow without him. By the time Garrett returned to England, early in April, the new 110-foot boat was more or less complete – and Nordenfelt was being pressed hard by the Turks, who already sensed that the delivery date was not going to be met. The Turks, dreading a Greek submarine onslaught at any moment, were demanding two submarines, on the counter, today, and were creating a rumpus which could easily have proved deeply embarrassing to Nordenfelt. Nordenfelt, presumably after consulting the Zaharoff Code of Business Ethics, countered by putting it about that the Turks had not paid him. While this tactical distortion was circulating in London, Agob Pasha, the Sultan's Treasurer, was protesting to the Grand Vezir that £14,000 (the first two instalments, as agreed) had been paid to Nordenfelt, with no sign of any submarines. Mr Foster, the Ottoman Bank's English General Manager, was advising default on the third payment, on the good-money-after-bad principle. The Swedish Ambassador to Constantinople, Mr Arenofa, was asked, not for the last time, to lean on Nordenfelt.

Nordenfelt responded immediately, once the pressure was coming from his own people: a telegram reached the Swedish Embassy on 5 April, saying that the two submarines were ready, and all the machinery running perfectly. This was, in fact, nonsense. The first boat was launched at Barrow on 14 April; the second boat was still very much under construction at Chertsey. Perhaps because of being built largely in Garrett's absence, the new submarine was far from perfect, as the Turks would soon discover. Immediately after her launch, Barrow registered her as a merchant vessel (with a gross tonnage of 68, a unique and very peculiar statistic), presumably for insurance purposes, to cover the (rather frantic) builder's trials and delivery voyage to Liverpool.

Nordenfelt's telegram had been meant to placate the Swedes while he continued to flannel and stall the Turks. Unfortunately, the telegram, like all diplomatic communications in Constantinople, was read by the Turks, and only made things worse for Nordenfelt and Garrett. The intercept, painstakingly translated into Ottoman, survives in the Grand Vezir's Archive.

A more truthful interpretation of Nordenfelt's telegram would have been 'Garrett's back'. In other words, des Vignes now had some chance of completing the second boat. A typical Nordenfelt touch to the telegram was an urgent request for the Ambassador to ask for names for the two boats, one of which was still largely a pile of steel plates as he wrote: he demanded a reply by telegram the next day. What he actually received was a personal visit to his London office from his Landskrona shipmate Commander Halil, the Turkish Naval Attaché: telecommunications, then in their infancy, could be something of a mixed blessing for an international commercial sleight-of-hand artiste. Nordenfelt was fortunate that Commander Halil did not go straight to Chertsey.

With Garrett back on site, work progressed flat out. The new submarines were considerably larger than the *Dykeri Pråm*, and included modifications ('improvements') to the machinery that gave trouble from the very start. The 250 horse-power engine was larger, more an attempt to deal with the vagaries of the Lamm system than a genuine upgrading in power.

Like the *Dykeri Pråm*, the new boats were to be submerged by means of two horizontal downhaul propellers, driven by independent 6 horse-power engines. On the earlier boat, these propellers had been mounted on sponsons on either side of the boat amidships. On the Turkish boats, they were moved to positions in a straight line fore and aft of the cupola, protruding oddly from the upper surface of the hull, in an attempt to deal with the underwater instability that had been such an alarming feature of the *Dykeri Pråm*. In their new position, the downhaul screws would actually make matters a great deal worse, emphasising the pitching motion they were supposed to prevent. As in the *Dykeri Pråm*, they could be connected to hydrostatic sensors which shut them off when a desired depth (or the hull's terminal depth) was reached. This supposed safety measure was *extremely* ingenious, and a Nordenfelt idea: for either or both of these reasons, it did not work. It was also potentially suicidal if it *did* work, or only slightly malfunctioned: the submarine might suddenly decide to inspect the enemy's surface vessels at the least convenient moment.

Unfortunately, one of the main causes of woe – the shape of the hull – remained substantially unaltered, except in sheer size: the new boats were 110 feet long, with a 12-foot beam amidships, displacing 160 tons – nearly three times the displacement of *Dykeri Pråm En*. The hull was the familiar cigar, but this had in fact undergone a significant modification. The coamings around the conning-tower, which had ruined the boat's attempts at semi-submerged stealth at Landskrona, had been (as Lord Sydenham of Combe put it) abolished, and replaced by a pronounced hump in the midships hull. This hump was under-drawn in the published drawings of the boat, and even – absurdly – in the rather abstract assembly instructions sent to Turkey: it is, however, clearly visible in all the photographs of the two submarines, and earned the first boat the unfortunate tag 'whale ship' on her first public appearance in Constantinople.

The other major horror of the *Dykeri Pråm*, the undivided ballast-tanks, with their deliriously athletic free surfaces, was just as evident in the new boats – but scaled up to match the new boats' displacement. From the start, once again, this was the boats' inexorable built-in nemesis.

On Saturday, 1 May 1886, Agob Pasha reported that Zaharoff had told him that the two submarines were to be loaded on board the steamer *Trinidad* at Liverpool on 8 May. For once, Zaharoff was telling a substantial percentage of the truth (fifty, to be precise): the *Trinidad* did indeed leave the following Saturday, carrying the first boat, which had been brought down from Barrow and dismantled. She reached Constantinople on 17 May.

The parts were off-loaded under the supervision of Captain Ismail Hakki, who was to take charge of the assembly operation. This would be done under cover, and in secret. Hakki found clear signs that the parts had been packed hastily and carelessly. Many parts were damaged: rather worse, several important parts were missing. The plans were vague or downright misleading (the modern euphemism is 'schematic'): Hakki, an experienced naval engineer, was not impressed, but set his men to work as best they could. After a particularly unpleasant exchange between Hassan Pasha and Nordenfelt, Garrett was despatched to Constantinople with a Mr Lawrie, a Nordenfelt engineer who had been working on the second boat at Chertsey. Mr des Vignes' men were left to do what they could to finish the second boat.

The boat had arrived in seven large sections. When Garrett and Lawrie finally drifted into Constantinople, in late June, assembly had progressed as far as the fourth and fifth sections. Garrett declared that it had taken nearly two months because of the incompetence of the Turkish engineers, but this was quite untrue. Work had in fact been held up by the need for the Turks to make several parts for the boat themselves, often having little more than guesswork to go on: at least one of the drawings that had been provided was for the *Dykeri Pråm*, and therefore useless.

On his arrival at Tashkizak, Garrett declared that all was going well, despite an understandably frosty reception from Hakki. After staying only a few days, he announced that his presence was not needed, and declared that he was leaving for Greece, to attend the torpedo trials of his earlier submarine. These trials appear to have been a figment of his imagination, as he did in fact return directly to London. He did, however, leave just in time to miss the arrival of the second boat, which had left with even more parts missing than the first at the end of a building process which had revealed, if nothing else, why Nordenfelt had chosen Barrow. It was claimed that the boat had undergone builder's trials on the Thames, but it is by no means impossible that she was merely prefabricated at Chertsey and despatched to Turkey without passing through a solid phase. This is certainly borne out by the experience of the assembly workers, who expressed wonderment that she had ever been put together in the first place. They may have been more right than they knew.

Meanwhile, the atmosphere at Tashkizak deteriorated. The assembly workers were supposed to be paid by the Nordenfelt Submarine Torpedo Boat Company's representative. By August, Zaharoff, who doubtless had far better things to do with the money, had not paid anyone for two months. Many of the workers drifted away. The remainder, contributing in their own way to the Sultan's drive for modernisation, went on strike. Hassan Pasha came close to panic after a harrowing interview with the Grand Vezir, who made it clear that the Sublime Porte saw the submarines as a strategic necessity: more necessary, at any rate, than Ministers of Marine who had difficulty running a shipyard.

The assembly work was taken over by naval ratings and soldiers, who were paid in the normal manner. Every month, an appropriate bill was sent to Zaharoff; every month, he ignored it. Relations between the Turkish Government and the Nordenfelt Company were less than cordial.

The situation was not helped by a seemingly endless litany of missing parts and mechanical failures. One of the engine cylinders, made at Tashkizak, failed under test at 140 psi, resulting in yet another corrosive letter to London. Garrett sniffily pointed out that as the cylinder was of Turkish manufacture, he could scarcely be blamed for bad Turkish workmanship: there was no apology for what he blandly assumed had been the non-provision of the original cylinder. Hakki, commendably collected under the circumstances, replied that the original cylinder had indeed been supplied: it had failed at *80* psi. At this stage, parts one to five of the first submarine had been assembled, and six had been riveted to seven; it only remained to join the two sub-assemblies together. The least said about progress with the second boat, however, the better. Hakki said that he would be grateful for the presence in Constantinople of Mr Garrett.

Mr Garrett, however, was not to be had. Fond Eckerman, a Swede who had worked on the *Dykeri Pråm*, was sent to Constantinople as his deputy, only to take to his bed with dysentery the day after his arrival. Reluctantly, perhaps by now fearing for his safety in the face of increasingly hostile messages from the Turks, Garrett left for Turkey. By the time he arrived, the Sultan had intervened personally, declaring that work must proceed on the boats day and night. In an abject letter to the Grand Vezir, Hassan Pasha protested that the workers were in fact working as hard as they could, but made the reasonable point that the very cramped spaces inside the submarines restricted the number of workers who could operate within the hull at any one time. The Tashkizak engineers were doing their best, fabricating parts for a type of craft that nobody had ever seen before, without adequate drawings. For a country of Turkey's modest industrial means, the assembly of the two submarines was in fact an astonishing achievement, performed entirely with Turkish labour: if Garrett and Nordenfelt had attempted to foist these same half-finished construction kits on a European yard, it is likely that they would both have spent most of 1886 roasting in a blaze of litigation. The Turks bit the bullet and got on with the job.

On 17 August, the work was inspected by Admiral Starke (Pasha), a German who had followed the path taken by the Englishman Hobart Pasha, accepting a commission in the Ottoman Navy when life became dull at home. Hobart himself had died in Milan on 16 June: ironically, he had missed Turkey's submarine debut completely. There were in fact several foreign officers in the Ottoman Navy, most of them captains or higher: Abdul Hamid, despite a foreign-inspired attempt to reinstate his mad brother Murad in 1878 (when the Russians were virtually banging on the palace door), did nothing to discourage this. At this stage of his reign, he also employed men from the Empire's minorities in his government: for example, Agob Pasha, the Sultan's briskly efficient Treasurer, was an Armenian. This glimmer of liberality vanished when Abdul Hamid began the series of horrific Armenian massacres that his successors completed with near-genocide in 1916.

Starke reported to the Sultan that Hakki and his men were doing a wonderful job – as, indeed, they were. On 7 September, Hakki made his final report: the boat was nearly finished. Nordenfelt had declared that the inadequate plans were a security measure against spies: Hakki protested that if this were so, Garrett and/or Eckerman should have been present throughout the assembly to advise on problems like the replacement of the missing parts. As it happened, Nordenfelt's fear of spies was not entirely unjustified: as Hakki remarked, several European embassies had sent representatives to inspect the work, and some of these had shown more than polite interest. Hakki thought that the boat would be a useful weapon, but slipped in an observation that the speeds promised for the submarines were a little difficult to believe. This was in fact simply the professional judgement of a perceptive engineer (like Halil's comments at Landskrona), but it was far more than any European engineer had said in the early days of the *Dykeri Pråm*, on similar evidence: the Turks, for all of Garrett's subsequent protestations to the contrary, knew precisely what they were about.

The first submarine was launched at the Tashkizak wharf on Saturday, 18 September 1886. Apart from a substantial number of Turkish naval officers, the spectators included the Swedish ambassador Mr Arenofa and his two daughters, and the Italian Naval Attaché. Two sons of Tosun Pasha of Egypt had made the trip specially, and were not disappointed, as can be seen from the photograph of the occasion. The boat was launched from the slipway in the traditional manner, dressed overall. She flew two flags, one at each mast: the foremast carried the flag of Sweden, the mainmast that of Turkey. Garrett, who supervised the launch, declared that the submarine would be ready for inshore diving trials in three weeks, but was ominously vague about when she would be ready for full sea trials, and even vaguer about the progress of the second boat. He then went back to England.

Hakki had waxed unusually eloquent on the outrageous number of parts missing from the second boat. It is difficult to avoid the conclusion that the shortage of components was deliberate: it is impossible to believe that Garrett was unaware of the deficiencies before the boats' departure, even making due allowance for his absence when the second boat left Liverpool. Whatever the problems may have been at Chertsey, the des Vignes yard never built another submarine. Barrow, ultimately, built hundreds of them.

As usual, Garrett's three weeks were a grotesque underestimate.

The boat's first trials were not in fact held until the following February – five months later. He sauntered back into Constantinople early in December.

The boat made her first public appearance in the Golden Horn on 18 December, when Garrett, with fellow Nordenfelt drones Lawrie and Captain D'Alton (the latter Garrett's assistant at Barrow), took her for a brief spin on the surface to test the engines and steering gear. Inquisitive journalists were told that underwater trials would take place in the New Year in the Gulf of Izmit.

The first trials did indeed take place in early February 1887, but at Seraglio Point, under the supervision of another Englishman in Ottoman service, Captain Henry Harty. The boat's performance was observed by a Naval Commission consisting of Admirals Dervish, Süleyman, Starke and Woods (another Englishman) – and the newly-promoted Commodore Hakki, elevated in recognition of his efforts at Tashkizak. The chief of the Commission was Admiral Hassan Sabri bin Süleyman. The show turned out to be revival of the Landskrona Follies, as Captain D'Alton recalled:

> [The boat] had ... a total lack of longitudinal stability. Nothing could be imagined more unstable than [this] boat. The moment she left the horizontal position, the water in her boiler and the tanks surged forwards and backwards and increased the angle of inclination. She was perpetually working up and down like a scale beam, and no human vigilance could keep her on an even keel for half a minute at a time.[4]

At least one of what should have been the lessons of the *Dykeri Pråm* had gone sadly unlearned: the longitudinal instability of the new boats was even worse than that of their predecessor.

Three token dives were achieved, following the familiar pattern of flooding the tanks, starting the vertical motors and standing as rigidly still as nature would allow. The first dive lasted all of 20 seconds; the second, one minute and 20 seconds; the third managed 50 seconds.

After the first dive, Garrett was joined by a Turkish crew: command was formally handed over to a Turkish commander for the occasion. As these four men were the first naval crew of a modern submarine, they are worth naming in full:

Commander Halil Develioglu [Commanding Officer]
Lieutenant-Commander Ali [Engineer]
Lieutenant Sherafettin [Engineer]
Sub-Lieutenant Mehmet Salim [Engineer]

In subsequent trials, these would be joined by a stoker (a rating). The ratio of a single deck officer to three engineering officers would have confirmed the worst fears of the anti-engineer element in the European navies. In submarines, the tradesmen moved into the manor.

Among others, Captain D'Alton would later claim that it was impossible to crew the boats with Turkish seamen, who were supposedly too cowardly to take the risks involved: this is an unpleasant absurdity that tells us much about Captain D'Alton (who eventually reached the dizzy heights of Chief Engineer of the London Central Railway) and the prevailing condescending attitude towards the Turks. D'Alton even took this as far as claiming that any personnel assigned to the submarines promptly deserted. Quite apart from the fact that the crew consisted almost entirely of officers (not prone to desertion in the normal run of things), it shows a mildly hilarious ignorance of the frightening enforcement of discipline in the Turkish fleet. Desertion from the Ottoman armed forces was an *extraordinarily* bad idea. It *had*, however, been difficult to crew the *Dykeri Pråm* with Swedish civilians once her underwater instability had been discovered: they, unlike the Turkish seamen, actually had the option of leaving. Given the performance of the *Dykeri Pråm*, it is surprising that so few did so.

Perhaps fortunately, the three short dips, with a brief, tottering underwater crawl during the longest, were all the boat could manage at the time: as the Commission's report noted, there were *still* parts missing, preventing any diving trials beyond those already attempted. When called before the Commission to explain this, Garrett declared that what was missing was the depth-control mechanism (the automatic bob-and-lever contraption from the *Dykeri Pråm*), and that it would be necessary for the boat to be lifted out of the water for the missing gear to be fitted. After, of course, the gear had been made. Grilled over how much longer he expected the assembly of the second boat to take, he made carefully blurred noises about three months.

But Garrett, poor man, was distraught. He told the Commission that there was terrible illness in his family back in England – he was too worried to work properly. Having thus bared his soul, he disappeared overnight, without so much as a note to the Minister of Marine, taking Captain D'Alton and Zaharoff with him.

There was nothing wrong with his family, unless one counts

fatigue from the arduous chore of moving from Morecambe to a very plush house, 'La Plata', in Southampton. Garrett was in fact anxious to return to England to supervise the launch of his new super-submarine, then, as we shall see in the next chapter, nearly complete at Barrow. Unfortunately, the Commission's deliberations over the trials kept him too long: he missed the launch, which took place on 26 March. In any case, the Turks had rumbled him. The efficient Commander Halil had kept his ear to the ground, and had reported accordingly: he had been slightly misinformed, in that he thought that two boats were building, but he certainly told the Commission enough to provide them with ammunition. The Commission's report must have made interesting reading for the Sublime Porte:

> We observed that the bow and stern of the boat are not in balance ... According to our agreement with Nordenfelt, the boat's underwater speed should have been 10 knots, but only 2½ was reached: furthermore, we are certain that she cannot go faster than this.
>
> We are aware that two submarines are being built by Nordenfelt in England. If the boats now in Turkey are not good enough, we shall demand the ones in England as replacements. We do not believe Mr Garrett's statement that there is illness in his family: he has gone to England to work on the new boats.[5]

It is clear from this that a misunderstanding had occurred, or had been engineered. Nordenfelt had once again fudged the boat's underwater speed in the contract: the only way to extract ten knots underwater from this boat would have been to drop her into the water from the Galata Bridge. Otherwise, it was a mechanical impossibility. As he must have realised at the time, Garrett, who had had nothing to do with the drafting of the contract, had been dropped in it by the management.

The report ended with a forgivable tirade against Garrett, Nordenfelt and Zaharoff. The boat had taken more than ten months to assemble, and was even now incomplete; payment was demanded for the parts that had had to be made at Tashkizak; the assembly workers' wages had not been paid at all for most of the ten months. The Commission stopped short of recommending the rejection of the boats. Garrett, in one of his more serpentine performances, had pointed out that as full diving trials had not been carried out (because of the missing parts), the trials could not be counted as definitive and official. While strongly suspecting that the infidel priest was not all he seemed, the Commission swallowed this, and demanded that a formal protest should be made to the Swedish Ambassador. The Nordenfelt Submarine Torpedo Boat Company was, they reasoned, a Swedish concern (though by now it was part of the new Nordenfelt Company and registered in England): the Swedish Government seemed to be the only official body capable of turning the screw on Oscar II's wayward Royal Chamberlain. It does not appear to have occurred to them to protest to the British Government: given the opinion of Turkey then fashionable in London, they were probably quite right not to bother.

Mr Arenofa, the Swedish Ambassador, was shown the evidence, and agreed that the delays and malfunctions were entirely Nordenfelt's fault. He agreed to write to Nordenfelt, demanding an explanation. Depending on Nordenfelt's reply, he would, if necessary, take steps to ensure Nordenfelt's compliance with international law. Nordenfelt's antics (and therefore Garrett's) were proving a serious threat to relations between Stockholm and the Porte.

The result of Mr Arenofa's colourful correspondence with Nordenfelt was (as usual) more work for Garrett. Garrett, who had in fact returned to England for the delivery voyage and first trials of the new submarine, had collapsed from what looks like sheer overwork soon after his arrival. Having slaved through a difficult trial with his new boat, he was now expected to drop everything and return to Constantinople, to bring to life a boat in which he by now could have had little faith: his experiences in the new boat, while hardly all that might have been hoped for, had certainly reinforced, once and for all, the lessons of what had been wrong with his earlier designs. Nordenfelt, meanwhile, overcame his embarrassment over the Turks' mention of the new boat, and sold them an option on it.

Garrett had been driven to consult his medical brother William while in England: he seems to have developed a stomach ulcer in Constantinople (hardly surprising, under the circumstances). But business came first. Within days of Nordenfelt receiving a blunt threat from the Swedish Government and a demand for satisfaction from the Grand Vezir himself, Garrett was on his way back to Constantinople. As soon as he had re-installed himself at the Hotel Byzance, he wrote to Hassan Pasha in his best Uriah Heep mode:

June 2, 1887

Dear Sir,
I have this day arrived for the purpose of obeying the order His Majesty was pleased to give, namely that the Nordenfelt Submarine Boat should be experimented with on the 15th day of Ramadan.

I am extremely anxious that His Majesty should see with his own eyes that he has not been deceived by Mr Nordenfelt, but that he is really in possession of the best Submarine Torpedo Boat in the World. Can you please give me any idea of when and where His Majesty would like to see the boat?

I am
Your Excellency's Obt. Servt.,
George Wm Garrett[6]

The choice of the 15th day of Ramadan was significant. This was the festival of *Hirkai Sheroff*, one of the holiest days in the Islamic calendar, the day on which the Sultan was re-acclaimed as Caliph: as such, the day was of immense importance for the Sultan's prestige.

Garrett had left Fond Eckerman in charge of things at Tashkizak. With Garrett away, work seems to have progressed surprisingly rapidly. Having lashed together something resembling the boat's depth-keeping gear (for the little it was worth, in all candour), Eckerman mounted his own short series of trials, with a Turkish crew. By the time the 15th day of Ramadan came round, the boat was about as ready as she would ever be.

Garrett was fully aware that a genuinely impressive surface performance was by no means beyond the boat's capabilities, as was a carefully-staged diving demonstration, *if* the boat were to be crewed by experts. For the new trials, he insisted that the crew should consist almost entirely of Nordenfelt personnel – himself, Captain D'Alton, Fond Eckerman and Mr Lawrie, with a lone Turk stoking the boiler. In a clever psychological move, he asked Hassan Pasha for an assurance that a place would be chosen with water deep enough for the formidable diving powers of his submarine. Disasters excepted, it was extremely unlikely that the boat's hull would be required to live up to its 100-foot guaranteed depth.

Hirkai Sheroff fell on Tuesday, 7 June. The boat's first surface trials were to be held under the personal supervision of Abdul Hamid, who sent a steam-launch to fetch the submarine once the day's religious duties had been fulfilled.

Steam had been raised overnight, thus camouflaging the immense length of time required to get up steam for a submerged run, a defect the boat shared with the *Dykeri Pråm*. Garrett had, however, taken steps to alleviate the problem. The insulation around the boilers and the all-important hot water reservoirs was greatly improved, to the point where the pressure in the system, once steam was raised, would fall only 10lb in 24 hours, a loss made good by the consumption of 2 or 3 cwt of fuel. Given such a performance, it was thought practical (at least by Garrett) to keep the boat prepared to dive for days on end in time of war. This was at least a saleable arrangement, and an honest attempt to come to terms with a shortcoming that had been loftily ignored (or at best underemphasised) in the *Dykeri Pråm*.

The boat passed under the bridge at Galata at 2.30 p.m., earning a round of applause from the thousands who had gathered on the bridge. Once she was into comparatively open water, her grey paint-scheme rendered her barely visible from the shore. While this was an obvious military advantage (if a little annoying for Abdul Hamid, squinting at her from Seraglio Point), it had a more immediately practical drawback. Amazingly, nothing had been done to thin out the water traffic at the trials site, at the southern mouth of the Bosphorus: an assortment of craft poured, as usual, in and out of the Golden Horn and into the Bosphorus from the Sea of Marmora. It was like trying to give a plate-spinning demonstration in the middle of Hyde Park Corner. Garrett thus had a splendid (if unwelcome) opportunity to demonstrate the boat's manoeuvrability through a large number of boats and lighters. The boat also performed remarkably well in passing through the narrow space beneath the Galata Bridge, braving the strong cross-current in the process.

Well-advised by his ministers (Halil's perceptive remarks on the *Dykeri Pråm*'s behaviour in a seaway had obviously been noted), the Sultan commanded Garrett to keep station off Seraglio Point for fifteen minutes. The boat handled the strong current remarkably well, but was touched on a few occasions by the attendant naval launches, which bobbed about dangerously close until they were called inshore on Garrett's insistence. A passing lighter, lumbering *across* the Bosphorus in serene disdain of the Sultan's new wonder-weapon, was less fortunate, and had a hole torn in her bottom by the submarine's screw. The lighter reached the shore safely: the submarine sustained the loss of a few inches off one blade of the propeller. Hardly a good start to the trials, but not Garrett's fault – and, as he well knew, a useful excuse if he should suddenly need to stop the proceedings. The boat's propeller was the new submarine's primary improvement on her predecessor, making far more efficient use of the engine's power output – on the surface. No amount of propeller adjustment could help the boat's underwater performance, however.

The boat was then ordered to 'attack' a steamer lying off Scutari, on the other side of the Bosphorus. Garrett began the run with a turn across the current, well within the boat's own length – rather impressive. The boat's very low surface profile was noted as a considerable plus: much of the hull was concealed by the boat's own bow-wave.

Garrett marked the 'torpedo launch' by opening the bow caps of the empty torpedo-tubes. Unlike the *Dykeri Pråm*'s wholly external torpedo-tube arrangement, the new boat's torpedoes could be launched from inside the boat, an important improvement on the earlier design, though it carried with it a hidden danger that Garrett would encounter before long. Fortunately, with the boat on the surface and the tubes unloaded, all went well. Water rushing through the tubes and out through the vents caused two jets of water to be thrown up over the submarine, a touch of theatricality greatly appreciated by the crowd: the crowds who had hailed her as the 'whale ship' at Galata had their opinion confirmed at seeing her spout. The name stuck.

Returning to Seraglio Point on a wave of adulation, Garrett was instructed to run the boat against the current. The boat managed to steam at eight knots against a current of five, doing rather better than the supposed pilot boats, which constantly lost station and, far from guiding her, actually constituted a hazard to the submarine.

The final test was by far the most dangerous, given the still-parlous state of the boat's machinery. Garrett was ordered to repeat his attack on the steamer, but this time he was to make his final run submerged. Fred Jane observed the test:

> The [target] vessel being at no great distance, [the submarine] steamed slowly ahead so as to afford time for getting rid of the extra buoyancy, and closing up. Soon there was little to be seen of her but the hump-like dome, and having turned towards the enemy, it was very difficult to keep her [in] view. Suddenly she was lost sight of, to appear, however, shortly afterwards, rounding the bows of the vessel from the other side. She had, as it were, dived to deliver her blow, and then turned off to avoid pursuit.[7]

What Jane had seen was a simple 'dip-chick' manoeuvre that *Resurgam* could have managed – slipping briefly beneath the surface on the hydroplanes before bobbing up again on the reserve of buoyancy: this evolution, a sin against Nordenfelt's holy law of vertical submergence, was not supposed to be approved of by the manufacturers, but it saved the submarine's reputation. Once again, and for the same reasons, there was insufficient underwater speed to maintain depth, quite apart from the boat's instability, which would have been woefully apparent to the crew during their dip. The boat had not steamed slowly purely to 'afford time for getting rid of the extra buoyancy': she had been doing her sluggish semi-submerged maximum. The shape of the hull and the inefficient propulsion system were again conspiring to defeat the boat's purpose. The temperature on board the boat, closed up on the surface in the blazing Turkish summer, was murderous: as usual, Garrett neglected to publish figures on this detail. Atmospheric hygiene was as pristine as in the previous submarine: carbon monoxide, carbon dioxide, coal dust and candle-fumes all conspired to make the worst street in Constantinople (then enduring a mild burst of typhus) seem attractive. Once again, Garrett had achieved a 'successful' demonstration of a submarine's capabilities by the curious expedient of *not* demonstrating them.

The boat was ordered back to her moorings, at the top of the Golden Horn. Garrett chose to do this on reserve steam from the hot-water cistern, but left the hatches open, doubtless to the relief of the crew. At the end of the run, after two hours' running on the steam reserve, the gauge still showed 70 psi. Not bad at all.

The Sultan declared himself highly satisfied with the performance of the boat. Garrett's success was short-lived, however. The Naval Commission, using Garrett's own previous argument, pointed out that this was still not an official trial: the boat had not in fact been shown operating *as a submarine*. They thus proved themselves rather more perceptive than many of their European colleagues had been at Landskrona. However, as the Sultan had been impressed by what he saw, and it had been genuinely demonstrated that the boat had real potential as a low-silhouette surface vessel (even less visible than the dreaded Russian boats), it was agreed to pass the boat provisionally, and to press ahead with finishing the assembly of the second boat.

Garrett had brought with him a large case of parts for the second boat. These were not replacements, but components that had not been supplied when the boat arrived at Tashkizak. Garrett and Nordenfelt had expected the Turks to assemble the boat while a substantial proportion of the engine still lay in pieces in Chertsey.

The Turks had spotted this long before Eckerman, then the Nordenfelt man-on-the-spot, had been prepared to admit it, and had complained with appropriate stridency. Shipping large components aboard a completed submarine was even more difficult in 1887 than it is now, all the more so with the limited facilities then available in Turkey.

The official trials (by everyone's agreed definition) of the first boat were held in July, again at Seraglio Point, and were disastrous. The Turkish crew was re-convened, under Garrett's direction, though it seems by now that Commander Develioglu was beginning to tire of the excitable infidel: tempers rose in the searing heat of the closed-up boat, as Garrett gave out instructions that must have sounded outrageous. A commander in the Imperial Ottoman Navy was not used to being told to stand absolutely still – probably the most important duty for all concerned as the boat submerged. Without the very special skills (*how* special Develioglu and his men were only now discovering) of the Nordenfelt *équipe*, the boat's less desirable tendencies soon came to insist upon themselves.

Once again, the boat could only dive for an average of about fifty nightmarish, teetering seconds before returning to the surface, and this time the funereal underwater speed was neither overlooked nor forgiven.

It was, however, the torpedo-tubes which gave the most cause for alarm. Unlike the little game off Scutari, the official trials required a real torpedo to be launched while the boat was fully submerged. As Garrett had made no provision for counter-flooding to offset the change in trim when the torpedo left the tube (and this in a boat whose stability was hardly a strong-point to begin with), the result of firing the torpedo could have been predicted. Captain D'Alton, something of a fair-weather enthusiast, was there: 'Once, and ... only once, she fired a torpedo [while submerged], with the result that she as nearly as possible stood up vertically on her tail and proceeded to plunge to the bottom stern first'.[8]

The crew could be forgiven for believing they were about to be delivered to the arms of Allah, but Garrett had been this way before. Just when his priestly services might have been most useful, he had a congregation consisting entirely of Muslims – in a way, the story of his life, had he but realised it. The boat's watertight integrity had not been breached, so it was comparatively simple to bring the boat back to the surface – provided, once again, that everybody kept still, or at least quaked discreetly.

Although this exercise cannot in all conscience be deemed a success, we owe it to Garrett's memory to note that this hair-raising incident was the first known underwater firing of a torpedo by a submarine.

Nor was this the only potential tragedy. As at the Sultan's preview, no effort seems to have been made to clear the area of traffic. This time, fortunately with Mr Lawrie on board, the results were nearly terminal:

> On another occasion all hands were nearly lost. Mr Garrett was in the little conning-tower. The boat was being slowly submerged – an operation of the utmost delicacy – ... when a boat came alongside without warning. Her wash sent a considerable quantity of water down the conning-tower, the lid of which was not closed, and the submarine boat instantly began to sink like a stone. Fortunately Mr Garrett got the lid closed just in time, and Mr Lawrie, the engineer, without waiting for orders, blew some water ballast out. It was an exceedingly narrow escape.[9]

This seems to have been the only occasion on which the boat's emergency ballast-blowing capacity was used in earnest. One of the boat's much-vaunted inbuilt safety features, this was another of Nordenfelt's embellishments to the original Garrett design. The fact that it worked on this occasion probably indicates that the boat was at no great depth when Mr Lawrie did his duty; the underwater steam pressure of 150 psi was very dubious at the best of times, as would have been shown had the steam pressure been used to force out ballast at the hull's guaranteed depth of 100 feet. It is just as likely that at that depth water would have been forced *inboard* by the external pressure.

On 21 August 1887, the Constantinople newspaper *Tercümani Hakikat Gazet* announced the launch of the second submarine, which had taken place on 16 August, a mere sixteen months behind schedule. The same announcement also acknowledged the launch of the previous boat, which had been kept a semi-secret until the very public trials had rendered publicity not only inevitable but desirable. The *Gazet* was what we would now call a 'semi-official' newspaper, that exotic staple of modern Middle Eastern journalism: the paper printed what the Government told it to print, but was privately owned. When the time came to publish accounts of the boats' powers that were less than clinically accurate, this fond relationship between state and press would prove highly useful. The Government's exercise of official influence frequently

reached heights of absurdity that would raise a blush from the most
crass totalitarian régimes of our own time. For example, it was
forbidden to print anything concerning the assassination of heads
of state, anywhere in the world, lest anyone in the Ottoman Empire
started getting ideas. When President McKinley was shot, the
Turkish Press solemnly declared that he had died of anthrax.
'Indigestion' became a common euphemism for anything from
heartburn up to and including being blown in half, neither
particularly uncommon in Abdul Hamid's Turkey. Garrett does
not seem to have realised until painfully late that the Turks were
not to be trifled with.

No crew was assigned to the new submarine, but a caretaker
commanding officer was appointed, a Commander Tahir, who
handed over to one Commander Ismet just before the boat's trials.
Commanding officers apart, the two submarines would share a
single crew for trial purposes until the boats were formally accepted
and commissioned – when and if.

Soon after the launch of the second boat, Nordenfelt's obsessive
fear of spies was found to have been more than his usual paranoia.
A man was found loitering by the submarines' moorings, wearing a
heavy overcoat despite the late summer heat. The guards'
suspicions were aroused, and he was arrested. Underneath the
coat, the guards found a camera. Instead of a photographic plate,
which would have been normal then, the camera contained a metal
disk, holding six small individual plates: the disk could be rotated,
exposing each plate in turn, so that six different shots could be
taken. The lens was disguised as a button: all the operator had to
do was point himself in the appropriate direction and open the
shutter. The spy had taken six photographs of the two submarines
lying at their moorings.

Fortunately, the camera disk has survived, one of the more exotic
items of Garrett memorabilia. While the pictures are hardly
masterpieces of the photographer's art, they are an astonishing
technical achievement. Interestingly enough, a camera using a
remarkably similar film-disk has been on the market recently: there
really *is* nothing new, it seems. Not that the spy's technological
ingenuity did him any good. Despite the best efforts of Turkish
interrogational technology to extract the name of his employers, the
man kept an icy (or, more likely, rather noisy) silence throughout a
long night of the unspeakable: the records are eerily silent about
the methods used, which may be just as well. He was shot the

following morning. Reading between the lines, it needs no great insight to suggest that the spy was in the employ of the Russians, who had submarine plans of their own at this time and were disturbed at the prospect of being overtaken by one of their traditional enemies. Also, as we shall see, they were soon themselves banging on Zaharoff's door in search of their very own Nordenfelt boat.

Garrett managed to persuade Hassan Pasha that the problems encountered with the submarine were teething-troubles that could be ironed out given time: in any case, they would not recur with the second boat. Garrett's staying-power seems to have been matched only by his eloquence, doubtless the fruit of his time in the pulpit. Having saved the day for Nordenfelt yet again, he packed his bags once more and rushed back to England for the official trials, late in December, of the new submarine, in which he had at least a modicum of confidence. He was, however, working and travelling to a timetable which would be gruelling even today: in the 1880s, it verged on the suicidal.

The new, absolutely final, *really* definitive trials for both submarines were fixed for late January 1888, and a new Commission convened to supervise and assess them, chaired by Admiral Ahmet Retip. The other Commissioners were Admirals Süleyman and Starke, Commodores Hakki and Harty, and Commander Mehmet. There would be no excuses this time: also, these trials, as Garrett had requested, would be in deep water, in the Gulf of Izmit (or, as it was then spelt, Ismidt). Garrett, back in Constantinople by the second week of January, set to work on the boats in earnest. He would have been gratified to note the absence of one name from the Commission: Woods Pasha, who had been at the Southampton trials of the new boat, was too engrossed in his new position as Naval Attaché in London to be present at Izmit. He would not be there to make the embarrassing comparisons that would be all too obvious to Garrett.

Apart from engineer Lawrie, Garrett was alone in Constantinople: Zaharoff was busy peddling assorted modes of mechanised death (Nordenfelt's and others') in Europe, and Nordenfelt himself never once set foot in the place, being quite content to let others do the talking. Though he lived in considerable style in a lavish suite at the Hotel Byzance, Garrett's position was not entirely enviable. There are clear signs that he was far from happy in Constantinople. Garrett's letters simply show a man separated from his wife and family in a very strange land, a face of the eccentric inventor that the Turks would not have seen, though it would be little short of amazing if his personal mail went unread. The Garretts were a close family. Jane missed her husband sorely, and wrote frequently to tell him so. Garrett, freezing, overworked and miserable in an abnormally bad Turkish winter, was deprived of even this much contact with home when the inward mail was cut off by the weather. He continued to write home, however:

> January 16, 1888
>
> My only darling,
>   ... There are few wifes [sic] so loved as you, and you ought to be happy.
>   I have put the childrens' photos in the frame of my looking-glass, and every morning and evening they make me think of you and love you. Be happy, my dearest wife. The weather here is very severe, with much snow and storms, very hard on us for our work, so hot in the boat, so cold outside it ...[10]

Jane, learning that the mail was not getting through, sent him a telegram, which comforted him enormously:

> January 22, 1888
>
> ... The wire I got from you was a pleasure, for it told me my darlings were well and happy. I have been working my hardest for you, and am this day awaiting the order from the Sultan to begin the trials. I have one boat ready, torpedo and all, and steam up, waiting for orders. It is a great nuisance that in this country nothing can be done without the Sultan's order.
>   I expect to be sent to the Ismidt – you will find the Gulf marked in the Atlas. I shall be at the Eastern end of it for the next week or fortnight ...
>   With love and kisses to you all, I remain
>   Your own husband
>   George Wm Garrett[11]

On 24 January, the first boat was taken to Izmit, in company with the steamer *Salonik*, which carried the Commission. Despite fairly vile weather en route (a strong southerly gale and driving rain), the boat made good time: the 53-mile voyage took 6½ hours, with a ten-minute break half-way. As had been the case with both *Resurgam* and *Dykeri Pråm En*, the submarine was a remarkably good sea-boat – almost the only virtue of the hull-form.

The trials began at 9.45 the next morning: the boat was crewed by Garrett and the original Turkish officers, under the command, somewhat nominal in the circumstances, of Commander Develioglu. The first subject of the trials was the boat's ability to launch torpedoes. The submarine was trimmed down to the awash state (a matter of fifteen minutes) and paraded before the *Salonik* for 45 minutes at her usual stately semi-submerged pace. At 10.50 a torpedo was successfully launched from 200 yards in this condition, the *Salonik* acting as target: the trial log notes that the torpedo left the tube 'entirely normally' – because of the fractional remaining buoyancy, there was no repetition of the Seraglio Point nightmare. Altogether, the boat was run closed up for an hour and nine minutes. At this point, bad weather intervened, but Garrett had definitely had a good day. It had been realised that launching a torpedo while submerged was never going to be safe, given the boat's abominable lack of underwater stability, but it had now been established that launching in the awash state was a credible alternative.

The following morning, the boat sailed to the extreme eastern end of the Gulf. Night trials followed, again concentrating on the awash condition. The moon glinted on the cupola, but the boat was otherwise invisible: another torpedo was successfully launched at the *Salonik*, this time from 600 yards, well beyond the weapon's accurate range. Once again, the Commission's report was favourable: on a dark night, they decided, she would be completely invisible.

On 27 January, however, the bad news started being entered in the log. The boat tried to dive many times, but never succeeded in achieving more than the dip-and-stagger that had been demonstrated previously. Furthermore, her underwater instability was judged to be, if anything, worse than ever. The Commission noted bluntly: 'The boat cannot dive at all.'

Later the same day, the boat's surface speed was measured, and adjudged to be 10 knots. In total, the boat had been closed up during the trials for two hours and seventeen minutes. As a submarine, she had failed miserably, but she had shown other desirable qualities.

The following morning, Garrett was sent back to Constantinople with the submarine's crew to bring the second boat. On the way back, an exceptionally violent storm broke out, badly delaying his return journey to Izmit:

... At 8 o'clock in the morning I left Constantinople for Ismidt with Torpedo Boat No. 2. Due to stormy weather, I did not reach Prinkips until noon, and, seeing that the wind was going to grow stronger, I thought that it would be better to stop. At 10 p.m., while the boat was under the control of the Captain [Commander Ismet], my cables were broken and the boat was thrown ashore, causing damage to the large propeller etc. After very tiring work in very bad weather, I refloated the boat and tied her up at the quay again at 3 a.m. on February 2. At 9 a.m. I left Prinkips for Ismidt, where I arrived in good time on the afternoon of the 3rd.[12]

That afternoon had been set aside for the testing of the boats' guns, before the trials of the second boat, but the repairs to the second boat had to be attended to first. Working far into the night with the very limited equipment available at Izmit, Garrett managed to patch up the second boat sufficiently for trials to be attempted.

Garrett's memorandum on the following day's trials differs sharply from the Commission's log. According to the log, one of the Nordenfelts jammed after only being fired once. The log then contains a comment that comes as no surprise at all: for the first time, one of the most glaring faults of the boat's design was officially recorded: 'There is nowhere for the gunner to stand: firing the gun is therefore very difficult'.[13] In a seaway, the gunner would have been overboard before he could train the weapon. Garrett had made no attempt to cure a defect that had been just as obvious at Landskrona – but it had taken the Turks, whom he and the other Nordenfelt engineers never lost an opportunity to denigrate, to point this out in so many words. Garrett's memorandum, written as much for Nordenfelt's eyes as the Minister of Marine's, is – shall we say – different in emphasis:

I mounted the guns on boat No.1 and repaired the damage to No.2 as far as it was possible for me to do so. Before noon on the 4th, I manoeuvred boat No.1 and fired the guns to the satisfaction of the Commission.[14]

The last statement is quite untrue: after all the fuss that Nordenfelt had made over the guns, only a perfect performance would have satisfied them, and this had not been delivered. Tension began to mount between Garrett and the Commission.

The impatience felt by the members of the Commission is clearly indicated by their terse comments on the performance of the second boat, which was tested throughout the remainder of the day: 'No better than the first boat ... Cannot dive'.[15] When Garrett suggested a night trial, he was abruptly told that the trials were over. A ferocious argument erupted on board the *Salonik*, with the members of the Commission telling Garrett in no uncertain terms that they thought he and Nordenfelt were trying to swindle them.

It is clear that Nordenfelt had heavily oversold the boats to the Turks in the original contract, a mistake that was now coming home to roost. The contract had been drawn up by Zaharoff and Nordenfelt, and had made no concessions to the reality of the boats' limitations: had they been sold as semi-submersibles possessing a very limited submarine capability, the Turks would have had nothing to complain about – indeed, as semi-submersibles, the boats were a great success.

The Turks had long since realised that they had been taken in by a mixture of Nordenfelt-Zaharoff-Garrett salesmanship and (worse) Greek and Russian propaganda, though it is amusing to note that they had believed the stories of the Greek boat until Garrett's ostensible trip to her torpedo trials, when his very strange behaviour (to hide his efforts at Barrow) had planted the seeds of suspicion. When tempers had cooled a little, Garrett was allowed, at his own request, to write a memorandum of the trials as he saw them. He fell back on a carefully re-worded version of the old standby: the shortcomings of the trials had been caused by the Turkish crew. But he was finally prepared to admit that they could be trained to handle them as well as the Nordenfelt engineers: this was a wise psychological move that actually won him some sympathy from the Commission, if not quite the roar of approval that he suggests. The original memorandum is written in a shaky hand, in Garrett's execrable French:

> In the afternoon, I took boat No.2 beneath the sea, but the night put an end to the experiment, against my will. During the conference that was held today, I explained to the Commission that they had seen that the boats had all the power and machinery necessary for submarine boats, and that all that was needed was for part of the crew to be trained for the boat to do all that they required of it.   The Commission has expressed complete satisfacation with my explanation.[16]

Garrett ended his memorandum on a typically crafty note: the boat's faults would be attended to – after the Turks had commissioned them. While the two submarines were hardly loss-leaders – Nordenfelt was at least trying to charge considerably over the odds for them – it was vital to Garrett and Nordenfelt that what is now known as a *flop de scandale* be avoided if they were to sell the new submarine, whatever its improvements on the now slightly embarrassing Turkish boats. Some exposure of the Turkish boats' limitations was unavoidable, but a *flop d'estime* might be obtained with a little gentle massaging of the facts:

> I should like to add that it is very much the desire of Mr Nordenfelt and myself to make Turkey's submarine boats the most perfect in the world, and that it is only experiment which will show the improvements that need to be made to small details. I have already seen the small improvements that can be made to boats 1 and 2, and these improvements will be made at Mr Nordenfelt's expense after the boats have become the property of His Majesty the Sultan.[17]

Despite Garrett's pleas, however, the Commission had not relented when they came to compile their report. The concluding summary is blunt, precise and very damning:

> The boats are very dangerous to the crews ... They cannot be used to protect ports or the Bosphorus ... they have *no* naval use.[18]

Hassan Pasha's response to Garrett's memorandum was to suggest that the trials be held *yet again*, this time with a crew consisting entirely of Garrett's Nordenfelt All-Stars. Not wishing to push his luck even further (and knowing all too much about what the boats could *really* do), Garrett, acting on his own authority, turned the request down. By then, Woods Pasha had reported on the capabilities of the new boat back in England: with Woods' report on the Commission's knees as they watched the strugglings of the Turkish boats, there was simply nothing that the boats could do that would satisfy them. Garrett would brazen it out. There were in any case difficulties involved in consulting a higher authority, Unseen Friend always excepted. Nordenfelt, as ever, was in London, engrossed in the early stages of what would prove the Great Merger with his erstwhile chief rival Hiram Maxim: Zaharoff was somewhere between Paris, where he had bought a new home, and St Petersburg. Neither of them would want to be bothered with the junior partner's little local difficulty in palming off last year's model. Garrett would have to manage the situation on his own.

Ironically, in Garrett's darkest hour, des Vignes, who would have found a spaceship easier to build than Garrett's submarine, were back on the Turkish payroll. While Garrett sweated it out in Constantinople, the first of two new des Vignes torpedo boats, destined for Turkey, was undergoing trials at Long Reach.

Abdul Hamid at Constantinople, 1887. The ship in the background is an *Osmanieh class* ironclad (a British product).

James Bond, 1887. Disc of photographs taken by a spy at Constantinople, showing the two *Abduls* at their moorings. Smithsonian Institution, Washington.

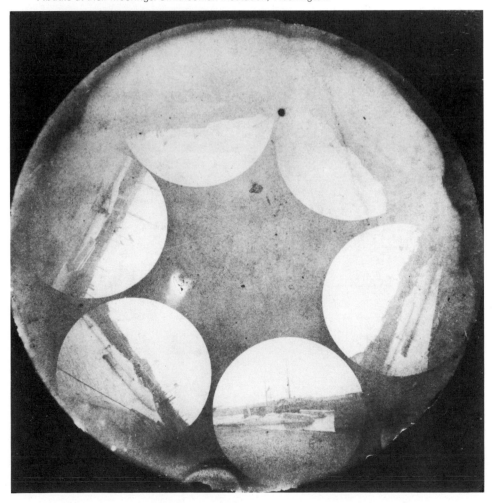

Commander the Reverend George
Garrett Bey, BA, in full regalia.

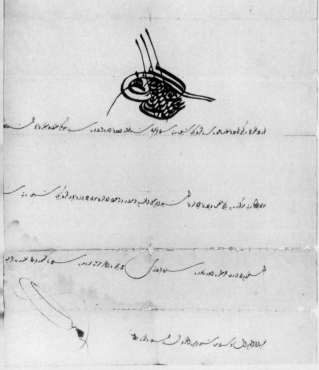

Garrett's commission in the
Imperial Ottoman Navy.
Smithsonian Institution,
Washington.

Whatever the realities of the two submarines, the political angle had to be attended to. A drastically different version of the Izmit Commission's report was issued to the European Press, who responded just as they had done in the case of the Greek boat. They believed every word. Violins soared, clouds parted and the moon rose over a Sublimely orchestrated submarine dream-sequence:

> The night on which the attack was made was beautifully calm and moonlight – circumstances powerfully against the submarine boat ... Owing to the extreme phosphorescence of the water, the Commission were enabled to trace the course of the submarine boat for a very long time, until suddenly it disappeared from their view, and they did not see it again till it blew its whistle [which it did not have] on the other side of the steamer from which it had departed, and at a distance of some 400 yards. This whistle had been agreed upon previously with Captain Garrett as the signal that the attack had succeeded, and it did so beyond question in the most unfavourable circumstances; those on board the Commissioners' steamer feeling that had it been in actual warfare they would have been completely at the mercy of the boat's commander ... Captain Garrett, to whom the Commissioners expressed their high approval of his skill.[19]

Meanwhile, back in reality, Garrett was summoned to Hassan Pasha's home on 27 February. It must have been a very uncomfortable walk, with unmistakable overtones of the headmaster's study. What followed was a truly remarkable interview, in which Garrett employed his diplomatic skills to their utmost to hammer out a settlement between the Nordenfelt Company and the Turkish Government, even going so far as (in effect) to place his own life on the line in the interests of the Ottoman Empire. Garrett's letter, summing up the agreement, is in its way an achievement at least on a par with the submarines themselves – a splendid concoction of half-truths, outraged innocence and surprisingly astute salesmanship, all put over with what looks curiously like sincerity:

> Dear Sir,
>   I write to confirm that at an interview which your Excellency kindly granted me at your private residence last evening you promised me that if I wrote to you a letter stating the result of the aforesaid interview you would never allow any one to either see it or know of its existence except His Imperial Majesty The Sultan.
>   This is the letter you promised to keep secret. Having explained to Your Excellency the great advantages which the Nordenfelt Torpedo

Boats have over the ordinary Surface Boats I admitted that the Contract had been drawn up most ambiguously and by persons ignorant of the subject and that it was quite possible that His Majesty had been led to expect that the boats would perform more than they have done.

And therefore, although at this moment there is not any profit on these boats, yet if His Majesty will accept in all honor [sic] these two boats and will contemplate the purchase of one more, Mr Nordenfelt will on his side be content to allow one half of the balance now due to him by Article XII of the Contract to remain unpaid until after the settlement of the contract for the new boat, and that if a new boat be bought the sum as left unpaid shall be deducted from the price of the new boat.

I have agreed to the above because I am extremely anxious that the Nordenfelt Submarine Torpedo Boats should form a part of the Ottoman Navy, because the defence of Constantinople and the Maintenance of the Ottoman Empire in its integrity is to the interest of England, and further because I believe that the defence of some Turkish Harbour, Strand or Sea will play an important part in the coming war, and if the Nordenfelt Submarine Torpedo Boats render good service in such a defence it will cause them to be adopted by the whole world.

I repeat that Mr Nordenfelt does not want to make money in Turkey, nor has he done so, but he wishes to be patronised by His Majesty and allowed to shew the value of the Submarine Boats in the defence of the rights of the King who has up to now done much to assist him to the success and fortune which he enjoys.

For my own part, if His Majesty adopts as part of his Navy the Nordenfelt Submarine Boats, I will do all that lays [sic] in my power to make them thoroughly effective and maintain them in good order, and I would propose as the best means of guarding the interests of His Majesty in this matter: That Turkish Captains and crews should be appointed to each of the Submarine Boats, but that I should hold a commission in the Turkish Service with a rank sufficient to enable me to control the Captains of the boats. I could not, of course, give my whole time to the Turkish Service in time of peace, but I would give one month each year, during which I would examine and service the boats and their crews. I would of course ask no salary for my services. For the first year, it would be advisable that two of my trained engineers should remain in Turkey to keep the boats in order and to instruct the Turks in the management of their machinery. These men would have to be paid by His Majesty.

By giving me the command of His Submarine Torpedo Boats, His Majesty would have the advantage of my experience, which will be continually increasing, and I should have the advantage of knowing that the boats were kept in good order and ready for use should they be wanted to fight.

In conclusion, I would wish to assure your Excellency that should I have the honor [sic] to serve under you either in peace or war, I will do my utmost to carry out your wishes for the guarding of the interests of His Majesty The Sultan.

I have the honour to be
Your Excellency's Obt. Servt.
George Wm Garrett[20]

The remark that the contract had been drawn up 'most ambiguously and by persons ignorant of the subject' is a very precise summation of the efforts of Nordenfelt and Zaharoff. But Garrett had not deserted the company, at a time when he could have been forgiven for thinking it had deserted him. His claim that there was 'not any profit' on the two boats would only have been accurate had the Turks ultimately decided not to make the final payment, which more or less represented Nordenfelt's margin.

Far from admitting defeat over the two submarines, Garrett even tried to sell the Turks the new boat, then basking in the glow of an only moderately bogus official trial, and on which they had already held an option. Not surprisingly, after all they had been through by now at the hands of Nordenfelt and his servants (including Garrett), the Turks did not take up this particular offer, but they were sufficiently impressed with Garrett's offer to place himself in the Sultan's service to accept most of his other proposals. The only real stumbling-block was the actual amount of money to be paid to Nordenfelt.

On 15 March, Garrett presented himself at the Imperial Admiralty to sign the final agreement:

Between His Excellency Hassan Pasha, Navy Minister, acting in the name of His Imperial Majesty the Sultan, and Captain Garrett, representing Mr Nordenfelt, the following has been agreed:

Article 1: The Imperial Ottoman Government accepts the two submarine torpedo boats constructed in Mr Nordenfelt's factories and contracted for on 23 January 1886.

Article 2: From the sum of £4,900 due to Mr Nordenfelt from the Imperial Ottoman Government, 2900 English pounds shall be deducted to cover the expenses incurred by the Navy Minister for materials employed in the assembly of the two boats.

Article 3: The sum of £1,488, in payment for two guns, and the balance of £2,000 shall be paid to Mr Nordenfelt next Saturday, the 17th inst.

Article 4: Mr Nordenfelt, conforming to the conditions of the contract of 23 January 1886, will designate two engineers to instruct the officers of the Navy in everything concerning the use of these boats. The appointment of these two engineers will be paid for by the Imperial Ottoman Government.

It has further been agreed that Captain Garrett, who, by order of His Imperial Majesty the Sultan, has been commissioned with the rank of Commander, will come every year to Constantinople, where he will remain without payment for one month, to examine and ascertain for himself the progress of the officers, and to indicate improvements to be made.

Article 5: Mr Garrett furthermore promises that in the event of war he will serve the Imperial Government without payment.

Done in duplicate at Constantinople, 15 March 1886.

George Wm Garrett   Hassan Pasha[21]

Nordenfelt had actually been demanding £6,388 in all, but it was made clear to him that he had come within inches of being sued for a great deal more. Two cheques were issued: one, for £1,488 – the price of the guns – went directly to the Nordenfelt coffers after the customary deduction for Zaharovian services. The second – £2,000, for the submarines themselves – went to Garrett, who, like everyone else on the Nordenfelt team in Constantinople, had not been paid for months.

Garrett's rank in the Imperial Navy was *binbashi* (pronounced 'bin-basher') – a 'leader of a thousand men', corresponding roughly to commander in the Royal Navy, and entitling him to the Turkish suffix Bey: this did not prevent Garrett from frequently styling himself The Reverend Commander G.W. Garrett Pasha, BA in the years to come. He was, after all, more entitled to it than the rather informal Captaincy that he had awarded himself since teaming up with Nordenfelt. In future, he would use both titles more or less as the mood took him.

It was an excited (and slightly confused) Garrett who wrote to his wife the next day:

My own darling Jane,
     Only yesterday the boats were officially accepted and I can say that I shall leave here with *perfect success*. It has been hard to stay away from you, but I have been working for you and your [sic] children and I *have* succeeded. *I am now a Commander in the Turkish Navy* (this is a degree higher than Captain). I have a regular Commission. You will see that this is very important, because it admits me to Naval and Military Clubs and circles all over the World. Besides, it gives a Social position to our Children which they would not have had if I remained a civilian.

I am working hard, and a few days will see me on my way to your arms.[22]

In his enthusiasm, Garrett has overlooked the fact that a commander/*binbashi* was (and is) a degree *below* captain/*miralay*, and that his commission was honorary. Apart from this tendency to play to the domestic gallery, Garrett also kept some of the darker aspects of his work from his wife, though he seems to have given an exceptionally lurid account of his life to his son (blockade-running and all). Jane went to her grave believing that Zaharoff was a semi-waif whom her husband had come across by chance in Constantinople: she always maintained that Garrett had given the poor man his first job as an interpreter. The fact was that by the time Garrett was in Constantinople, Zaharoff could have bought and sold him several times over – and Garrett was by no means a poor man by then.

Pausing only for a photographic session, at which his portrait was executed, twice, in full dress Ottoman naval uniform, fez and all, Garrett returned to England on a cloud of euphoria. Quite apart from his (apparent) triumph at Constantinople, the trials of the new boat were being well-received by the press. His long absence from La Plata, it seemed, had been worthwhile. After all that he had been through, it was, perhaps, a pity that he could not be in Constantinople for the submarines' commissioning ceremony, which took place on 3 April 1888. The Turkish ensign was finally hoisted on the two boats, and the submarines were given names: the occasion was reported the following day in the faithful *Tercümani Hakikat Gazet*. Ironically, Garrett was one of the very last to learn the names of the boats, despite the fact that Nordenfelt had asked for this information very early on, and had been ignored. Two weeks later, he received his *firman* (commission), with a letter from his brother British officer in the Sultan's service, Henry Harty:

My dear Garrett Bey,
    I have much pleasure in forwarding your Firman, which I received last week from H[is] E[xcellency] the R[eis?] Pasha. Please acknowledge the receipt of same. I have nothing new to mention to you about the Boats, only that by his I[mperial] M[ajesty]'s orders the boats are to be named *Abdul Hamid* and *Abdul Medjid*.
                    With kindest regards,
                    Yours very truly
                    Harty Bey[23]

It is possible – but unlikely – that the Sultan had the eighteenth-century Sultan Abdul Hamid I in mind rather than his exalted self when naming the first boat. Abdul Medjid had ruled from 1839 to 1861, and had been a reforming, liberalising, popular Sultan – everything 'Abdul the Damned' was not. Giving the new submarine this name – while the submarines were being passed off as the new maritime guardians of the Empire – was an utterly bogus attempt to link Abdul Hamid's reign of terror with the Empire's less vicious recent past. It is very unlikely that anyone was impressed: in the event, the submarines' subsequent fate neatly epitomised the fate of Abdul Hamid II and all he stood for.

For all of Garrett's promises, and the dark hints of maritime doom to Abdul Hamid's enemies issued in the name of the two *Abdul*s, the two submarines, once commissioned, were never refitted or used for so much as a training exercise, apart from one very brief surface outing at Seraglio Point for propaganda purposes – the only time the two boats were ever seen together in public. After the appalling trauma that had been experienced in bringing them to a state of very doubtful war-readiness, it was not thought to be worth expending further time, money and (conceivably) lives on developing them further. The two boats were towed to Sütlüce and dragged ashore, to rust in a shed overlooking the Golden Horn. As a final grand gesture, Garrett's cheque was bounced: it remains a Garrett family treasure. Needless to say, Nordenfelt did not make good the loss: nor did he overlook the fact that, on close inspection, the financial success of the two Turkish boats had turned out to be rather marginal. Garrett kept his honorary rank, however, without being bound to the chore of training more Turkish submarine officers or fighting in the Sultan's wars. It is possible, considering the whole affair from the Sublime Porte's point of view, that returning to Constantinople might not have been in his best interests.

Like their Greek predecessor, *Abdul Hamid* and *Abdul Medjid* became a ghostly fleet-in-being, a sabre to be rattled in the face of the Greeks and Russians, but only on paper. Had the Turks but known it, they were half a knot *slower* under water than the Russian pedal-boats which had caused so much *angst* at the Naval Ministry. The actual contribution to the naval balance of power of three piles of rust deployed at either end of the Aegean is impossible to determine, but it was certainly in excess of their material capabilities: as such, they were, perhaps, not the failure that they must appear to be. After all, our own modern submarine-based deterrent is based on potential rather than use: we measure its success by the extent to which it is *not* used. So, perhaps, by our own twentieth-century standards, Garrett's three Mediterranean submarines were a strange sort of success – but definitely a success of sorts.

While the ultimate fate of the Greek boat is unknown, beyond indications that she was scrapped soon after 1900, the sad end of the two *Abdul*s is a little better documented. In July 1909 (ironically, the year of Abdul Hamid's deposition), a poignant report emerged from Turkey, almost by way of light relief amid reports of massacres in Armenia:

> Amongst other oddities to be disposed of shortly by the Turkish Government is one of the oldest submarines in existence. It has been reposing in a weather-beaten shed in the Golden Horn for more than a quarter of a century. It is literally dropping to pieces from rust and neglect, whilst the grass is growing knee-deep around it.[24]

There were, of course, two hulks. but even this was not quite the end. When the German Military Mission arrived in Constantinople in 1914, they were still there, and were inspected by General Liman von Sanders. The Germans even made a half-hearted attempt at re-conditioning them (a near-surreal idea), but this was soon abandoned. At this point, hidden in a mist of decay and semi-comedy, the two *Abdul*s finally disappear from view. Twelve years earlier, their creator had himself gone almost literally to the scrapyard.

Despite their faults – they were essentially larger, worse versions of the *Dykeri Pråm* – *Abdul Hamid* and *Abdul Medjid* marked a milestone in the history of the submarine. They were the first submarines ever to be commissioned into a Navy; *Abdul Hamid* was the first submarine ever to launch a torpedo under water; Turkey became, by a very considerable margin, the first nation to have submarines in her Navy. And a curate from an obscure Manchester parish had become the Reverend Commander G.W. Garrett Pasha, BA. Perhaps he thought 'Bey, BA' sounded awkward.

CHAPTER SIX

Nordenfelt

After the sale of the *Dykeri Pråm* to the hapless Greeks, Mediterranean political intrigue and the commercial propaganda of Nordenfelt and Zaharoff combined to turn submarine construction into a profitable, even booming enterprise, at least to outward appearances. The Garrett family had bought 'La Plata', in Southampton, early in 1886. During his increasingly frequent and protracted absences in Constantinople, Jane and the children were cared for by a small retinue of servants: the genteel poverty of Greenheys Hall had been replaced by something not at all unlike wealth. When not serving in the Sultan's new submarines, Garrett had a yawl, the *Lodestar*, in which to practise his maritime skills and teach them to his eight-year-old son John, now showing signs of interest in the black arts of engineering and seamanship. Garrett, not the most literate of men ('wifes'), himself often rendered his boat's name as 'Loadstar': he does not seem to have found her name particularly ironic. While working on the new boat at Barrow, Garrett would live at Grange and potter over to the yard on the *Lodestar*. Life, if extremely exhausting, was at least prosperous.

Garrett's position within the Nordenfelt empire, however, was not what it seemed. To him, the submarines were everything; to Nordenfelt, they were a sideline that was already beginning to look shaky even before the *Dykeri Pråm* was sold. In January 1886, while Garrett was still paving the somewhat devious way to Nordenfelt's Chamberlainship, Nordenfelt patented a method of discharging smoke from surface torpedo-boats through valves below the water-line, a clear spin-off from work on the submarine and something of a threat to it: for Nordenfelt, there should be no more need for the agonies of totally submerged navigation if only the problem of early visual detection could be solved for fast surface torpedo-vessels. Submarines were simply proving more trouble than they were worth, and Nordenfelt was looking for the least troublesome alternative. Nordenfelt's new invention, a system of non-return valves linked to the boiler, did not live up to its promise: it was tried out on the *Dykeri Pråm*, not necessarily the best test-bed. This setback, and the Chamberlainship, may well have saved Garrett's career for the comparatively brief time it had to run. But it was dramatic developments in Nordenfelt's other activities that would ultimately lead to Garrett's professional demise.

The Nordenfelt Gun and Ammunition Company, for all its international pretensions – offices in London, factory in Sweden and world-wide distribution network – was in fact a comparatively small concern, though by 1886 Nordenfelt had at least stopped actually working in his own workshops, which he had done for many years on his way up. However, the appointment of Basil Zaharoff (by now the personification of the 'distribution network') had led to an expansion in business that came close to outstripping the company's production capacity. Zaharoff was simply unstoppable. One Monday morning, he bet a War Minister £10,000 that the next day would be Thursday; he sold an admiral a new steam yacht for £10 – nothing was too outrageous, dangerous or lunatic to shift the merchandise. There was also a new, potentially threatening face in the machine-gun world.

Hiram Stevens Maxim was a colourful American mixture of homespun philosopher, gunsmith, electrician and all-round 'chronic' (his word) inventor, born in Sangerville, Maine in 1840. His first invention had literally been the 'better mousetrap', though the world on that occasion had not beaten a path to his door. A succession of jobs that had included boxer, barman and factory weaver had produced a degree of personal resilience very unlike the urbane Nordenfelt, who had more or less walked to prosperity from the age of twenty.

Maxim's system of incandescent electric lighting, one of the earliest, was fitted to HMS *Agamemnon* in 1881, his first foothold in the naval world in an area – electricity – of which Nordenfelt seemed to have a near-morbid dread. Meanwhile, Maxim's most celebrated invention, a machine-gun that was lighter, fired faster and needed a smaller crew than Nordenfelt's, began to attract attention. In 1883, Randolph Symon, the Vice President of the Mexican Central Railway, introduced Maxim in London to Albert Vickers, the Sheffield steel magnate, and convinced Vickers of the wisdom of investing in the American's weapon. Although the Vickers firm had produced a great deal of steel for making guns, they had not previously made the weapons themselves. In 1884 the three jointly founded the Maxim Gun Company, with a capital of

£75,000: Maxim set up shop in a small factory in London's Hatton Garden, now better known for its jewellery.

By 1886, the Maxim Company had become a full-scale menace to Nordenfelt. Though produced in small numbers at this stage, the Maxim gun (especially the heavy-calibre version, introduced in 1885 and already a runaway success) soon gained a reputation for reliability and ease of operation that Nordenfelt could not overlook. Nor, indeed, could Zaharoff, who had seen the Maxim gun demonstrated in Switzerland and had watched the potentially lucrative French market wilt before it. The crunch came with a Maxim gun demonstration for the benefit of the Italian Navy, held at La Spezia in 1886. Nordenfelt had more or less assumed that the Italian naval contract was his for the asking, and was distraught when the American snatched it up. The Swede did his worst: he sent in Zaharoff to deal with the interloper.

It is extraordinarily difficult to portray Zaharoff as anything other than the moustache-twirling villain of melodrama: he looks precisely the sort of man who ties heroines to railway lines. His dealings with Maxim confirm this impression. At a demonstration of the Maxim gun in Vienna, attended by the Emperor, Franz Josef, and the Austrian War Minister, all seemed to be going well for the American. Before long, the Maxim gun would be the standard machine gun in the Hapsburg Army.

Maxim was joined by Archduke William, a field marshal in the Imperial Army, who told him that an 'agent for another company' had advised him not to bother himself with baking in the summer heat to watch such a poor weapon as the Maxim, which 'never works'. Zaharoff, of course. Although the demonstration was a huge – indeed, definitive – success for the Maxim gun, the following day's Viennese newspapers declared that the *Nordenfelt* gun – which had not been demonstrated – had won the day. After the trial shoot, a man in a frock coat and top hat (guess who) had patrolled through the ranks of the press declaiming, 'A wonderful performance, gentlemen. Marvellous! Nobody can compete with this Nordenfelt gun.'[1] The reporters, apparently affected with the same gullibility virus that scythed down the cynics at Nordenfelt submarine demonstrations, reported a Nordenfelt triumph.

These comic-opera tactics resulted in an embarrassing official inquiry into the press statements and Zaharoff's activities. But the Man from Tatavla (or wherever) was not finished yet. Maxim's weapon was approved, but the Austrians asked him to adapt it to take standard Austrian cartridges, to which he readily agreed. When he returned and demonstrated the gun again, using Austrian cartridges, it chugged fitfully, then jammed: 'I took the gun apart and found, very much to my surprise and disgust, that the greater part of the dovetail that secured the side-plate to the barrel had been milled off and a loose piece riveted on, the whole being blackened over to deceive me'.[2] Zaharoff had taken Maxim's English foreman to lunch and drugged his wine; while the foreman slept, Zaharoff bribed a miller to sabotage the gun.

This insane tale of industrial nobbling was unearthed by Count Nicolai, the Kaiser's chief of Intelligence (not a man known for his sense of humour), while investigating Zaharoff during the First World War. The Austrian contract still went to Maxim, but, at only 140 guns, it turned out to be smaller than he had hoped. Zaharoff, never a man to undervalue his own achievements, recalled: 'Maxim was furious, but he forgave me, and from that trick emerged a new armaments firm – Maxim and Nordenfelt'.[3]

Zaharoff had realised that the 600-round-a-minute Maxim gun was the horse to back; he would act, in his own interests, to bring about a merger of the two companies. This would in fact take him the better part of two years – 1886-8. The Sangerville ex-boxer and the Constantinople ex(?)-pimp had much to discuss: in later years, Maxim would refer to Zaharoff with near-affection as 'my friend Mr Zedzed'. They did, of course, have an acquaintance in common: it had been Albert Vickers' brother Tom who had been given the lecture on submarines at Zaharoff's Athens hotel. During the two critical years, Garrett and Nordenfelt, when not trying to run rings round the Porte, would be hard at work on a new and potentially revolutionary submarine, with neither of them apparently aware that Zaharoff was busy digging their commercial graves.

There is no record of the laying-down of the fourth Nordenfelt submarine – Barrow's Job No 149 – but the most likely date for the keel-laying is October 1886, shortly after Garrett's return from the launch of the *Abdul Hamid*. It was just before this date that Garrett bought a second home at Grange-over-Sands, where he stayed during the construction of the boat whenever business in Constantinople allowed. Sometimes, Jane would join him, leaving the children in Southampton with their governess.

Having disposed (presumably with relief) of the *Abdul Hamid* – or at least seen her off, in bits (give or take the odd engine cylinder), to her proud new owners, then twitching with war-fever and submarine-deprivation – Garrett and the engineers at the Barrow Shipbuilding Company were free to start work on a completely new boat which departed radically from the other Nordenfelt submarines. His chief assistant, with whom he enjoyed a progressively more corrosive relationship as the months went by, was Captain P.W. D'Alton, a real (ex-army) captain, who seems to have been as suspicious of Garrett as the Turks.

Garrett, with the horrendous facts and statistics of the *Dykeri Pråm*'s tribulations (and the grim prognosis for her lately-departed Turkish sibling) to wave under Nordenfelt's nose, had finally won the argument over the shape of the hull. The new boat would have a largely cylindrical hull, coming to a wedge-shape at either end: this was inherently far more stable than the earlier cigars, and much more like a modern submarine. At 160 tons, which rose to an imposing 230 on diving, she would also be a great deal larger than the other submarines: she was 125 feet long, with a maximum midships beam of 12 feet.

At last, Garrett had realised that *something* needed to be done about the ballast tanks: in the new boat, there were ten separate tanks, as opposed to the swirling, surging three of the earlier boats. Garrett was finally working with the warship-building professionals: on the drawings, each tank is inscribed with a value for stability moments. But not, alas, for free surface: either Garrett or D'Alton (not Nordenfelt, whose free surfaces were confined to his bath) has calculated each tank's effect on the boat's stability as if its contents were solid. There was no internal sub-division within the tanks: while the free-surface effect would be less marked than in the earlier submarines, it would by no means be cured.

Garrett considerably revised the Lamm steam system for the new submarine. Instead of one boiler feeding a hot-water reservoir, there were now two boilers. The larger, heavily-insulated forward boiler doubled as a hot-water/steam tank. To prepare the boat for sea, both boilers were stoked. When the required underwater/ awash pressure was reached in the forward boiler, it was disconnected from the steam system until the boat was required to dive: at this point, the other boiler was disconnected and the machinery connected to the stored hot water, to operate in the same way as in the earlier boats. When the boat was used as a surface vessel, only the after boiler was used. This system had the marked advantage of reducing the time required to raise steam for diving, but it still took a great deal longer than raising steam in the normal manner: overnight preparation was still required.

Alas, no consideration was given to the water in the two boilers from the point of view of stability. As a combined result of this oversight and the water in the ballast tanks, the new boat was still a white-knuckle experience when submerged. As usual (as *ever*), Garrett found this out the hard way.

Bulkheads divided the interior of the boat into five sections, as much to discourage movement within the hull as to strengthen the structure. The only means of access between the forward and after ends was an exciting *Resurgam*-style crawl over the top of the two boilers: communication between the nine members of the crew was by a system of speaking-tubes. There were two hatches, under matching cupolas at either end of the boat. The forward cupola was the captain's observation station: here, beside the controls for the boat's planes and rudders, were the controls for releasing torpedoes from the two forward tubes, now completely enclosed within the hull and with storage space for two reloads. The captain was also supplied with a depth gauge, an inclinometer and a compass: no attempt was made, however, to compensate the compass for the boat's varying magnetic field. The seriousness of this deficiency with ace navigator Garrett at the helm is, of course, debatable.

The after cupola was for the engineer. Garrett had finally made provision for the captain and the boat's engineer being two men, rather than a frantic individual. The engineer had plenty to occupy his time. The engine, supplied by the cheerfully-named Messrs Plenty, of Newbury, was a 4-crank double-compound unit, which, apart from driving the boat's screw, was expected to supply vacuum to an appalling battery of auxiliary motors – blower, ballast pumps, submerging engines, two sets of steering gear, torpedo compressor, steam capstan – an astounding eleven subsidiary engines in all. While this brought the boat up to the 1886 state of the art as far as automation was concerned, it was also introducing a degree of mechanical complexity that offered rather more occupational interest than the average marine engineer would have liked. Designed maximum surface speed was 17 knots. In the matter of submerged speed, Nordenfelt finally took the plunge into the unknown territory of commercial frankness, and announced the underwater maximum as 5 knots, hedging it about with lavish reminders of the boat's reserve of buoyancy and her wondrous performance when running awash: he was within inches, in fact, of overtly marketing her as a semi-submersible.

The inevitable downhaul screws were now mounted in wells right forward and aft: even in this, the ultimate steam submarine, there was to be no nonsense about neutral buoyancy. Submergence was as before: ballast down to a reserve of buoyancy, then claw her down on the horizontal propellers. As in the earlier Nordenfelt submarines, these were linked to hydrostatic sensors, which would shut them off if the boat's safe depth were exceeded. Or so the theory went. The boat may be slow, said *The Times*, but she is apparently sure: should the craft sink deeper than is desirable or safe, she would ascend as naturally to the surface as a runaway horse makes for the stable door.[4] An odd metaphor for a warship.

Construction continued under Nordenfelt's very remote supervision during Garrett's absence in Constantinople. To Garrett's sorrow, this included the launch, which he missed, due, as we have seen, to the continuing haggling with the Turkish Commission over the theological definition of a submarine trial. He was, however, not unrepresented.

Job No 149 slid down the ways on 26 March 1887. The boat was sent down the slipway after a traditional douching with champagne: the bottle was wielded by Jane Garrett. Jane was accompanied by her eight-year-old son John, now not merely a son but a disciple of the Latent Heat Apostle. Jane named this ship the *Nordenfelt*, and asked God for the usual concessions to the boat and all those who sailed in her. Unfortunately, He seems to have been otherwise engaged that afternoon, and made His presence felt by giving Barrow a particularly severe lesson in the physics of flotation.

The *Nordenfelt* came off the ways and into the water, recovered, and then settled. And settled. The stern drooped forlornly, mutely announcing a serious miscalculation in the boat's trim: 9 feet aft and 4 feet 6 inches forward. The definitive Bad Start had been made.

This was the first – and last – formal builder's launching of a Nordenfelt submarine (the *Abdul Hamid* had only received this treatment after re-assembly): to mark the occasion, the Barrow Shipbuilding Company presented Jane with a gold card-case. Nordenfelt beamed his benevolent Royal Chamberlain's smile, basking in the glory of it all: the company were now openly trying to woo the glamorous Swede onto their board. The submarine wallowed serenely in the background, a spectacle that does not seem to have dampened the Barrow directors' enthusiasm for Nordenfelt. As usual, any problems, if anyone asked, were Garrett's fault. He, of course, was in Constantinople, attempting to account for another submarine's little foibles, and trying to touch the Turkish Commission's iron heart with a sad tale of sickness in the Garrett household. Unless Jane managed to contract a hangover at the launch party, the Garrett family (even Mary, for once) was in excellent condition.

The builder's trials began on 30 April, when Garrett and D'Alton returned. Captain Palingen, a Swede from the Palmcrantz yard, acted as engineer. Captain D'Alton appears to have begun drifting into disaffection the moment he saw the *Nordenfelt* actually in the water. He was already having a gruelling, if informative (and indubitably absorbing) time as Garrett's assistant in Constantinople, and was developing a low opinion of his boss that oozes out between the lines of his reminiscences. Garrett found himself being subjected to a harangue from D'Alton about the boat's trim and questionable habits. What had happened was not in fact all *that* bad. John Holland's first submarine was ballasted without considering the salinity of the water, and demonstrated the flotation characteristics of a house-brick when launched: at least the *Nordenfelt* stayed afloat.

The *Nordenfelt*'s trim was corrected by the application of science: several tons of stone ballast was resolutely shovelled in to the fore-ends, causing a predictable loss of speed. So much for Nordenfelt's 17 knots. The effect of the news on Garrett was rather more ominous, however.

Having made the gruelling journey from Turkey fully expecting to be greeted as the heroic creator of a wonderful new submarine, Garrett took the news of the boat's eccentric trim very badly. His initial response was to plead that the trim would have been corrected by the weight of the four torpedoes once these were shipped, but this would still have left him with an embarrassing waterline once the torpedoes had been expended: this does not seem to have been explained too kindly to the shattered pioneer. Garrett's own ballast must have shifted heavily: he collapsed, and was taken back to Grange, gibbering quietly.

A 'nervous collapse' was diagnosed. While nothing like a full-scale nervous breakdown, it does show the very parlous state that Garrett was in by this time. He was, quite simply, being worked into the ground. His health had never been robust: the now very extended periods in his submarines, alternating with lengthy and frequent journeys between Turkey and Britain (hardly a reasonable commuting distance, especially in the 1880s), were clearly taking their toll. Nor had it 'only' been his lungs that had shown signs of wear (his coughing fits inside the boats had caused his collaborators to worry about infection, and they were not far wrong). From time to time, the handwriting in Garrett's letters and papers degenerates into an infantile scrawl, and the grammar and spelling – never very strong – sometimes take on a dynamic independence all their own. In what may be another sign of the condition that had haunted Greenheys Hall, Garrett's intellect shows clear signs of having been subject to what one might call the occasional flicker. The collapse at Barrow was the worst incident so far; it would not be the last.

It was about this time that an interesting document arrived at Nordenfelt's London office. This was a circular from the US Navy Department, inviting proposals, in competition, for the construction of a steel submarine torpedo-vessel. The specifications required were stringent – indeed, too stringent for the worldwide state of submarine development at this stage. The submarine they wanted had to be capable of operating in three conditions:

1. *Fully submerged*, where the displacement was not to exceed 200 tons, and the power endurance was to be at least two hours at eight knots, all connection with the atmosphere being broken off.
2. *The covered condition*, when she was meant to be protected by at least three feet of water, but at the same time have means of observing the object of attack through air.
3. *The light condition*, or *ordinary surface condition*, when she was to have some freeboard, and a power endurance of at least 30 hours at 15 knots.[5]

Maximum diving-depth was to be 150 feet.

While fully realising that his own submarine came nowhere near these requirements, Nordenfelt thought it was at least worthwhile trying to interest the Americans in her, and added them to the guest list for the first demonstration *after* the diving trials – if there were going to be any unpleasant surprises from the new submarine, Nordenfelt wanted to see them first. This was a wise precaution. In the meantime, he submitted her design for consideration.

The American demands were frankly unrealistic for 1887 – the underwater speed and endurance specified were not achieved until shortly before the Second World War. Equally, however, they were largely a product of precisely the sort of inflated claims that Nordenfelt used as a routine part of his sales technique. A bluff was being called.

While Garrett was being nursed by Jane at Grange, Captain D'Alton prepared the submarine for her delivery voyage to Southampton – yet again, the longest journey by a submarine boat up to that time. Well or not, Garrett rose from his bed to deliver the *Nordenfelt*. His experience in delivering submarines from the north of England to the south may not have inspired confidence, of course: the precise fate of *Resurgam* was probably a taboo subject in the Nordenfelt camp. Relations inside the new boat were not excessively cordial: D'Alton was his usual grumpy self, and Captain Palingen was already beginning to consider his position, only weeks after joining.

The boat left for Southampton on 24 May, encountering a storm en route (Garrett had paid his customary close attention to meteorological factors), but the *Nordenfelt* acquitted herself well, averaging 100 miles for every $1\frac{1}{2}$ tons of coal. Only the after boiler was used, without forced draught.

The *Nordenfelt* arrived, unharmed, on 26 May – perhaps, for Garrett, laying the ghost of the *Resurgam*. Nordenfelt had arranged the usual gastronomic shovel-party at the South Western Railway Hotel, after which an impressive array of naval and military luminaries was herded to the jetty in the South-Western Dock (now the Princess Alexandra Dock), where the boat lay.

Among the guests were General Nicholson (Sir Andrew Clarke's successor as Inspector-General of Fortifications), General Harding Steward, General Sir Gerald Graham (a Nordenfelt board member), Admiral Morgan Singer (a Nordenfelt employee), Sir James Garrick and Sir James Lorrimer, all of whom helped themselves at Nordenfelt's groaning table. More fastidious, perhaps, was the local contingent, which joined the revellers at the jetty. Admiral Sir George Willes, Commander-in-Chief at Portsmouth, General Sir George (and Lady) Willis and Captain Seymour arrived aboard the steam-yacht *Fire Queen*. Torpedo-boat 23 brought the Awkward Squad – the technical specialists who always caused Nordenfelt more trouble than their quarter-deck-oriented colleagues; rather too many of the visitors to the Nordenfelt sales-drives seem to have overlooked the outrageous proportion of supposedly independent guests who were directly involved with the Nordenfelt Company. On this occasion, the harder heads belonged to Captain Long, of HMS *Vernon* (the Torpedo School) and Captain Domville, of HMS *Excellent* (the Gunnery School).

Captain Garrett, like the rating foolish enough to return late the night before Navy Day, was given the difficult task of threading the guests through the boat, four at a time (including Lady Willis, bustle and all, through a hatch that was barely two feet wide). The boat's virtues were remorselessly explained, with Garrett and Nordenfelt drawing special attention to the inch-thick plating on the upper surfaces of the hull, capable of withstanding the fire of any known machine-gun. Including, of course, the Nordenfelt guns that had been sold so hard to the Navy. More perceptive listeners would also have detected a broad hint that the boat was primarily meant to be operated on the surface.

The procedure for total immersion was explained, immediately followed by a regretful announcement that 'due to the inexperience of the crew and the recent arrival of the boat'[6] there would be no demonstration of this extraordinary feat that day. The guests contained their disappointment, and piled aboard the steamer *Alexandra*. Meanwhile, Garrett ballasted the boat down to the awash condition and closed her up. The two craft trundled along to Netley Hospital at 5 knots, with occasional startling bursts of 8 knots from the submarine; her widely bored-out cylinders coped well with the reserve steam. Like the *Abdul Hamid, Nordenfelt* was painted a neutral grey: the assembled worthies were impressed by her low profile and lower visibility, all the more so when she steamed ominously round HMS *Invincible*, anchored in Cowes Roads. The lack of smoke, and the boat's perfectly genuine capacity for making a stealthy approach to an enemy, were much appreciated, though even at this stage there were murmurs of doubt concerning her underwater capabilities.

Garrett restored the boat to normal surface trim and fitted the two funnels, a fidgety and faintly comic business: the funnels did not telescope, but had to be removed and replaced as whole units, and manhandled up and down the hatches. One guest was unkind enough to observe that this could be a diverting business under fire. The demonstration ended with a sprint back to Southampton, the boat almost entirely concealed by her own bow-wave. Garrett announced, to great acclaim, that she had touched 15 knots. Yet again, the gentle application of propaganda and cognitive dissonance had resulted in a successful non-demonstration. SSS

(Submarine Steamship, apparently a Garrett coinage) *Nordenfelt*, her noseful of rock notwithstanding, had made an auspicious public début.

The following day, private speed trials took place in Stokes Bay. With all the stops out and on a glassy sea, the boat reached 14 knots: Garrett had doubtless been overcome with excitement when making the previous day's declaration. The steam plant, designed to produce 1,000 IHP, managed to develop 1,300: this was probably a tribute to the inventive powers of the engine's indicators. Nobody, not even Garrett, took IHP all that seriously: what mattered was the power that made itself felt through the screw. A second trial was held off Calshot Castle the next day, confirming 14 knots as the boat's ceiling.

After a few precious days with his family, Garrett set off again for Constantinople for the next round with the Turks. D'Alton, by now not the best of travelling companions, went with him. Meanwhile, the Nordenfelt sales force – Zaharoff – set about seeking a market for the *Nordenfelt*.

Late May 1887 finds Zaharoff in St Petersburg. He was not, officially at least, in Russia on Nordenfelt business, but was there as agent for the Austrian Mannlicher rifle company, one of several agencies he held in pluralism with his Nordenfelt job. However, while he was about it, he wrote to the Navy Minister requesting an interview. Zaharoff was his usual charming self:

My firm is the agent of no one power. The Turks have bought two submarine boats from my firm. In the event of war, the Turkish Navy can, thanks to these submarine boats, menace your ships in the Black Sea and strike where you least expect them. What the Turks possess you, too, can have, in greater numbers, if you wish. I propose that while two submarine boats are sufficient for the local needs of a small power like Turkey, four should be necessary for your own security as a great power.[7]

The Navy Minister duly fell into discussions with Zaharoff, now blatantly doing Nordenfelt business on Mannlicher time, for which the Swede was suitably grateful on his return. Zaharoff explained that the new, improved Nordenfelt submarine boat would be demonstrated at the forthcoming Spithead Review (a considerable Nordenfelt coup, via his friend the Prince of Wales), where the Tsar would be able to see the marvel with his own eyes. The Minister, not under the same pressure of apparent impending doom as his

Greek and Turkish counterparts had been, agreed to consider the matter. Zaharoff, meanwhile, reported back to a delighted Nordenfelt. While he was in London, Zaharoff was visited by Captain Mordovin, the Naval Attaché at the Russian Embassy, who confirmed that the Russian Navy were indeed interested in the new submarine, and that the Tsar would be encouraged to take a special interest in her at the Spithead Review.

Now higher than ever in Nordenfelt's esteem, Zaharoff set off for Constantinople. There, on Nordenfelt's time, he showed Hiram Maxim round the city: Mr Zedzed, the 'amusing Russian gentleman',[8] was, however, nowhere to be seen when the Turks went looking for him with a wages bill.

Early in June, Nordenfelt had announced his intention to build a large, modern armaments factory at Erith, close enough to Woolwich Arsenal for the British Army, his best customers, to think of it as the local cash-and-carry. The choice of site was significant. Nearby, at Crayford, Maxim had already done the same thing, aiming at the same market. The two armourers were in head-on competition, which neither company was large enough to survive. The major European arms manufacturers – Krupp, Skoda, Armstrong – could and did give huge credits to their clients, a facility which the smaller companies simply could not offer. As Zaharoff saw it, merger between Maxim and Nordenfelt was the only chance for survival. He made no secret of his belief that Nordenfelt was too timid, too orthodox and (at 45) too old for the modern armaments business, all of which was music to Maxim's ears (making due allowance for Maxim being 47). Maxim and his Mr Zedzed were now plotting with gusto.

Back in London, Nordenfelt seems to have been blissfully unaware of all this, having just received £50,000 as his personal rake-off from the share-issue that had been made to pay for the new factory. While Garrett's reports from Constantinople were hardly stimulating reading, all seemed to be going well with the *Nordenfelt*, apart from her having yet to undergo diving trials. For that, Garrett was needed, but he was busy staging mock sinkings off Scutari. Like animals in a circus (a parallel that sometimes seems a little too close for comfort), the Nordenfelt submarines only seemed prepared to perform for their trainer. Fortunately, the Amazing Garrett would be back at Southampton in time for July's Royal Performance.

The 1887 Golden Jubilee Fleet Review at Spithead would mark the end of the Queen's Golden Jubilee celebrations, and was beyond doubt the prime showcase for a new naval vessel: Nordenfelt had lobbied long and hard to obtain permission for the submarine to appear. On the day, the impression made by the *Nordenfelt* was not unlike the now rather more famous appearance of the *Turbinia* at the 1897 Review. The *Nordenfelt* drew appreciative crowds; the belief that this tiny craft threatened watery doom to the ironclad dinosaurs that thronged in Stokes Bay thrilled the more imaginative observers.

The Review gathered together 128 Royal Naval vessels in a carefully-staged demonstration of naval might: it was made clear that the Review was the prelude to an important programme of Fleet manoeuvres in the Channel, and not an empty parade, like the naval reviews of the despised Sultan. The Royal Navy mustered a daunting armada, including three squadrons of ironclads and cruisers (24 ships); five flotillas of coast defence vessels, gunboats and torpedo craft (73 ships), six training craft and thirteen troopships. Her Majesty's enemies, it was hoped, would get the message: they, in turn, were themselves represented in force by units of their own fleets.

In order to have time to raise ample reserve steam for the big day, Garrett brought the *Nordenfelt* round to Portsmouth early on the morning of Friday, 22 July, the day before the Review. The previous evening, Jane had had an opportunity to exercise her skills as a hostess on a social connoisseur: the Garretts were treated to a home visit by Basil Zaharoff. This was the first time that Jane had met him. Like most women who came into contact with the most dangerous barman in history, she found him witty and charming, as indeed he probably was. He wished Garrett well for the coming day's adventures.

En route to Portsmouth, Garrett found himself steaming in company with HMS *Tamar*, an Indian troopship that had been temporarily docked at Southampton. The submarine did not go unnoticed:

> [The *Tamar*] was steadily followed from Southampton Docks by a craft which, looked on from the great height of the *Tamar*'s taffrail, more resembled in hue and shape, but certainly not in speed, a huge slug than anything else. This was the submarine torpedo boat, the *Nordenfelt* ...⁹

Fred Jane, at this stage of his career a Nordenfelt submarine enthusiast (he later recanted), was impressed by all the usual things:

On the run down to Portsmouth the *Nordenfelt* just kept the position with regard to the troopship that she liked best. She was not nearly submerged; yet the target she presented was extremely small. Coming bows on 200 yards or so in the wake of the *Tamar*, little could be seen but an upheaved mass of water.[10]

His faith in the wonderful powers of the submarine's bow-wave (something of an article of faith in the Nordenfelt cult) touched the mystical:

Unlike torpedo boats, which, when going at speed, lift their bows out of the sea, the *Nordenfelt* keeps on an even keel, and raises in front of her a curious wave, which is rifle-proof and probably proof even against machine guns, because the solid mass of water deflects bullets upwards at such an angle that they clear the hull.[11]

While there will have been *some* truth in this, hiding the boat's numerous shortcomings behind it is a feat of marketing that must command respect: never mind the stability – look at the froth. Lord George Hamilton had proclaimed that the Review would include 'every variety of the most modern warships, from torpedo boats with their gossamer skins to the mammoth ironclad with its pachydermatous hide of two feet of iron:'[12] these were now to be joined by a vessel protected by an impregnable girdle of water. Statements like this did much to add to the unreal, semi-magical aura which always surrounded the Garrett/Nordenfelt submarines, and deflected (like the bullets) unwholesome suspicion of the boats' actual capabilities. The *Nordenfelt* never – ever – launched a torpedo, submerged or otherwise, but still managed to exude menace to an extent that repelled military reality for a surprising length of time.

The submarine, flying a colourful pennant emblazoned with her name, spent the day at Spithead patrolling the fringes of the Fleet, closely inspected by avid parties of enthusiasts in small boats. Of course, none was allowed aboard this highly secret vessel. Before the Queen passed up the lines (at three o'clock), Garrett was permitted to take *Nordenfelt* on a spin through the awesome lines of ironclads and cruisers. Many saw, and believed:

The *Nordenfelt* appeared to be the very incarnation of destructive power. There was not one of the magnificent and costly men-of-war reviewed by her Majesty that could do anything to avert destruction by the *Nordenfelt*, if that destruction were contemplated, save take to their screws as fast as she could.[13]

Among the admirers, as Zaharoff had been promised, was Tsar Alexander III, by now, after years of experiment and cloak-and-dagger bluff with Drzewiecki submarines and other dubious devices, something of an old hand at underwater warfare. His father, Alexander II, had even celebrated his coronation with an underwater serenade from four musicians in a Bauer submersible. While no enquiries about the *Nordenfelt*'s acoustics were made, the Tsar was impressed by what he saw (a telling phrase). His naval advisers would inspect the submarine: if she lived up to the promise of that joyous July day, she would join the Imperial Russian Fleet. More to the point, she would be invited to breed.

It was announced that the submarine would be demonstrating her dreaded underwater powers later in the year, once Captain Garrett had returned from further urgent experiments in Turkey. Fortunately, the Turkish Ambassador and his naval attaché kept their faces straight. The hosts of foreign representatives were seeing precisely what Nordenfelt wanted them to see. The contents of the forthcoming underwater trials were carefully trailered:

> She could run quite close up to a ship without availing herself fully of her submarine powers, and her chances of getting away unhurt, after discharging her torpedoes, would be very good. But she could approach within a mile of an ironclad at anchor; take her bearings accurately and then go down, and proceed under water until she had run the requisite distance ... and immediately afterwards deliver a blow which would send a great ironclad to the bottom. The *Nordenfelt* had rendered ... naval operations against forts and harbours nearly impossible. No commander dare lie near a harbour from which a submarine boat could be despatched to blow up his ship.[14]

Having thus made his mark, Garrett dutifully took up station alongside the *Tamar*, and stood stiffly, rapturously at attention as the little old lady peered down from the *Victoria and Albert*. Captain the Reverend Commander Garrett Pasha/Bey BA was touching the very peak of his career.

The Fleet was to be illuminated on the evening of the Review, but there was precious little *Nordenfelt* above water to illuminate, and there were (very) private diving trials to arrange, so Garrett took her back to Southampton, just missing the only serious mishap of the day: a gun on board HMS *Kite* exploded, dreadfully injuring the gun-crew. One man, whose arm had been in the gun's barrel at the time, died later. It is very odd to note that this unfortunate accident (which he missed) was in fact the closest that Garrett ever came to seeing anything like naval action.

A few days later, Garrett and D'Alton took the submarine out for preliminary diving trials in the Solent, and discovered the worst. The ballast that had been added to restore respectable surface trim played havoc with the boat's underwater attitude, as did the still all-too-free water in the boat's boilers and tanks. There were several unplanned trips to the bottom, with the boat careering out of control if the crew's movements exceeded the statuesque. The nine Nordenfelters soon discovered that working the submarine would have passed for a branch of yoga. Only the shallowness of the water prevented disaster: the boat's keel became horribly familiar with the Mother Bank Shoal.

Wishing to test the boat in deep water (not a universally popular decision), Garrett took her to Land's End. D'Alton's description of events at this maritime graveyard *de luxe* is as bleak as it is concise: 'It was found impossible to sink her in the Channel without risking the life of all on board'.[15] There was no attempt to launch a torpedo. After the horror experienced when this had been attempted in the *Abdul Hamid*, Garrett and D'Alton were in no hurry to press the *Nordenfelt*'s claims in that direction.

It was decided to play down the boat's underwater potential in favour of stressing her still-undoubted capabilities as a surface vessel, though it still looked ill-advised to attempt a torpedo-launch, even on the surface. Although he had very partially solved some of the problems caused by the cigar hulls of the earlier boats, Garrett had hardly designed the super-submarine that he and Nordenfelt desperately needed to create if they were to carry any degree of credibility into the future. For the present, it was almost a relief for him to return to Constantinople.

It was a mortally exhausted and ill Garrett who staggered into Southampton just in time to prepare the *Nordenfelt* for the next demonstration, which was scheduled for Monday, 19 December. While this was not billed as an official trial, it was rather more formal than the May beanfeast, and considerably more so than the Spithead performance. As usual in Nordenfelt/Garrett submarine demonstrations, however, it was not lacking in theatrical invention.

Once again, Nordenfelt gathered together a lavish cross-section of the British military Establishment. A special train left Waterloo containing General Sir Gerald Graham, RE, Colonel Armstrong, RE, Mr W.H. White (the Director of Naval Construction) and Captain Drury of the Woolwich Works Committee, all representing

(Left) First page of the official log of the Izmit trials. *(Right)* The world's first naval submarine commander: Commander Halil Develiogiu.

Nordenfelt ready for launching, March 1887.

Nordenfelt does her stuff at Southampton, December 1887: (above) in surface trim and (below) awash.

domestic interests (and in Graham's case, Nordenfelt's, too): these were joined by the disappointingly-lowly Lieutenant Jacques of the US Navy, who had been sent specially to see how the *Nordenfelt* matched up to the requirements of the Senate Circular. A second carriage contained the Naval Attachés from the embassies of the United States, Italy, Austria, Germany, Spain, Japan and Turkey. The newly-appointed Turkish Attaché, to Garrett's horror, was Woods Pasha, one of the Commission who had seen the *Abdul Hamid* and had *not* believed. At Southampton, they were joined by Commander Batten, of HMS *Vernon*, and Major Orde Browne, of the Royal Artillery.

The boat lay in the South-Western Dock in surface trim, funnels raised and steam up: the usual overnight fire rituals had been observed. Garrett opened the demonstration with a declaration that work had been done on the engine's valves to enable the boat to reach the fabled 17 knots: this had been D'Alton's doing, wrestling with the arcane hieroglyphs that Garrett tended to offer as working drawings. Two other major alterations had been made. Following protestations from Palingen and other malcontents who found 60°C unnecessarily stuffy when running on the surface, a ventilator had been fitted between the funnels. Also, anticipating the sorrow of the Turkish gunners, who correctly feared being washed overboard, a flat deck had been fitted between the conning-towers, a humdrum task entrusted to Oswald Mordaunt and Company.

Garrett gave the standard pep-talk on the mechanisms of the boat, her safety, and even a brief historical dissertation on Bushnell and the *Turtle*. So smooth was the *Nordenfelt*'s transition from the surface to the depths, the pilgrims were told, that the crew could be kept in ignorance of whether the boat was afloat or submerged. Garrett told them that the crew consisted of the captain (himself), the mate, two seamen, an engineer, an engineer's assistant, two firemen and cook, all veterans of the Land's End adventure, which had, of course, been a great success, Gentlemen.

The celebrities boarded the *Alexandra*, once more employed for the occasion, and proceeded in company with the submarine to Calshot Castle. Garrett managed to convince his audience that they had seen 15 knots. New valves or no, 17 knots was never achieved: it is hardly likely that Garrett was surprised by this.

The *Alexandra* then turned back towards Southampton. Once she had put 500 yards between herself and the *Nordenfelt*, the submarine gave chase in the now-standard demonstration of her small end-on profile. Once again, the application of grey paint, much helped by the dull December weather, seems to have done as much to conceal the boat as any inherent virtues of her design. The funnels disappeared behind the bow-wave; once, when a passing cloud obligingly cast its shadow directly onto the boat, she seemed to the observers to disappear completely. The demonstration was declared a success. The second test would be a night attack on the *Alexandra* by the submerged boat – precisely what everyone had come to see.

An atmosphere of carefully-managed peek-a-boo anticipation spread among the observers as the light faded:

> It was known that Captain Garrett would submerge the boat in the docks, but as it was supposed that he might attempt a surprise attack from some unknown point of the compass, a long and weary watch was kept up on board from 5 o'clock until near upon 8. The moon came out and cast a shimmer of light upon the water, and it was thought that the enemy would be certain to be detected in crossing the ray. Presently, however, a nimbus cloud came floating across the scene from the north-west, and rain began to fall, followed by total obscuration.[16]

While the observers were enjoying their *frisson* of expectation, Garrett was experience a *frisson* of his own. He was lost. He had submerged the boat, with the usual agony, just before six, and had spent nearly two hours lurching about (in three dimensions) trying to find the *Alexandra*, which suffered, as Garrett discovered a little late, from a mast light 'of indifferent brilliancy'. Like the Turks, the Southampton authorities had seen no reason to disrupt traffic for the sake of the submarine, and the harbour had rapidly filled with traffic, including a German mail-steamer which Garrett had some difficulty distinguishing from the *Alexandra*. It does not seem to have occurred to him to count the masts: it *was* getting dark. Finally, as if on cue from a malevolent examining officer in a submarine commander's test (such as the Royal Navy's dreaded 'Perisher'), a fleet of fishing boats puffed in, without lights. Garrett made frequent visits to the surface – the boat's lack of underwater speed gave him no choice – fearing that his efforts might be rewarded at any moment with a loud crash, followed by an all-too-convincing diving demonstration that the observers would probably miss.

Life inside the boat was chaotic. Captain Palingen seems to have spent the two hours underwater drafting his resignation, not an unreasonable attitude under the circumstances. If a man in the after part of the boat moved so much as a couple of feet forward, the submarine rewarded him with a nose-down attitude that resulted (according to Garrett's calculations) in a 36-feet-per-minute dive – just under three minutes to the boat's nominal crushing depth of 100 feet. Nordenfelt's beloved automatic depth-keeping system was now further 'enhanced' by being linked to pressure sensors in the hull, as was the automatic shut-off to the downhaul screws: predictably, these devices chased each other's effects in a frenetic display of mechanical feedback. The boat's inherent tendency to see-saw was magnified into a terrifying multidirectional oscillation. The two-hour 'dive' was in fact a nightmarish chain of rollercoaster dips between largely uncontrolled surges to the surface, punctuated by an occasional sickening crunch on the bottom. Meanwhile, Garrett was back in his worst Lake Boren mode, full of a confidence little shared by his colleagues in the crew.

Finally, at ten to eight, he found the *Alexandra*. When 500 yards (the supposed range of a Whitehead torpedo) off the steamer's starboard bow, he gave a blast on the boat's whistle – *Nordenfelt* was the submarine with everything – and skulked round to the other side of the ship, an evolution that took the submarine a rather suspicious twenty minutes. At ten past eight, the observers were astonished to hear a loud, grampus-like snort announcing the boat's long-awaited return to the surface and the supposed success of the 'attack'. 'There she blows!' yelled a comedian on board the *Alexandra*.[17]

Garrett explained that the regrettable noise was caused by water in the boat's whistle, but the loudness of the sound and the time since the boat's previous appearance suggest that something may in fact have gone wrong (or rather, more so) aboard the submarine. What the observers heard may well have been Garrett blowing out the tanks with steam-pressure as an emergency measure: this belief is strongly reinforced by the fact that the boat was seen to pop up and settle at *surface* (light) trim, rather than the awash condition which would normally have been intended. Having thus brought the boat up, Garrett blew another blast on the whistle and showed a light: the observers, who may have been close to witnessing a tragedy, were deeply impressed. Or so they said. While the sceptics pointed out that an electric searchlight might have picked out the boat during one of Garrett's all-round looks, others declared that the same light would have betrayed the *Alexandra*'s position. Garrett, who had spent most of the previous two hours searching for any sort of light, did not comment.

As Garrett explained, it was of course impossible to demonstrate the *Nordenfelt*'s diving drill at night: this would be done the following morning. By this stage in his career, it is quite simply impossible to believe that Garrett was unaware of the degree of deception involved in these semi-public trials. A 'diving demonstration' *invariably* meant a short, vertical up-and-down dip on ballast and submerging engines, with the whole crew rooted to the spot: what the observers never saw was the boat *running* underwater. When this was demanded (as had happened with the Turks), the boats' instability and near-total lack of underwater manoeuvrability became all too apparent, with unfortunate effects on sales potential. But the boats were always marketed as *submarine* boats; like a metallic mutation of the South Sea Bubble, their true underwater potential was always going to be revealed at some future date. So it was with this demonstration of the *Nordenfelt*.

The visitors were taken round the boat, four at a time, as before. When everyone had seen the bunks, the galley, the eleven auxiliary motors and everything else that made *Nordenfelt* the most modern submarine ever, the boat was closed up and the vertical diving routine gone through several times. The boat, gasped *The Times*, 'appeared and disappeared like the floats of an angler, to the manifest astonishment of the company and a considerable assembly of casual spectators'.[18] The demonstration had been a considerable public relations achievement.

Much was made of the boat's notional 1,000-mile surface range (achieved by filling the ballast tanks with coal), which, it was pointed out, would allow her to steam from England to Constantinople, with a coaling stop at Gibraltar. Whether a Nordenfelt Submarine Demolition Derby was intended at the end of the voyage is unclear, but this was an inevitable implication. The trial also triggered a great deal of soul-searching on the morality of submarine warfare; perhaps for the first time, mechanised submarine warfare seemed close enough to reality for this to be a legitimate topic for agonising over. One comment would have been of great interest to the former bare-knuckles Champion of Trinity College:

> In these days of attempts to revive prize-fighting, we shall certainly hear much about the manliness of standing up face-to-face with your foe and the cowardice of hitting below the belt. Without doubt, there seems to be a touch of cowardice in hitting even such an adversary as an ironclad below her armoured belt and sinking the whole crew at one fell stroke.[19]

Others published the Nordenfelt line in a more robust form:

> Mr Nordenfelt has got a start in the race which will enable him to keep
> ahead of all possible competitors. We may – we hope we shall – have
> quite a little fleet of Nordenfelts when Christmas comes round again.
> When once Columbus had shown the way to America the route was
> freely traversed.[20]

The first man to set foot in the New World had actually been
Columbus's servant, but the management received the credit.
Garrett would have known how he felt.

Another day, another show. Garrett prepared to leave for
Constantinople, where the audience was far harder to please, and
where he would be expected to please them with inferior
equipment. On the day he left, however, he received a visit from
Captain Palingen, who had had enough:

SSS *Nordenfelt*, Southampton   December 31st, 1887

> This is to certify that Captain Palingen has filled the position of 1st
> Mate on board the SSS *Nordenfelt* ... and that during this period he has
> shown himself a competent officer and has given every satisfaction.
> Moreover, he has carefully studied [!!!] the peculiarities of the
> Submarine Steamship *Nordenfelt* and is in my opinion competent to
> command a similar vessel.

signed
George Wm Garrett[21]

Captain Palingen had no intention of ever setting foot on another
vessel even dimly resembling the *Nordenfelt*: he took his reference
and went back to Sweden. As far as is known, he did not undertake
further study of the peculiarities of submarines, not even when the
erstwhile Palmcrantz engineer Enroth built a frank and fearless
freelance version of a Nordenfelt boat at Stockholm in the
mid-1890s. Whatever else the Nordenfelt company was, it was
never a school for submariners.

In February 1888, while Garrett was being dragged over the
coals in the Gulf of Izmit, Nordenfelt was formally invited onto the
board of the Barrow Shipbuilding Company, now completely
re-vamped and expanded as the Naval Construction and Armament
Company. The board was chaired by the Marquis of Hartington,
with a now-obligatory sprinkling of retired admirals making up the

numbers. Obviously, Nordenfelt had started something when he
invited Cooper-Key to be chairman of the Guns and Ammunition
Company. As part of his dowry, Nordenfelt brought with him the
Nordenfelt, which passed formally into the new company's
ownership until a final buyer could be found. The Russians, of
course, were still the most likely customers: Zaharoff was hard at
work trying to convince them. Or so Nordenfelt thought.

While Nordenfelt was settling into his new director's chair at
Barrow, Zaharoff was deep in negotiation, not with the Russians,
but with Lord Rothschild and Sir Ernest Cassel, two financiers
who shared his and Maxim's enthusiasm for uniting the Nordenfelt
and Maxim companies. Once agreement had been reached over the
distribution of shares in the eventual united company, the process
of picking off the shareholders of the Nordenfelt company began.
By the time Nordenfelt realised that anything was going on, it
would be too late. By floating off the weakest part of the Nordenfelt
Company – the submarine business – and taking it to Barrow, he
had made his enemy's task that much easier. What followed was in
fact not so much a merger as a hostile takeover.

Meanwhile, fast in the delusion that his business career was
ascending new heights, Nordenfelt promoted his wares as usual.
The press proclaimed the glad tidings: 'The United States
Government has, we understand, decided in favour of Nordenfelt
boats, as a permanent arm, and is carrying its decision into
practice'.[22] This attempt to bounce a government into bed with
Nordenfelt (now, of course, in the form of the Naval Construction
and Armament Company) was virtually the new company's first
corporate act, and its first failure. The inconspicuous-looking
American lieutenant at the December trials of the *Nordenfelt* must
have been more observant than many of his colleagues: the
Americans rejected the Nordenfelt/Garrett design out of hand.
Ominously, the Americans awarded their first submarine contract
to John Holland, who had finally emerged as a competitor to
Garrett and Nordenfelt, who were, perhaps, fortunate that the
Cramp shipyard (ironically, the yard that they themselves had
nominated to build their design) let Holland down. The following
year, Holland won a re-run of the same competition, but this time
was prevented from building by the Navy Department deciding
they wanted surface craft instead. These two factors – wavering
interest in submarines and John Philip Holland – ultimately spelt
doom to the Garrett/Nordenfelt submarines.

Nor was this the only sign of trouble for the *Nordenfelt*. On 23 March, Nordenfelt attended a meeting of the Institution of Naval Architects in London, where a paper on submarine boats was given by the young Lieutenant William Hovgaard of the Danish Navy. Hovgaard, offering a tentative design of his own, came down firmly in favour of electrical propulsion beneath the surface. Nordenfelt, of course, defended 'his' steam system, in a ponderously patronising reply to the paper, but Hovgaard, heavily armed with statistics, unquestionably won the argument: electrical propulsion, given the recent improvements in accumulators and electrical equipment, had all the advantages of weight, efficiency and habitability over the Nordenfelt system. Nordenfelt countered with the suggestion that what the Powers 'really' needed was a torpedo vessel with a low surface profile, capable of submerging to avoid danger. This was precisely the argument that had caused much of the friction between himself and Garrett, and it was no more impressive to the institution than it had been to Garrett, then on his way back from Constantinople in his hard-earned fez.

Even as they spoke, several European designers were working on electrically-propelled submarines. In France, the veteran naval architect Stanislas Dupuy de Lôme's submarine *Gymnote*, with her 564 (!) accumulators, was being completed in near-pathological secrecy by Gustave Zédé (de Lôme had died in 1885), and Claude Goubet's little electrically-driven boat was already receiving much attention.

In England, James Waddington, ironically the successor to Jack Aitkin at Cochran's (and the son of a clergyman), had designed his *Porpoise*: this amounted to an electrically-propelled Nordenfelt boat, and shared a distressing number of the fripperies of the earlier Garrett/Nordenfelt designs, including the dreaded depth-keeping mechanism in all its too-clever-by-half glory. This was supposed to have been a Nordenfelt invention, but no attempt was made to enforce the patent rights on a gadget that Nordenfelt himself had so obviously lifted from the Whitehead 'secret'.

Porpoise also shared the Nordenfelt downhaul screw system, and therefore the instability that went with them and the depth-keeping gear. Unlike the Nordenfelts, she carried a caustic-potash carbon dioxide scrubber for atmospheric cleansing, precisely as Garrett had originally recommended to Nordenfelt. Far more like the Nordenfelt boats, however, was the *Porpoise*'s fate: she eventually spent many years rusting on a Tranmere beach.

On the Nordenfelt boats – even the latest – the absence of electricity had been taken to almost Puritan extremes: it was a cause of much amusement that the lighting on the *Nordenfelt*, ostensibly the most advanced submarine in the world, was supplied by candles at a time when electric lighting was starting to appear in the more prestigious surface vessels. Events, in fact, were moving fast to overtake the Nordenfelt/Garrett system: it was perfectly possible that the *Nordenfelt* would pass from innovatory wonder to embarrassing anachronism in the time it would take to sell her.

Garrett spent two months recovering from his Turkish efforts, mulling over the implications of the new state of things with Nordenfelt. The *Nordenfelt* huddled miserably against the Southampton dockside until June, when she was inspected by a party of Russian naval officers. Garrett and the usual team demonstrated the boat to them, but found themselves faced with a level of understanding and competence distressingly close to that of the Turks. The Russians, who, after all, had their own submarine pioneer in Drzewiecki, knew precisely what to ask, and were not impressed by the answers. A dreadful gloom settled over Garrett as they departed to make their report.

On 12 July, matters grew even worse. Sufficient Nordenfelt shareholders had succumbed to the blandishments of the Maxim lobby for the illicit Maxim-Zaharoff affair to be consummated. At an extraordinary meeting of the Nordenfelt Guns and Ammunition Company, it was proposed to wind up the firm and merge with the Maxim Gun Company. The motion was passed virtually unopposed.

On 19 July 1888, the Maxim-Nordenfelt Guns and Ammunition Company was floated on the Stock Exchange at an impressive £1,900,000, and was sold out in under two hours. Maxim, who had started out with only £75,000 four years earlier, was bringing to the new company patents worth an estimated £1,000,000. At the first board meeting, the following week, there were some new faces: Hiram Maxim brought with him Albert Vickers and the two bankers Rothschild and Cassel. Another erstwhile Nordenfelt shareholder simply sold out, and found himself wealthy (or wealthier) overnight: Zaharoff wanted influence and cash, not shares. He immediately became an agent for the new combined company, a post he had held *de facto* for at least two years.

Although Nordenfelt was forced, politically, to seem the prime mover behind the merger, he must have seen the writing on the wall for his own future. Totally outgunned on the board of the new company, the Barrow directorship became more or less his main job. This was a considerable wrench: he had never thought of himself as a shipbuilder. He had been a gunsmith who also built submarines. Meanwhile, the Naval Construction and Armaments Company began to think hard about their suddenly-powerless Swedish director and his curious (and commercially doubtful) submarine.

Nordenfelt, shaken by recent developments and now fearing a damning report on the submarine, tried his old tactics. He announced that the Russian Government had bought the *Nordenfelt*, in the hope that the traditionally secretive Russians would be embarrassed by the publicity into actually doing so. Unfortunately, this sort of sympathetic magic was no more successful with the Russians than it had been with the Americans. A lofty notice appeared in *The Times* on 24 September:

> Captain P. Mordovin, of the Imperial Russian Navy, naval attaché to the Russian Embassy, asks us to state that the submarine Nordenfelt torpedo boat has not been bought by the Russian Government. He is officially authorised to say that the boat was tried at Southampton and rejected by the Special Commission of Officers appointed by the Russian Government, the boat being found 'entirely unsuitable for naval and fighting purposes'.[23]

Mustering his now slightly tattered dignity (and Zaharoff), Nordenfelt convened a hasty conference with Captain Mordovin, probably soon after October 9, when Garrett came to London and was surprised to find Zaharoff staying in his hotel (the Buckingham Palace Hotel). After much wrangling, it was decided that the Russian Government would accept the boat after all, but purely on an approval basis. No money would change hands until the boat had been thoroughly tested and passed by the Russians themselves at Kronstadt, the Russian Fleet's Baltic base. After all, as Mordovin pointed out, the Commission had only seen the boat demonstrated in shallow water, and 'Any boat might undertake trials in shallow water which could not be repeated in deep water: should she at any time show an undue tendency to hit the bottom ...'.[24] Of course not. The boat was to be made ready as soon as possible for the passage to Kronstadt.

In late October 1888, the *Nordenfelt* sailed from Southampton in company with Garrett's yawl *Lodestar*. From the very outset, this trip, a shambling recapitulation of the *Resurgam* fiasco and the Swedish canal trip, seems to have been doomed. Captain Palingen had never been replaced, and several of the Swedish contingent in the original *Nordenfelt* crew had left. For the delivery voyage, Garrett's longest-ever submarine journey, setting a record that would last into the next century, Garrett filled Palingen's berth with his ten-year-old son John. The rest of the crew were a similar variation on earlier Garrett/Nordenfelt standards: the likes of D'Alton, Lawrie and Norström were replaced by a motley collection of seamen of modest competence and immodest thirst. The only names to come down to us are 'Bosun George', 'Swede Anderson' and the otherwise mysterious Thomas Arm, probably a fireman. Whoever they were, they were not employed for long.

The two vessels crossed from Southampton to Le Havre, detained only by the discovery that the crew of the *Lodestar* found the Channel a little too challenging. The submarine therefore towed the yacht. Keeping within sight of land, Garrett continued up the coast to Ijmuiden, where a brawl broke out between Swede Anderson and Bosun George: Garrett separated the combatants and entered the Noordzeekanal. After a surprisingly trouble-free passage, the expedition tied up at Amsterdam. The crew went ashore and hit the town, taking young John with them. After a highly educational evening 'sampling the sweet champagne,[25] the now very unsteady John was invited to walk the plank by his equally befuddled shipmates. He accepted, and dropped into the canal while his father sulked in the saloon of the *Lodestar*.

The following morning, the crew worked off their hangovers on a passage through the Zuyder Zee. Garrett then threaded his way between the Frisian Islands and the coast, finally limping across the Heligoland Bight and into Cuxhaven. Limping, because, 1000-mile steaming radius or no, the submarine's engines were giving trouble. A three-day stay at Cuxhaven was needed for repairs, after which the convoy began the northward passage up the coast of Schleswig Holstein. One more call was made, probably at Tönning (Garrett's records are very vague), before disaster struck, off the Danish coast.

At 1 a.m. in the semi-compulsory Garrett gale, both vessels grounded on Jutland's celebrated Horn Reef, off Blåvands Huk. Garrett later explained that this was due to the 'officer of the watch' mistaking the lights on the coast, though there is reason to believe that he himself was on watch at the time. His son, understandably embarrassed by this particularly obvious example of incompetent seamanship, even claimed later that the submarine and the *Lodestar* had fallen victim to wreckers, who swung lanterns on shore to confuse passing experimental submarines. No doubt. Perhaps the 'sweet champagne' had been passed round again. Be that as it may, the expedition was in serious trouble:

> It was blowing a gale of wind and after futile efforts to kedge the *Lodestar* and navigate the *Nordenfelt* out of the maze of sandbanks, at 2.00 p.m. the next day we were forced to abandon them, as the bottom of the *Lodestar* had crashed in and the *Nordenfelt* showed signs of rolling over, which would have trapped the crew.[26]

The yacht's windlass and bulwarks had carried away: the decision to abandon ship was in fact made over lunch in the saloon – a typical Garrett sop to convention. It was lunchtime, whether the ship was breaking up or not.

It was at this anxious moment that young John decided to indulge in one of his quaint childish pastimes:

> I [John] was the last man off the ship, having jumped aboard to get my rifle in order to take a shot at some seals that were laying in view on the sandbanks [that were] exposed at low tide. This action caused me some grief, as my father had been, as he supposed, the last man to leave the ship, as usual in the good old British custom. Also, one of the men got his hand crushed, fending the boat off until I could get back.[27]

After a few very un-churchmanlike words with his son, Garrett distributed the crews of both vessels among the yacht's lifeboat and dinghy, with the remainder going into a Berthon collapsible from the submarine (surely the first to carry this standard feature of early Naval submarines). The two smaller craft were towed by the lifeboat, under Garrett's command. After a long pull through fairly heavy seas, they reached Esbjerg at 2 p.m.

The shipwrecked submariners put up in a hotel for the night, where John, who had never seen a feather quilt before, lay awake freezing under the gaudy bedspread in the belief that the blankets had been left off. He vented his dissatisfaction with the hotel's management and the Danes at large by shooting the gold ball off the top of the hotel's flagpole. As an adult, he would eventually become a champion marksman and a leading figure in the USA's National Rifle Association, with his targets used as advertisements by the rifle companies: on this cold Danish morning, all the hotel management saw was a crazed juvenile sniper. His father, who had enough to think about already, gave him another sermon. Possibly with his belt.

Next morning, the crew went back overland to Blåvunds Huk to inspect the wrecks:

> The natives had stripped them of everything movable, even the piano from the salon of the *Lodestar*. With some difficulty and the payment of a considerable sum, we recovered most of our personal belonging.[28]

Nothing could be done for the moment. John and most of the crew were sent back to Harwich on the steamer, a trip which Master Garrett enlivened by finding a barrel of pigs' offal and falling into it.

Two weeks later, the *Nordenfelt* was pulled clear of the reef and towed into Esbjerg. Although she was thought to be in surprisingly good condition, the Naval Construction and Armaments Company petitioned to have her declared a Total Constructive Loss, on the grounds that the Russians would be unlikely to complete the sale after such an incident. The Russians themselves do not seem to have made any specific statement one way or the other, and have no record of being asked.

An unseemly dispute broke out over the salvage rights to the vessel, which further delayed the settlement with the insurers. Nordenfelt made curiously half-hearted attempts to find another buyer, to no avail. The boat would lie ashore at Esbjerg for some years before being broken up for scrap, without so much as the spurious deterrent powers of the Greek and Turkish submarines to hide her discomfiture. While there is certainly no clear evidence to suggest that the boat was deliberately wrecked for the insurance, nobody seems to have been particularly heartbroken over her loss: however, Garrett and Nordenfelt were almost certainly spared a great deal of embarrassment at Kronstadt.

Christmas 1888 might have been expected to be a rather fraught affair at 'La Plata', but Garrett and the family continued as usual. Garrett's most pressing concern turns out to have been a replacement for the *Lodestar*. He bought another yacht, the *Alert*, and a little tender, the *Boomerang*.

When not sailing in the Channel in his new status-symbols, Garrett worked on a new improvement to steam power that would take it halfway into the realm of the internal combustion engine. The key to the system was a new type of vapour generator, a device not unlike a normal steam condenser: however, instead of cold water being passed through the tubes, steam or hot water was to be pumped in. The cooling surface of the condenser thus became the heating surface of the Garrett generator: petrol or paraffin was sprayed over this heating surface, vaporising it. The resulting gas could then be used to operate an ordinary steam engine. This was an ingenious idea, not least in its non-combustive use of the oil-based fuel, but, for now, Garrett had to be content with patenting it. The generator was ostensibly designed as an aid to submarine propulsion – probably its least realistic application; this at least made it possible for Garrett to work on it under Nordenfelt auspices, but, with the ground now almost audibly crumbling under Nordenfelt, there was no outside industrial interest.

There are tantalising, veiled references to Nordenfelt attempting to negotiate a contract to build submarines for the Royal Navy – even a contract for twenty submarines is mentioned, but there are no details, and it is quite certain that nothing came of the scheme. British Government records have nothing to say on the matter: it must be said that such a deal would have been directly counter to the prevailing anti-submarine trend in the Admiralty at the time. There was never any serious Royal Naval interest in the *Nordenfelt*. Even after officers from HMS *Vernon* and elsewhere had inspected the boat, their comments had not been thought worthy of inclusion in the Torpedo School's Annual Report: clearly, the non-use of the torpedo tubes and the fearsome heat inside the boat (at least by Royal Naval standards) had not gone entirely overlooked. Nor had the makers' strange reticence over her underwater powers. The only sympathetic response to the boat came from Captain Albert Durston, the Chief Engineer at Portsmouth Dockyard, but his was a lone voice in the anti-*Nordenfelt* wilderness.

If anything, the Nordenfelt probably acted as a setback to submarines in the Royal Navy. Not that the Navy entirely ignored their existence: while the Torpedo School had turned their noses up at the *Nordenfelt*, the French submarine *Gymnote* received a faint squeak of apprehension in *Vernon*'s 1888 Report. The submarines to worry about, it seems, were not Nordenfelt's.

Meanwhile, ghostly contracts apart, Nordenfelt had other troubles. Virtually from the beginning of their supposed partnership, Maxim and Nordenfelt detested each other: the suave Scandinavian gentleman and the American ex-boxer had little in common professionally, and nothing at all personally. Nordenfelt was very much the junior partner in the company: within months of the merger, he had become little more than the manager of what had been his own factory at Erith. An insight into how closely the two men worked can be gained from Maxim's withering report that he had obtained American tools for 'his' Crayford factory for far less than Nordenfelt had paid for the same equipment at Erith. By the middle of 1889, both factories had been largely turned over to making Maxim guns, which had just been accepted by the British Army. The Nordenfelt gun was already becoming a curiosity, not helped by Zaharoff applying the same zeal to denigrating the weapon abroad that he once employed to sell it.

As part of the merger deal, some sections of the original Nordenfelt company (apart from the submarine arm) had been floated off, to be run separately by Nordenfelt himself, ostensibly in order to maintain a degree of Nordenfelt independence, but actually because Maxim and Zaharoff saw them as what we would now call 'lame ducks'. They included the Swedish works at Carlsvik, which now became a sub-contracted supplier to Maxim-Nordenfelt.

The adoption of the Maxim gun by the British Army coincided with a series of lucrative successes for Zaharoff, who obtained large orders in Europe for the heavy-calibre weapon. Unfortunately, this boom in orders was not matched by a corresponding increase in income: some of the governments involved, more used to dealing with the European armaments giants, turned out to be excruciatingly slow payers. By August, the company was in a severe cash-flow crisis: wages were cut at Erith and Crayford. Despite assurances that everything would balance up eventually, the Amalgamated Society of Engineers, the main Maxim-Nordenfelt trades union, initiated a programme of action (or rather, inaction) that culminated in a bitter all-out strike in November. Men who worked through the strike were subjected to burnings and intimidation: for two months, Maxim-Nordenfelt was in serious danger of collapse.

For Thorsten Nordenfelt himself, however, the position was much more stark. His own businesses could not survive the pressure. With the Maxim-Nordenfelt Company slowing down and then ceasing production, Nordenfelt's firms had no one to supply. They – and he – went into liquidation. Nordenfelt was forced to sell out his holdings in both Maxim-Nordenfelt and Naval Construction and Armaments. The buyer, to nobody's surprise, was Zaharoff. Zaharoff, who had reportedly cried with gratitude when he was given his first £5-a-week agency by Nordenfelt, was rewarded with a £1,000-a-year sinecure as the firm's 'foreign adviser' to add to his already mountainous income.

When Nordenfelt's co-chairman seat on the Maxim-Nordenfelt board became vacant, it was filled by Albert Vickers sufficiently quickly for many of the shareholders to suspect a plot. Nordenfelt, a broken man, gathered up his patents and what was left of his fortune and went to Paris, where he set up the Société Nordenfelt with his nephew Per Nordenfelt. This was a glorified dealership, with Thorsten working in the back office. There would be no more Nordenfelt submarines.

There is, however, a footnote to the Garrett/Nordenfelt submarine story. In 1885, Nordenfelt had licensed the patent of the *Dykeri Pråm* (to which he owned all the patent rights, despite Garrett having done most of the actual designing) to the German Imperial Navy. The Germans appeared to take no further interest: it is not impossible that the Reich's good relations with Turkey had resulted in a flow of intelligence concerning the *Abduls*. In 1890, however, two orders were placed at Kiel (the Howaldt yard) and Danzig (Kaiserliche Werft). The resulting submarines, listed as being of the 'Nordenfelt type', were known simply as *U1* and *U2*, and were attached to the torpedo squadrons at Kiel and Wilhelmshaven respectively. Both took part in the 1890 Imperial Fleet Manoeuvres.

Although the two first-ever U-boats were undoubtedly built to the Garrett/Nordenfelt design, there is no record of either Garrett or Nordenfelt having anything to do with their construction or trials. It is therefore interesting to find that their performance, while not good enough to encourage the Germans to build more of them, was rather better than the Garrett-supervised originals. Although their surface speed was a rather humdrum 12.2 knots, they managed 9.3 knots awash, and an astonishing 6.5 knots submerged – almost half as much again as the Greek or Turkish boats on which they were based. It is not impossible that the Germans simply took advantage of Nordenfelt's sudden bankruptcy to build the boats, knowing that he would be unable to pursue what should have been his (and, at a remove, Garrett's) royalties.

With Nordenfelt's fall, however, Garrett's career in submarines, at least with the Maxim-Nordenfelt Company and its offshoots, was over. Zaharoff had long since lost interest in the boats, and he was now a dominating influence in the Company. Maxim, for his part, was beginning to turn his attention in the diametrically opposite direction: he had built his first wind-tunnel, and was considering the difficulties of adapting the steam-engine for powering a flying machine. As was pointed out at the time, it was curious that undersea and aerial travel were plagued by the same problem – the inflexibility of steam propulsion.

Captain Garrett, now much given to loafing on his yacht and attending to the social side of being a Great Inventor, could no longer claim to be resting between engagements: apart from the work on his new vapour generator, which he briefly continued on his own account after the Nordenfelt collapse, he was unemployed. In Britain, as an acolyte of the fallen Nordenfelt, he had no conceivable prospects. He would have to look further afield. Perhaps it was fitting that a man who had worked so hard to conquer the depths should go such a long way to find the abyss.

CHAPTER SEVEN

The Land of Wonder

Oh! to be over yonder
In that land of wonder ...
John Garrett, D.D.[1]

George Garrett, who had weathered many lesser storms in his submarining career, faced the crisis of his life in 1890. Nordenfelt, his backer and supposed partner, had sailed off the edge of the industrial world, helped along by hearty puffs from Zaharoff and Maxim: this left Garrett high and dry, with no visible source of income. He was by no means a poor man: he had been well paid during his time with Nordenfelt, and was spending his enforced leisure in considerable style, with a large house, servants and two yachts to alleviate the boredom. But he had no independent source of income. With no opening for his talents in Britain, he would either have to look for work abroad or find himself yet another new career. In the event, he did both, and both were disastrous.

Jane, who at least saw more of her husband than at any time since their marriage, developed a talent for entertaining in the high Victorian style. Although Zaharoff came no more (probably in the interests of personal safety), the Garretts were not short of visitors to their lavish (*too* lavish) Southampton establishment. Among the family's guests in 1890 was a remarkably young American, 25 years old and newly graduated from Harvard with his Bachelor of Science degree.

John Jacob Astor IV is now best known as the man who built the Waldorf Astoria, or as the unfortunate (if stupendously wealthy) Corpse No 124, fished from the sea in the aftermath of the *Titanic* catastrophe. But the remote, aloof Colonel Astor, last seen seating his pregnant wife in a half-filled lifeboat, was a very different creature before being cut off by an ocean of money when his father died. The young man who sought out Britain's leading submarine engineer was himself a scientist and inventor of immense talent. One of young Astor's inventions was an electrical accumulator,

185

which he installed in one of his yachts (Garrett must have winced at this); he later moved on to marine turbines and his own internal combustion engine, the latter, of course, a subject that greatly interested Garrett. They presumably discussed Garrett's new engine. Astor dreamed of space-travel, weather control, germ war-fare – and submarines. Interestingly, having met Garrett, Astor does not seem to have made the same effort to seek out Holland on his return to America. After Garrett, the relatively sane Holland might have been something of an anti-climax. Jane always remembered Astor and Zaharoff as the glittering highlights of the Garretts' social life in Southampton: a strange combination.

It is possible that the enthusiasm of the young American may have influenced Garrett in his eventual decision to emigrate to the USA. The news was received with horror when he went back to Christ Church to announce his decision to his parents, who were now ageing and (in Georgina's case) visibly fading: Jane was also less than enthusiastic, but opposing Garrett once he had made up his mind was pointless. He was the sort of man who walks off the edge of a cliff to prove that the map is not out of date.

While the family's affairs were wound up in Southampton, Garrett sent the children for a holiday in Ireland with Jane's family. In what must have been something of an adventure for them all, the five children, under the (armed?) protection of John, were placed on the train together, to be met at Liverpool by a Mr Knewing. An outing was arranged to New Brighton, a resort which Garrett had the odd distinction of only having seen from passing submarines. John, it is no surprise to record, made a bee-line for the nearest rifle gallery.

Garrett already had family connections in America, both on his own and his wife's side. His uncle, Alexander Garrett, was Missionary Bishop of North Texas, doing God's work in Dallas. Perhaps of more immediate relevance to Garrett, however, was Jane's brother James Parker, who was making his name as an attorney on New York's Wall Street; another brother, Percy, lived in Cheshire, Connecticut. Garrett must have felt that he was not entirely taking a leap into the unknown: he would certainly not be travelling in the steerage from one hovel to another, like so many emigrants. He was moving on to better and greener pastures.

Garrett was not alone in breaking new, romantic ground. Basil Zaharoff was taking the first steps in a long, tortuous chain of events that would eventually bring his world back into contact with Gar-rett's with almost comically savage irony.

Late in 1889, Zaharoff was travelling on a train between Athens and his new home in Paris when a particularly attractive young woman caught his eye over dinner. Later, while lying in his sleeping berth engrossed in sales figures and promising intelligence of forthcoming wars, he heard muffled screams coming from the next compartment. Hearing a door open and the commotion continue in the corridor, Zaharoff, never a man to miss even a small war, went to investigate. The apparition from the restaurant car fell into his arms, bawling '*Monsieur, monsieur*, please help me. Hide me, I beg of you. My husband wants to kill me.'[2] Zaharoff might have been expected to snatch up a sales opportunity – but no. At 38, and with one highly peculiar marriage behind him (to a woman who may not have known his real name), the self-styled Mystery Man of Europe had met the love of his life.

Maria del Pilar Antonia Angela Patrocinio Simona de Muguiro y Beruete, more concisely known as the Duchess of Villafranca, was then all of seventeen years old. Her husband was, indeed, an abominable man who beat her, and was known throughout Madrid for activities with stable-boys that would have sent even Mr Zedzed to the reference books. Unable to resist or refute the lady's protestations of impeding violent extinction, Zaharoff challenged the young lady's husband to a duel, and won. It is quite clear that Basil's granite heart was at least chipped by the Duchess: in his own, grimly methodical way, he set about winning her for himself.

In the normal run of things, buying a clutch of doctors and getting them to sign one's rival into a lunatic asylum would win the fair lady, but Zaharoff had reckoned without the Duchess's devout Catholic faith, which prevented her from divorcing her husband and marrying her saviour. Zaharoff was doomed to lay siege to Maria (etc) until her husband's death in 1924: never let it be said that Basil Zaharoff was an impatient man. In the meantime, he would be spending a great deal of time in Spain on business – and not.

Back at the more prosaic end of Europe, Garrett was considering his plans for America. He seems, in fact, to have decided to retire from engineering, at least in a professional capacity. Instead, he would take up farming. His initial choice was California, but further research turned him towards the possibility of a high profit for a modest outlay in Florida, where the first steps were being taken in the creation of potentially vast sugar-cane and rice empires. He would be coming in, as it were, on the ground floor.

Nor would he be entirely among foreigners: the centre of the new agricultural promised land, Osceola County, was something of a British enclave.

It is impossible to tell exactly who or what turned Garrett's thoughts to agriculture as an alternative career, but it may not be necessary to look further than Nordenfelt. Although their relationship as partners had never been personally close, it is quite clear that there was no acrimony between them over the end of their submarine adventures. However much Nordenfelt may have wavered as a submariner (by proxy) in the past, the dissolution of the partnership was due to forces entirely outside his control: Garrett understood this. The two men had disagreements, but they were colleagues.

Nordenfelt had always been interested in farming, and would eventually make a small comeback in the agricultural machinery business. In 1885, he patented a process for obtaining albumen from blood, an extension of industrial methods to the exploitation of animal products: the fact that he himself made no immediate use of the invention may have had something to do with the faintly macabre idea of an armaments manufacturer finding a use for what might be regarded as one of his by-products. Albumin, it should be added in Nordenfelt's defence, was highly valued in printing and photography: the modern process for refining it is broadly similar to his method.

Nordenfelt, like many wealthy men, wanted to retire to the farm one day. It hardly seems to be straining the evidence to suggest that Garrett may have taken a cue from him and, indeed, beaten him to it. But there may have been another reason for the change. Six years of absurd overwork on the Nordenfelt boats had nearly killed him. Garrett's lungs – and probably quite a lot else – had almost certainly been damaged by the grotesque physical environment that his work had involved (this had been true all the way back to Pneumatophore days): in any case, he was definitely showing florid, recognisable symptoms of tuberculosis by this time. The knowledge that he was suffering from the greatest killer disease of the period should have made him positively anxious to move to a better climate and a healthier life. So the romantic rural dream may also have been a matter of medical urgency; with three doctors in the family, Garrett was hardly short of clinical advice.

Having sold up in Southampton, Garrett booked passage, first class, for himself, Jane and their five children, aboard the White

Star liner *Teutonic*. The ship was not a random or casual choice: Garrett had seen the ship at the 1889 Spithead Review, when she had been fitted out as the first armed merchant cruiser. He had been impressed, as had the Kaiser, who had been moved to instigate the mercantile equivalent of the naval race. In August 1890, *Teutonic* took the westbound speed record twice on successive voyages, crossing to New York in 5 days, 16 hours and 31 minutes on the second occasion. Marine speed stastistics were always an interest (and a talent) of Garrett's: his mind was made up.

After tearful farewells to his parents (whom he would never see again), Garrett sailed for New York on 26 November 1890. 'Captain' Garrett and his family had a comfortable suite of rooms (one *each*), and shared the palatial first-class lounge with such luminaries as the Governor of Bermuda and the evocatively-named (but historically inscrutable) F. Roosevelt.

The ship had much to interest Garrett. Because of her narrow beam (a form adopted in the sacred name of Speed), *Teutonic*'s two propellers overlapped by five and a half feet: the starboard propeller was six feet further aft than the port, which will have had interesting implications for the vessel's steering. She was the first transatlantic liner not to actually *need* auxiliary sail, though she did in fact carry canvas on board, as did every liner up to and including the *Queen Mary*.

Garrett kept a day-by-day record of the ship's progress along the 2,850-mile icy season outward track. This was not quite the navigational feat it sounds – the figures were supplied by the captain and spaces provided in the ticket booklet for recording them. A day out of Liverpool, *Teutonic* found herself sailing into the teeth of a strong westerly gale that roared all the way to New York: Garrett carefully recorded its progress from 'strong' to 'whole' to 'violent', presumably amid harrowing scenes among those passengers who lacked his highly specialised oscillatory experience. He seemed to attract gales.

This was not one of the ship's record-breaking passages. *Teutonic*, having barely averaged 350 miles a day in the atrocious weather, finally reached New York on 5 December: the Garretts tottered ashore to a new life. They booked into the Fifth Avenue Hotel to recuperate. It cannot have been a pleasant experience for the children, especially the delicate Mary, but it can be safely assumed that most of the *Teutonic*'s passengers – poor emigrants, largely from Ireland – recovered from their nautical trauma in somewhat less comfortable surroundings. The Garretts, as first-class passengers, will also have been spared most of the indignities routinely heaped on immigrants at New York.

The family continued their journey southwards by rail, finally reaching their temporary Florida base, Ocala House, Kissimee, early in January. From the speed of Garrett's subsequent transactions, it is clear that Jane's brother had done much of the legal spadework for them in advance of their arrival. Garrett entered into an agreement with one Albert Drought, President of the Kissimee City Bank, Director of the Florida Midland Railway and (apparently) generalised small-time tycoon, to buy 100 acres of land at Narcoosee for cultivation. The asking price was $5,000, on which he and Jane made a down-payment of $1,000. The bond, dated 3 April 1891, was registered jointly in Jane's name: not for the first time, Parker money had come to Garrett's rescue. Garrett would cultivate the land, or improve it and sell it on in 20-acre chunks: the proceeds would pay off Drought, with the profits going to the Garretts. The bond was open-ended, so this apparently relaxed rustic deal should not have been too onerous. Or so Garrett thought.

A further $1,000 went, in agonising, dribbling stages, to Mr E. Nelson Fell, whose company felled (Felled?) the trees, cleared the land and prepared it for cultivation, then fenced it and threw up a few cabins. The Garrett-Fell correspondence soon deteriorated into a yapping exchange of small bills, petty demands and pettier refusals that grew all the worse when Mr Fell, himself a landowner, decided to lay claim to a chunk of the land, at the edge of Lake Kissimee. Not much further north, a feud would have broken out at this point and the varmint in the dog-collar would have bitten the dust, but Kissimee seemed to have been a relatively civilised place, where disputes were settled by exchanging threats in one of Mr Drought's many offices, on those rare occasions when Drought returned from arcane doings in New York.

By August 1891, the Garretts had moved into their dream home, Lake Cottage, Narcoosee, Osceola County. A weird air of unreality is imparted by its address – Bayswater Road. Connoisseurs of Greek tragedy with a passable knowledge of the Seminole language would have advised against this move. The man whose life had been shaped by the machinations of the Manchester Temperance Movement may not have realised that Osceola (the name of a fallen Seminole Indian Chief) means 'hallower of the black drink', a definition so obscure that it almost seems to have needed Garrett's presence to explain it. Now, after years of tempting Nemesis in the lurching, searing heat of his submarines, Garrett jumped down its throat.

Rice, as Garrett soon realised, is a very labour-intensive crop, requiring, for preference, armies of financially unpretentious workers to tend it. In Florida, this simply meant blacks. But they had to be paid, not in itself a problem if the crop is reasonably strong and plentiful. Garrett soon discovered why rice was new to Osceola County. He would also discover one of the reasons for growing sugar-cane in Hawaii.

Sugar-cane is still grown in Florida, but further south than Osceola, at Lake Okeechobee, where farmers who had learned from the experiences of people like Garrett began growing it in 1931. Compared with other regions (particularly Hawaii), yields are low, for the elementary reason that the climate is not hot enough: it is necessary to replant every year. The region has a peculiar climate: the heat that attracts the tourists in summer is far more variable in winter. In some years, temperatures can and do drop precipitately below freezing in January, killing the cane and just about everything else. Averaged out over several seasons, this is a reasonable agricultural risk. If a farmer is struck by a 'Florida freeze' that wipes out all of his very first crop, he can find himself in diabolical trouble if he is even marginally over-extended to begin with. This is precisely what happened to Garrett.

One cold morning in January 1892, the Garretts woke to find that their entire crop, cane and rice, had been destroyed overnight. Typically, Garrett had sunk nearly everything into the voyage from England and setting up the farm: the family had no financial reserves. Garrett was not financially embarrassed, hard up or (like Nordenfelt) 'ruined': a single night's frost had effectively pauperised him.

Not knowing which way to turn, Garrett had the agreement with Drought re-drafted. Drought stood no chance of receiving his money under the standing agreement. However, the new arrangement, again drawn up jointly with Jane, took the $1,000 the Garretts had already paid to compensate the unfortunate Drought for his sorrows, and absorbed a further $300 that had been paid as a show of good faith when the original agreement had been signed. Drought, $1,300 the richer on no perceptible expenditure, still wanted $5,000. The new bond more or less turned the Garretts into slaves on what was nominally their own land, though part of the new agreement involved giving Drought power of attorney over all the property. This was the side of the American Dream that the emigration agents (and probably Astor) had neglected to mention.

Garrett had intended to be a 'farmer' in the English-gentleman sense of hiring large numbers of wage-slaves and watching *them* farm. For the first time in his life, he experienced real, grinding hardship. Food and clothing became short: Lake Cottage's furniture had to be sold. In one noticeable gesture of defeat, Garrett finally stopped calling himself 'Captain'.

The family's agonies began to pile up: Mary, whose health had always haunted him on his trips abroad, died, aged eleven years. Almost before Garrett had time to recover from this blow, news came from England that his mother had died, on 12 November 1892. He was in no position to return to Britain to join in the family's mourning after her funeral, which took place in Exeter: the psychological impact of this on Garrett, a very proud man, is difficult to imagine. Nor can his next move have come easily to the erstwhile Garrett Bey.

Early in April 1893, Attorney Parker received an angry note from Mr Drought, now all but pawing the ground for his money:

> Referring to Mr Geo. W. Garrett, I wish you would inquire of that gentleman whether he has abandoned all idea of doing any further work on the Narcoosee property, and if I am to consider that his agreement with me for the purchase of the entire property is at an end.[3]

It was indeed at an end. Drought had had to write to Garrett through Parker because Garrett had fled: the Garretts had crept off into the night with as many of their possessions as they could carry. Drought never received another penny from them: they had none to give him.

After a brief stay in Savannah, Georgia, the Garretts finally made their way to New York, where they took a tiny apartment at 352 East 9th Street. The little furniture that they still had was left behind in Narcoosee, where it was sold off, painfully slowly, by a Mr Butler,another victim of the 'freeze' who was also one of Fell's surveyors and a friend of the family. Garrett was well on his way to rock bottom, but, incredibly, the Reverend Commander still had some way to go.

For the first time, Garrett now needed a job, not as a matter of pride or to bail out his father, but to survive. He tumbled headlong

The commander in decline. Garrett in US naval rating's uniform, Texas 1897.

Garrett (with hand on heart) as a corporal in the US Volunteer Engineers — the last known photograph.

into the industrial working class, becoming one of the people he may once have noticed in the corner of his eye at Cochran's or Tashkizak. The best he could find, astonishingly, for a man of his experience and credentials, was a position as a fireman on a New York railway, where he vanished into anonymity. Had he joined the board, or even the engineering staff, of such a company, his name would have survived in some form: as it is, loco firemen came and went like the dew, and it is not even possible to discover the name of his employers. Whoever they were, they were careful with their money: Garrett and his family were brought to the edge of starvation.

In order to eke out the tiny income from his railway work, Garrett advertised himself as a visiting tutor: in the evenings, 'George Wm. Garrett, BA, A. Dep. Eng.' (the latter qualification is news), or, more poignantly. 'Rev Commander G.W. Garrett, BA, Imperial Ottoman Navy, Visiting Tutor' would offer his services to the dimmer children of the New York semi-rich who needed extra coaching in mathematics, science and classics, the last a surprising hangover from his days at Rossall.

The news of what amounted to his son's downfall must have come hard to Dr Garrett, now approaching retirement at Christ Church: Jane kept up a steady, if very depressing, correspondence with the family. This included a studiously optimistic account of her husband's job, presumably promoting him a few grades for the old man's benefit.

Dr Garrett's own circumstances, of course, had been much reduced: the widowed rector was himself on the edge of poverty, though it cannot have been much comfort to him to know that George was well into the real thing – if Jane's letters ever let as much slip. However, if fate had been less than charitable to George, it had been keeping something especially gruesome in store for the chairman of the world's first submarine company.

The Manchester press had grown used to featuring Dr Garrett's sermons in its columns. In years gone by, these had often been highly newsworthy tempests of abuse aimed at the rector's critics, but the opposition had won in the end, and, especially since being widowed, the Moss Side Savonarola had quietened down. Dr Garrett settled for the usual run of loaves, fishes and Samaritans, with the occasional poke at the Pharisees, who seemed rather more real to him than to most clergymen. By the late summer of 1893, he had already resigned the living (for what it was now worth to him), and had arranged the handover of the parish to the Rev John Challenor, who was then on the bishop's staff at Manchester Cathedral. Dr Garrett had seen Christ Church fall from a (supposedly) wealthy living to a young churchman's first solo appointment. He sat down to write his farewell sermons.

On Sunday, 24 September 1893, Dr Garrett took as his subject an old standby of the gloomier Victorian ecclesiastical thunderers, and interspersed it with reminiscences of his life at Christ Church. For the last, awful time, a Garrett sermon made the newspapers:

> Ten minutes after commencing his sermon, his speech became thick and indistinct, and it was at first thought he was much affected by the recapitulation of his experiences and his resignation, but on his son [Thomas] approaching him, it was seen that something serious had happened. The reverend gentleman sank in a heap in the pulpit. It was announced that he had had a stroke, and he was shortly afterwards removed home, where he died at about seven o'clock. It is a remarkable coincidence that the last sermon he preached was about sudden deaths. He warned the congregation that they were liable to be taken away without a moment's notice ...[4]

Even the staid *Evening News* could barely resist a smirk behind its deadpan mask: the old stager had gone out with panache. 'He was in some things an eccentric person' was the paper's summary of forty-eight years in the pulpit, presumably including his service in the now-forgotten Garrett Sub-Marine Navigation and Pneumatophore Company.

There was, of course, another side to this sepulchral comedy. Just when it seemed that life in America could grow no worse, Jane received a letter from her sister-in-law, Thomas's wife Katie, only a couple of weeks after a typically exhortatory epistle from the rector:

> My dearest Jane,
> Hard indeed it is to tell you that we have lost dear Father ... he was conscious until half past two, when he fell asleep and never awoke again. Tom buried him in Exeter beside dear Mother. His end was peaceful – he just passed away in his sleep: two deep sighs and he was gone. We did all [laid him out] ourselves: he looked so like himself in his nice clean surplice, hood and stole.
> I believe he wrote to you on the Friday before he died. I am so glad the dear old man had the joy of hearing from you before he died. your letter gave him such relief, for he grieved about you all. Dear Jane, how I wish you had never gone away from us all.

He never suffered a bit, and did not know he was ill. He asked, when they brought him home, why they stopped him from finishing his sermon. He got confused all of a sudden when preaching: Tom went to him at once and he fell into his arms. The left side was paralyzed completely, eyes and all: he could only look to the right. He had a second stroke after he became unconscious, and then the right side went.

May God bless and comfort you, dear Jane, and take care of you and all your darlings.

Ever your loving Sister
Katie[5]

Once again, Garrett had to remain in America while the family grieved. His work on the railway seems to have been sporadic: there are signs that it may even have been casual labour. At one stage, the family was literally down to the last dollar, and had to move to an even humbler apartment at 352 East 91st Street. His health grew steadily worse: it must have occurred to him that Mary had been the fortunate one.

As late as December 1895, nearly three years after the Garretts' flight to New York, they were still desperate for the pathetic income from their furniture, which was now being sold to victims of another 'Florida freeze'. One of their letters, far from being a bearer of glad financial tidings, is a glimpse into a pit of terrible poverty, where tiny sums are bargained for like gold-dust:

Dear Garrett,
 Herewith $3.50, which I would have sent sooner, but had been expecting for a long time to collect $2 on your sofa. The freeze stopped Tysen taking it, and it stayed at Haycock's house till last July, by which time it was badly moth-eaten ... I suggest trying to sell it to any buyer now for $1, sooner than give it away, which is what it otherwise amounts to. I regret not having found a purchaser for your window-shutters, which are still on hand ...
 Hoping you are in better circumstances than the freeze left us in,
Yours truly,
H.T. Butler[6]

It is entirely reasonable to wonder why a man of Garrett's experience and qualifications should have had such difficulty in finding employment, even given the comparatively mild recession then taking place in American engineering. Ironically, there were plentiful vacancies for farmers and stockmen in the West, and even an upsurge in the Florida orange industry, but the further upheaval

and financial outlay involved were far beyond the Garretts' now
negligible means. In any case, to borrow one of John Garrett's more
enterprising understatements, it had been established with some
certainty that Garrett was 'not temperamentally suited to the life of
an agriculturalist'.[7]

The most likely cause of Garrett's appalling lack of success in
New York was his declining health, which can only have been made
far worse by his work as a fireman. His illness may also have kept
him off work: returning to the footplate would have made him ill
again – a vicious circle. However, it is still remarkable that he was
unable to find work as an engineer or in the shipping industry. He
was, of course, rather old to be starting work as anything lowlier
than a corporate partner, which would not have helped; nor would
his nervous, over-forceful manner, which many people found
alarming.

By 1896, Garrett's prestige as a submarine designer was virtually
non-existent: his best-known creations, the Nordenfelt boats, did
not carry his name, and were in any case all but museum pieces,
even this soon after their heyday (in so far as they had one). That
year, Garrett finally came into contact, if at something of a remove,
with the man whose submarine work had overtaken his own: John
Philip Holland.

In a sense, the two men had clashed before. The Turks had
inspected Holland's *Fenian Ram* in 1881, but had gone on to buy
two Garrett/Nordenfelt submarines. Holland had nursed his pride,
while forging ahead with his designs, until 1887, when he beat
Nordenfelt in the Navy Department's competition, only to lose the
contract when the Cramp yard decided they could not build his
design. The following year, Holland won another, similar
competition (this time with Nordenfelt and Garrett out of the
running), but by then President Cleveland, who had backed the
submarine proposal, had been replaced by the uninterested
Benjamin Harrison, and the anti-submarine faction ruled once
more. Holland had to wait until Grover Cleveland's 1893
re-election for his next chance. By 1896, he had founded the
Holland Torpedo Boat Company, and his submarine *Plunger* was
on the stocks at the Malster yard at Baltimore.

When the 1888 US Navy Committee chose Holland's design over
Nordenfelt's Garrett-designed submission, they gave as their reason
one of the key points of difference between the Nordenfelt and
Holland submarines:

It embodies the ideas of a fixed centre of gravity, of an exact compensation for expended weights, of a low longitudinal metacentric height, and of quick diving and rising, by the effort of the propeller pushing the vessel against the resistance of her mid-ship section only, down or up inclines, the angles of which were to be determined by horizontal rudder actions.[8]

Put simply, the Holland boat dived on hydroplanes – like *Resurgam*. Unlike *Resurgam*, she remained submerged on ballast: the reserve of buoyancy was abandoned, as was Nordenfelt's dogma of the necessity to submerge vertically on an even keel. There were therefore no vertical screws. Careful design of the tanks eliminated the free-surface horrors of the Nordenfelt boats. Neutral buoyancy was now a reality. Holland's boat was, in fact, the modern submarine: in many important respects, Garrett was shown to have been wrong all along. The means that he and Nordenfelt had chosen to control underwater instability had only made the situation worse, with the whole problem looping back on itself when vertical submergence was proclaimed the one true, safe (!) mode of submerging for all but the briefest dives.

The Holland *Plunger* was propelled by steam on the surface. The engine drove a dynamo, which charged a bank of accumulators, which in turn powered the vessel under water. This was the system that had been adopted by de Lôme and Zédé ten years earlier. It did at least share Garrett's system when the boat was surfaced. However, Holland found the temperature inside the surfaced boat too high (which would have raised a hollow laugh from an experienced Nordenfelt crewman): he had been forced into using steam by the US Government's over-ambitious speed and endurance requirements. In 1896, he was working on combining the internal combustion engine of the *Fenian Ram* with the electrical system of the *Plunger* to produce his sixth boat, which became, in essence, the archetype for all future submarines.

Holland's hulls leapfrogged history. His early boats adopted the tear-drop form eventually employed in nuclear submarines, ideal for high submerged speed, but this shape was misguidedly 'superseded', in the interests of improving surface running, by the less efficient wedge-ended cylinder, not unlike the *Nordenfelt*: in the short term (in fact, for more than seventy years), Garrett was ahead on this one point, but, paradoxically, he was still 'wrong'.

In 1896, then, Holland was a famous man, whose submarines had all too clearly taken up, not where Garrett had left off, but largely where Garrett had never looked. Garrett could not have chosen a less auspicious time to decide on a comeback in submarines. Nor could he have made a worse choice of yard in which to seek employment.

At the end of May, Garrett (now 'Captain Garrett' once again for the occasion) wrote to William Cramp and Sons in Philadelphia, offering his services as a submarine engineer. He had heard that they were being considered for a contract to build submarines for the Government. The firm that had let Holland down in 1888, and to whom he had never returned, were not anxious to take on that sort of work now. Garrett had, of course, chosen them because of his now somewhat tenuous link with them via the 1888 competition – which was precisely what they would rather forget.

Cramp's reply was brief to the point of being brusque:

Dear Sir,
   In reply to your letter of the 31st ult. we remark that, in view of the amount of large construction on our hands, we have decided not to undertake any of the submarine torpedo-boat work now under contemplation at the Navy Department. We are aware of your connection with previous experiments to which you refer, and have no doubt of your efficiency.
   We have understood that the Chas. Hillman Ship and Engine Building Co., Beach and Palmer Sts., this city, is disposed to undertake this class of work, and would therefore refer you to that concern.
Very truly yours,
Henry W. Cramp, Treasurer and Secretary[9]

If he had been taken on, Garrett would have been employed building Holland boats, a harsh enough irony in itself. However, Hillman were of no use to him either – or he to them. Leaving aside the fact (for it was one) that by now his name was absolutely not the one to conjure with in submarines, the contemplated Government contracts evaporated: the first Holland submarine to be commissioned by the US Navy (his sixth, internal combustion/ electrical boat then building at New Jersey) was only accepted in 1900, twelve years after the commissioning of the two *Abduls*. By 1900, a great deal had happened to Garrett.

Later in 1896, another industrial wild goose chase took the ailing Garrett all the way to Galveston, Texas: no details have survived, but the Todd Shipyard seems a likely destination. In any event, nothing came of it, though, for once in his American career, Garrett may actually have been fortunate in missing this opportunity:

Galveston, Todd Shipyard and all, was devastated by a tidal wave in 1900.

On the way to Galveston, Garrett, entirely unannounced, visited his Uncle Alexander, who had risen from Missionary Bishop of North Texas (a species of ecclesiastical sheriff) to bishop of Dallas (a marshal) in 1895. The shabbily-dressed (and probably very tired) Garrett presented himself at the bishop's house in Greenwood, and eventually managed to talk his way in. He was received by his uncle's wife Letitia, whom he had never met before. What must have been a rather edgy interview with this total stranger resulted in Garrett being sent back to his hotel, the run-down but aptly-named St George, to await the return of his uncle, who was out of town on business.

When her husband returned, Letitia told him about their strange visitor. There followed a classic Hollywood encounter, with the overjoyed bishop rushing to the hotel to collect his long-lost nephew, who stayed for several days. Garrett had not seen his uncle since childhood, though he had followed his uncle's adventures (bringing Christ to the cow-towns, after earning his spurs among the Canadian injuns). Of course, he now had a few adventures of his own to relate. He left behind a bundle of photographs of his submarines: unfortunately, all were lost when the house burned down some years later. The Garrett trail, never easy to follow, has had a strange way of covering itself as the years have passed.

While in Galveston, Garrett, for whatever reason (nostalgia, pride or plain eccentricity) had himself photographed in a US naval rating's uniform, smoking a pipe. It is not inconceivable that he attempted to join the Navy as a rating (future events would bear this out), but this strange picture offers no clues: it may have given the family a smile on his return to New York.

In June 1897, Garrett decided to return to Europe, on his own, in search of work. This last, desperate journey home may have been a result of his visit to Dallas, as the same month brought Bishop Garrett to the Lambeth Conference with a spectral, supernumerary 'assistant, a member of the bishop's family' in his entourage – presumably the bishop's nephew, who would easily have passed as a servant by now.

Garrett sought out his old acquaintances and contacts, only to find that they had all evaporated or moved on, out of reach. What little was left of Maxim-Nordenfelt was in the process of disappearing forever. Yet again at the instigation of Zaharoff (with a little help from the trusty Rothschild and Cassel), the company was bought by Vickers at the knock-down price of £1,353,334, reflecting the firm's thin times in the recent past. In 1894, they had even tried to give Zaharoff notice, a monumental act of folly for which they were now paying. Zaharoff's close friendship with Alfried Krupp had given him ample leverage in the new negotiations.

Naval Construction and Armaments disappeared into the Vickers empire at the same time, resulting in the powerful naval (and particularly submarine) yard now thriving at Barrow. At this stage, however, the anti-submarine orthodoxy was at its height in Britain (a state of affairs which, as we have seen, was partly Garrett's fault): no one was interested, Vickers least of all. Another three years would see a change of attitude and a Holland boat under construction at Barrow, but 1897 was the bottom of the market for submarines in Britain, and the worst possible time for Garrett to be seeking work. Even Holland, who by any standards (and especially compared with Garrett) was *succeeding*, was in the process of being devoured by the Electric Boat Company, due to his own rather incomplete business abilities. At the best of times, submarine engineering was a questionable occupation at the close of the nineteenth century – and Garrettt's best times were behind him.

The obvious contact for Garrett to try was, of course, Thorsten Nordenfelt. It is clear that Garrett had made no attempt to reach him (or anybody else) by mail before coming over to Europe. Nordenfelt, now permanently living in Paris, was understandably surprised to hear from him out of the blue. Garrett actually went to Paris before writing to Nordenfelt, only for the letter to be sent to London by a sleepy clerk at the Société Nordenfelt office. Nordenfelt's reply to Garrett gives some idea of the change in both men's lives: relatively speaking, they had fallen a similar distance. But the fact that Nordenfelt's plunge had a much higher starting-point made a world of difference:

> 8, Rue Auber, Paris,
> August 7, 1897
>
> Dear Mr Garrett,
>   I am pleased to hear from you again! Your letter of August 3 has reached me from London.
>   I would be very glad to assist you to find employment, but do not know where to turn – I am working here quietly in my nephew's office, and

have no work that would suit you. The Barrow yard has been bought by Messrs Vickers and Co of Sheffield, who have also bought up the Maxim-Nordenfelt Co, so that with Mr Albert Vickers as head, I have no influence there. Mr Durston is, I am told, now a great swell in the Admiralty – could not he do what you wish?

If you can suggest any special way in which I can be of use to you, kindly let me know – and you know from experience that I am not lazy. The only line in which I am of no use is £.s.d. – my pockets are shallow, and there are holes in them!

A Frenchman, a *litérateur* [sic], called upon me last year, asking for details of the submarine boats, but I had none to give him. He however only wanted them for a book on submarine boats, probably of no great value.

Let me know how you get on.
                    Yours very truly
                    T.W. Nordenfelt

I was astonished to find that you are in France. I thought you were in Yankeeland, where I heard that you were getting on well.[10]

Nordenfelt was merely short of cash; Garrett was all but destitute. Nordenfelt was in fact being as kind and helpful as he could: the only shadow on the letter, Garrett's gently-rebuffed begging aside, is the interesting glimpse of the acrimony that had surfaced in the Maxim-Nordenfelt merger. Whatever the friction between Maxim and Nordenfelt, it was as nothing compared with the blazing detestation between Nordenfelt and Albert Vickers.

'Mr Durston' was indeed a great swell at the Admiralty. The only naval officer to have spoken up for the *Nordenfelt* was now Vice-Admiral Sir Albert Durston, KCB. But times – and submarines – had changed. Although British naval policy was still some way off accepting the submarine, very tentative feelers were being put out to investigate Holland's achievements in America: the first Royal Navy submarine would be a Holland boat, built at Barrow – to Garrett, the worst of all worlds. For him, the entire naval establishment carried a 'no vacancies' sign.

A month later, Garrett and Nordenfelt still had not met. Nordenfelt wrote to Garrett from a hotel in Holland, where he was pursuing his new interest: he had been exhibiting (among other things) the Nordenfelt Patent Butter Churn at the Scheveningen Dairy Show. Guns were now largely behind him: he left all that to nephew Per, Signor Ristori (another nephew – presumably his sister's son) and Per's partner Carl Holmström. The Société

Nordenfelt, despite its Anglo-Nordic origins, was now sufficiently Gallicised for Per to be calling himself Per *de* Nordenfelt.

Garrett must have wondered whether the newly-bucolic Nordenfelt was the same man who had brought him and his submarines to the fringes of royalty. At their meeting, amid the mooing and milking of the Islington Dairy Show in September, Garrett finally realised that the Nordenfelt circus, as far as he was concerned, really had left town. The two men never met again.

Garrett lingered in Britain another month, staying with his brother Thomas, now practising medicine in Manchester. Fully expecting to find work suitable for a Reverend Commander, he had not booked a return passage to America, and had no funds to do so; he was virtually disintegrating before his brother's eyes. The family noticed (as they could hardly fail to do) changes in him that were more than the result of poverty. He looked ill; he *was* ill. He had no clothes: his brothers' wives rummaged through their husbands' wardrobes for acceptable cast-offs.

Rather more worrying was his behaviour. He had always been constitutionally over-wrought to the point of eccentricity and beyond, but now there were disturbing flashes of something worse. He wrote to his brother Oliver:

> Be sure Tom is a clear-headed business man, who will never miss a post or a point. And I assure you he has cards in his hand that will make you sick, sore and sorry you crossed him if you make a clip.[11]

This was language as strange to Oliver as it is to us: Thomas was an unassuming, dedicated man, the quietest and most pious member of the family. George, if not actually raving, was at least becoming slightly unhinged. Oliver, frightened by his brother's condition, decided to pay his fare back to America, first class:

> You will sail on the 16th inst. [December] on the SS *Mississippi*, Atlantic Transport Line, from London. I shall send you a first class ticket. You will have one pound in your pocket for the voyage and to get home properly when you arrive in New York. Neither your position nor your health can permit your going in any other way.[12]

There may have been more than fraternal charity to this. Garrett was now showing obvious signs of tuberculosis: there was a chance that he, as a non-citizen, might not be re-admitted to the United States if his condition was spotted, even with Jane and the family living (just) in New York. There was far less chance of this happening to a first-class passenger.

Garrett arrived in New York just in time for another bleak Christmas. The only work he had not sought was in the Church: although he still occasionally styled himself 'Reverend', that side of him had been consigned to the past, buried with his father. With all he was going through, however, he will have needed some sort of faith: he needed it all the more soon after getting home.

Oliver's act of kindness had turned out to be very nearly the last thing he ever did: he died suddenly, aged 49, on New Year's Day, 1898, at his home in Dinard, Brittany. Garrett was caught in a deluge of misery and misfortune that only occasionally moderated to a drizzle. The stoking and the teaching, the pallor and the ominous coughing went on.

Not least because they probably could not afford a newspaper, the Garretts would not have noticed that riots had broken out in Cuba on 12 January, but the shock waves from Havana would reach them soon enough.

The inhabitants of Cuba had been agitating for independence from Spain for many years, but tensions on the island had been greatly heightened since 1895 by a vitriolic campaign of anti-Spanish propaganda in the American press, particularly in those papers owned by William Randolph Hearst, who actively wanted to see America wade in on the side of the Cubans against their oppressors. And, while they were about it, liberate (so to speak) the Philippines. So far, almost comically unsubtle diplomatic pressure on the Spaniards had placated the war fancy, but a heavy-handed Spanish campaign against the Cuban insurgents in 1897 and the steady creep of yellow fever across the Straits of Florida from the island's shattered population brought matters to a head at the turn of the year. The possibility of war with Spain was now a party-political issue: President McKinley's Republicans feared they would not be re-elected in 1900 if McKinley failed to get a decent war under way, as recommended in Mr Hearst's papers.

On 25 January, the 10-inch-gunned cruiser USS *Maine* arrived in Havana harbour, ostensibly on a courtesy visit. It is at this point that Garrett's tormentors begin to appear as malevolent ghosts on the periphery. The Spanish Minister in Washington, cursed with the task of handling the diplomacy of the situation, was Enriqué Dupuy de Lôme, a relative of the French naval architect whose submarine had driven the *Nordenfelt* off the Royal Navy's agenda. One of de Lôme's letters, in which he described President McKinley as a 'spineless politician' (fighting talk in 1898) was widely leaked: Hearst thumped the tub all the harder, and war loomed. Hearst, for some reason, never leaked Vice-President Theodore Roosevelt's description of McKinley as having 'no more backbone than a chocolate éclair'. War-mongering is a selective business.

On the night of 15 February, USS *Maine*, swinging at her buoy in Havana, was blown literally into the air by a massive explosion, nearly breaking the ship in half and killing 143 of her crew of 328. Sabotage was the obvious diagnosis: large numbers of Cuban suspects were rounded up and interrogated. Modern research (notably by Admiral Rickover, the founder of the American nuclear submarine fleet) has shown that the explosion was almost certainly caused, not by a mine, but by an explosion of dust in the ship's bunkers that took a magazine up with it. Nothing less wicked than a Spanish infernal machine would placate American opinion at the time, however. The Hearst papers were screaming 'Remember the *Maine!*' within days.

Mr Hearst was not alone in trying to start a war between the USA and Cuba. One of the men interrogated after the explosion, while pleading that he knew nothing about the destruction of the ship, declared that he had been told by a Spanish officer that 'an agent of the Maxim-Nordenfelt Company' had been agitating violently for war in Madrid. By then, the firm was Vickers, Sons and Maxim, but the rest fits. Early in 1898, Basil Zaharoff was indeed in Spain, using the free time between trysts with his Duchess to sell a few tons of weapons for use against the Americans.

The war, partly precipitated by a Dupuy de Lôme and joyfully promoted by Zaharoff, finally erupted on 17 April. Among the troops who found themselves looking down the wrong ends of a great number of Maxim guns (and even the occasional Nordenfelt) was George Garrett.

Garrett, once a naval commander and known for much of his adult life as 'captain', became a corporal in the First New York Regiment of the US Volunteer Engineers. The fact that he was accepted at all shows that the medical inspections at the recruitment centres were either performed by doctors of very circumscribed talents or were not carried out at all. It is ironic to find that during the war there were many complaints in the regular army about commissions being handed out to the ranks like confetti, a situation which obviously did not apply in the Volunteers.

Fortunately, Garrett was not in the firing line for long, which, considering the state of his health, was just as well. To enter the army, he had to become an American citizen, thus finally cutting the ties with home. This was not a decision that would come easily to a man who had been reviewed by his Queen in the midst of her Fleet while showing the world a warship of his own design. Garrett had less reason than most to think of America as the Land of Opportunity, far less the Land of the Free; he had just returned defeated from an attempt to escape from it. It is frankly more than unlikely that Garrett joined the army out of patriotism for his new-found home; the grim reality is probably that he simply signed up for the money. He swore his oath on 21 June and enlisted the next day.

The war was all but over when Garrett became involved. General Miles and the 22-stone General Shafter had had their moment of glory at Santiago: all that remained was the mopping-up of Puerto Rico, the operation for which the Volunteer Engineers were specially raised. The main force left Guantanamo the day before Garrett enlisted and had already been fighting (but not a lot) on Puerto Rico for nearly two weeks when the Engineers arrived. The highlight of Garrett's active military career was not exactly Gettysburg: he was actually in the field for about a week.

The problem for the Engineers, however, just as it had been for virtually all the American army forces deployed in the war, was actually getting them to Puerto Rico. The American people had been treated to a veritable cavalcade of military incompetence and graft. The standing army, which had not been mobilised since the Civil War, was more or less ready, but the organisation of the volunteer regiments almost beggared description. Many men were sent into the summer heat of Cuba in winter clothing; fatuous scandals blossomed over the sale to the army of semi-decomposed 'contract beef', a substance which soon entered the language as 'embalmed beef' and brought down far more American soldiers than Spanish bullets ever did.

The Volunteers were taken upstate to Peekshill for their basic training, an irritating formality for the adventurers among them, who felt, correctly, that the war was ebbing away while they were melting on the parade-ground. It was probably at this time that some perceptive officer made Garrett a corporal.

From Peekshill, the men were taken to Bedlow's Island and shoehorned into an ancient steamer, the *Chester*, where they were left to simmer in the suffocating heat for nearly a week while the Army tried to nail together a plan of attack. Dithering of this sort had been the hallmark of the entire campaign: compared to what soldiers had been put through in Tampa earlier in the war, the Engineers were doing fairly well. The situation at Tampa had degenerated into a race between yellow fever, malaria and malnutrition: on the *Chester* the race was merely between heatstroke and the Armistice. The men, and their commanding officer, Colonel Griffin, became genuinely worried that they might miss the war if they did not depart soon. On 18 July, a strangely Garrettesque problem broke out below:

> It was found last night that the engines would run reversed all right, but they refused to work the other way. Anxious as were the members of the 1st New York Regiment of Volunteer Engineers to get to the front before an armistice is declared, they did not relish the idea of sailing backwards over summer seas.[13]

Chief Engineer Bain and his men beavered away, apparently unaware of the nearby presence of a man who had once been one of the most celebrated marine engineers in Europe. The *Chester*'s decrepit machinery finally began grinding in the desired direction: the ship, allegedly capable of fourteen knots, doddered gamely through the Narrows, pursued by mocking cries of 'You'd better rig your sails!':[14]

> The Engineers didn't care, so long as they got far enough away to prevent the War Department recalling them. They wanted to sniff the ocean breezes and see the verdant stretches of sub-tropical Puerto Rico ...[15]

They would have to start sniffing and seeing fairly quickly. The anxiety over missing the war was partly due to the Spanish Government having been so unsporting as to open negotiations for peace three days earlier.

Undaunted by such underhand tactics, Colonel Griffin and his Engineers pressed on, and reached Puerto Rico before an armistice could be signed. Puerto Rico 'fell' to the Americans after a virtually unopposed landing. Total casualties in the operation were three dead and forty wounded: Garrett was not in either group. Embarrassing questions were asked (and suppressed) about the precise origin of the supposedly 'enemy' fire. The customary fistfuls of medals compensated for any red faces. Theodore Roosevelt summed it up: 'It wasn't much of a war, but it was the best war we had.'

Unfortunately, the Engineers had not only walked to victory: they had also walked into a fever-trap. Within days, rudimentary sanitary facilities and frightening ignorance of basic hygiene brought the same rewards to the Engineers that their colleagues had reaped on Cuba – dysentery and typhoid broke out, accompanied by the now almost-banal malaria and the lethal yellow fever. By 8 August, when the general American withdrawal began, there were nearly 4,000 cases of fever in the army. While nearly 5,000 men were killed in the war, only 379 were killed in action: the rest died of disease.

The army, Engineers included, was so disease-ridden, in fact, that the American Government hesitated to bring it home, for fear of starting an epidemic. Only energetic political agitation forced the Government to relent: 'This army must be moved at once, or it will perish,' pleaded Roosevelt.

The Engineers were finally deposited at Montauk Point, at the easternmost end of Long Island, in mid-August, but were not allowed to leave, in the interest of public health. The Montauk Point Camp was a clearing house for the whole Expeditionary Force, and rapidly deteriorated into a concentration camp for sick and dying soldiers. By the time Garrett was demobilised, in late September, another 257 men had died from an assortment of entirely avoidable diseases. Four-fifths of the force – 20,000 men – were officially admitted to be 'ill' on leaving Montauk Point. It would be more than surprising if Garrett, in questionable health when he joined, was anything other than a shattered man when he was finally released to his family. After his father's death, John Garrett put his demise down to 'exposure and contract beef'.[16] Those soldiers who had been given winter outfits for the sultry days had been given nothing for the freezing nights: exposure is not recommended in cases of tuberculosis.

Garrett returned to what would be his last home, 452 West 151st Street, and took up where he had left off – the same grind of stoking and coaching. In 1901, he made one last attempt to revive his career. On 10 April he met two gentlemen, Thomas MacConnell and William Beam, at the Hotel Earlington on West 27th Street. This was a business meeting – or, rather, a sad parody of one – to discuss the prospects of one of Garrett's inventions.

The invention concerned, which he now proudly named the Garrett Motor, was the hybrid steam-petroleum vapour engine that he had patented in 1888. Even in 1888, the motor had been a rather doubtful proposition: in 1901, with the internal combustion engine a daily reality and the diesel engine already far more than a curiosity, Garrett's device, though ingenious, was a non-startaer. Its only conceivable use might have been as an adjunct to large marine steam engines, but the costs involved in retrofitting all the equipment for the Garrett motor would act as a powerful – terminal – deterrent to its acceptance. Curiously, an engine that uses an oil-based spirit without consuming it might receive a more sympathetic hearing in our own oil-starved times, but fossil-fuel conservation was the last thing on anybody's mind in 1901.

Garrett sold 51% of the rights to the motor to Beam for one dollar, on the understanding that Beam would put up $500 within thirty days to meet the costs of building and demonstrating the machine. If the deal and the motor had succeeded, the new machine may, in all seriousness, have been known as the Beam Engine. What with Fell the tree-feller, Drought the land-speculator and Beam the engine-developer, all occupying a landscape of tears and tribulation, Garrett sometimes appears to have wandered into the All-American Morality Play.

Closer inspection of the contract reveals the probable real reason for Garrett resurrecting an invention he must have known to be commercially hopeless: he was to receive $15 a week from Beam for eight weeks, while he worked on the engine. It was, perhaps, just this side of fraudulent, but it was preferable to stoking, and much better paid.

Garrett did his eight weeks, received his salary, and failed again. There were no takers, just as there had been none in 1888. But Jane and the family had been a little more comfortable. This sad little game with marginal technology – in a way, what he and Nordenfelt had been up to with the *Abduls*, but on a pitiful, tiny scale – was Garrett's final appearance on any industrial stage.

On 23 January 1902, Dr G.F. Brewster was called to a cramped apartment in West 151st Street to attend a 49-year-old railroad fireman suffering from advanced pulmonary tuberculosis. There was nothing that could be done for him, but Dr Brewster arranged for him to be moved to a charity ward at the Metropolitan Hospital. By then the patient appeared to be delirious, muttering some nonsense about appearing before the Sultan in a submarine boat. His family seemed used to it.

The Reverend Commander George William Garrett Bey BA died on 26 February 1902, at 1.25 pm. He was certified as having died of *phthisis pulmonaris chronica* – tuberculosis – and exhaustion. On 1 March, he was buried in an unmarked pauper's grave at Mount Olivet Cemetery, Maspeth. Only his son John went to the burial, riding shotgun on the undertaker's cart as it crossed to Queens on the ferry. Before long, two other, nameless men were buried in the same grave, on top of Garrett. Only the fact that he had been in the US Army kept his name and location in the cemetery's records.

Fortunately, Jane and the family were not prisoners of poverty for much longer: whatever demon had pursued Garrett died with him. Garrett's two sons, John and George, prospered (with a Mr Zimmermann) in the early years of the motor trade; in later years, John even moved back to Florida. Georgina and Janie married and brought up families of their own. Jane lived with Georgina, now Mrs Cullinan, in New York, until 1920, when they moved to Plainfield, New Jersey, where Jane died in 1926. At 78, she was a respected member of the Plainfield Community, and had lived to see her great-grandson, John Hendrickson, who was Janie's grandson.

One car that was never sold or serviced in the Garrett-Zimmermann Garage was the Nordenfelt. This, one of the earliest mass-market cars and an almost unmitigated failure, was the last machine to be produced by the Société Nordenfelt before Thorsten retired to Sweden in 1903: he died, a comfortable if regretful man, in 1920. There is no reason to suppose that he knew of his erstwhile partner's fate.

Of the original personnel of the Nordenfelt Submarine Torpedo Boat Company, only one man achieved the wealth and fame that Garrett had expected when he joined forces with the Swedish gunsmith: it is no surprise that the lucky man was Basil Zaharoff. By the time of his death – in his bed, in 1936 – he had been knighted (for extremely shadowy services to the British Government during the Great War), and had amassed a barely calculable fortune from his arms sales. One of his sources of income was the Electric Boat Company, builder of the Holland submarines that had superseded Garrett's: he was on the shareholder's list before

Garrett died. The Duchess of Villafranca finally married Zaharoff in 1924, only to die in 1926: his return on 35 years of waiting was eighteen months of married life. It – she – was his only questionable investment. He died in his very own town – Monte Carlo.

George Garrett's reputation was dead long before he was. His immense talent had been swamped in a wave of over-promotion and increasingly farcical accidents and failures. But for the extreme pressures on him – to build the boats, sell the boats, promote the boats, keep quiet about the limitations of the boats – he would almost certainly have been able to develop his submarines in a rational way, building on the successes and analysing the disasters. That, however, was not the way things were done in the armaments business: more and more, Garrett and Nordenfelt were selling the *idea* of submarine warfare, with the hardware almost an afterthought. In some ways, very little has changed. Today, we are bombarded with claims that system *x* is the final, ultimate war-machine by precisely the people who know that such a weapon does not exist and never shall: at least Garrett knew that a workable submarine was a *possibility*.

The Nordenfelt partnership saved Garrett's career early on, but it also marked the end of the chain of careful, step-by-step development that had taken him from the pneumatophore to the 'egg', and from there to *Resurgam*. The commercial 'realities' of the 1880s were his scientific death-knell – to Nordenfelt, research and development were two very long words. Progress was by intuitive leaps, or it did not happen at all. Miscalculation was cured by applying plenty of ballast at the other end of the argument and claiming that the result was an improvement.

Garrett's misfortune was simple enough. He was the first mechanical submariner, the trailblazer – but he blazed the wrong trail. If *Resurgam* had reached Portsmouth, he may have come back to the idea of controlling the submarine's buoyancy, which was the principle of his 'egg' and the idea that Holland pursued to glory: with Nordenfelt, Garrett was locked inside a single idea of what a submarine should be, and never escaped.

Garrett was certainly capable of original, innovative thought – the vapour generator (the key component of the would-be Beam Engine) that he designed after the loss of the *Nordenfelt*, when her namesake was too preoccupied to get in his way, is ample evidence of this. But, with the submarines, Garrett simply could not win. When the Nordenfelt boats appeared to succeed, Nordenfelt received the credit; when the Nordenfelt empire fell, it was Garrett who had to emigrate. Suddenly, the boats were his idea after all, when nobody wanted to know.

Of course, Garrett was hardly blameless in his misfortunes. He was a proud and often frighteningly foolhardy man. Unfortunately, the recklessness that took him down in his submarines was the same quality that let him invest his every penny in the Florida farm scheme. Once his material situation and social position had dropped below the level his pride expected, he seems to have almost switched off his personality: there is an aimless, sleepwalking aura around the last American years that suggests something stranger, and much sadder, than mere bad luck. He was ill for most of his life, and ill men do strange things, especially those who cannot bring themselves to admit to anything being wrong. Tuberculosis was dreaded in the same way that cancer is dreaded now: to admit to suffering from it was tantamount to handing in one's notice to the world. It is simply impossible to believe that Garrett thought he had a nervous cough or a perpetual chest-cold – but he may well have made himself believe it.

In an important sense (apart from the literal one), he never stopped being a curate. It never seems to have occurred to him that what he was doing was in any way unusual, beyond the obvious fact that other people were not going to sea in submarines. He was not – absolutely not – the sort of man who *did* such things. The attitude, the sheer, po-faced respectability, was purest Victorian clergyman. Whatever his original reason for joining the clergy, he was far more clergyman than mariner: he was not a parsonical adventurer, but an adventurous parson. And after a period in the engineering novitiate, he became Nordenfelt's curate: he was never fully admitted to *that* priesthood, either.

But this strange, paradoxical man, a man who typified his age, yet who died an outcast, deserves far better from history. His submarines, for all their faults, *were* the first practical undersea warships: in their doubtful war-worthiness, they are perhaps closer to our modern weapons than we care to admit. He was the first in the field, and the first to be forgotten.

The arrival on the scene of the *Nordenfelt* was likened at the time to Columbus discovering the new world. But Columbus, judged by the task he set himself – to find a western route to the Orient – succeeded in doing something very different: he established where Japan was *not*. No one curses the map maker for marking the dead ends in the road system: if Garrett's boats were a dead end in the history of the submarine, they were not less worthy or smaller achievements for that. They were the first steps on a dangerous road that we are all still travelling: it would not do our pride any harm to remember that Trident, Polaris and their opponents were born at a Manchester church fête.

Jonah, the first submariner, cried: 'The waters closed in over me, the deep was round about me; weeds were wrapped about my head at the roots of the mountains. I went down to the land whose bars closed upon me for ever, yet thou didst bring up my life from the Pit, O Lord'.

Surely, we should follow the divine example, and do the same for George Garrett.

Epilogue

Garrett's submarines had a way not so much of disappearing as of fading out of history. *Dykeri Pråm En* and the *Abdul* sisters all drifted into the mist, with their precise fates unknown; *Nordenfelt* was nibbled away at Esbjerg over an indefinite period, and the fate of the little 'egg' is a total mystery (though a fairly easy guess). *Resurgam*, however, is a different matter – in her own way, the only survivor of Garrett's boats, awaiting resurrection from the bottom of Colwyn Bay. This book has been written during the preparation and execution of what should be the final, definitive *Resurgam* rescue mission, the latest in a chain of events that have mixed historical devotion, expertise, lack of expertise and near-slapstick in a manner that will be horribly familiar to those who have read thus far. If George Garrett's spirit lives on anywhere, he haunts the remains of his *Resurgam*, ready to inflict stony-faced farce on all who are foolhardy enough to draw close.

The visitor to modern Rhyl might well think that *Resurgam*, denied the choice of disappearing literally into nowhere, did the next best thing. With the driving rain reducing one's map (perkily headed 'Sunny Rhyl') to sodden rags as one stands in the shelter of the boarded-up hotel that dominates the promenade, one soon acquires a suitably funereal frame of mind for approaching the submarine's grave. When the rain stops (*if* the rain stops) and a few brave holidaymakers emerge, with that oddly post-nuclear look and the air of having realised precisely why Uncle Ernie went to Torremolinos this year, it soon becomes obvious that all Rhyl lacks is tumbleweed to underline its indubitable status as Boot Hill On Sea.

The exact location of the wreck has been a mystery since Garrett's wintry ordeal of 1880. George Price's account of the loss is not only unhelpful but discouraging, suggesting as it does that the submarine may have foundered virtually anywhere between Mostyn and Anglesey. However, there has been a persistent local tradition (for want of a better word) to the effect that *Resurgam* actually sank near the harbour entrance at Rhyl: as the boat had been at sea for 36 hours when the hawser parted, this will require explanation. Garrett may well have been carrying out experiments with the submarine; he had certainly put to sea for precisely this purpose on at least one occasion after the refit, and it is not impossible that this was in fact another such trip, rather than the final departure that it has always been understood to be. Garrett would hardly have bothered to tell the local press, any more than he did on the previous known Rhyl trial. Equally, he may have decided to return to Rhyl for further repairs to the *Elfin*. *Resurgam*, therefore, may have been under tow *back* to Rhyl when the disaster occurred. With no firm documentary evidence, all of this is entirely speculative, but it does at least serve to fill the gaps in the Price narrative and offers some basis for the faith of many down the years.

Fishermen's reports of foul ground aside, the first documented sighting of the wreck in modern times dates from about 1930, when a Mr Birchall reported having come into 'light contact' with a 'rusty cylindrical object of considerable size' while (too) close inshore off Rhyl in a motor cabin cruiser. Birchall, not unreasonably, speculated that this may have been the *Resurgam*. As the incident only came to print in 1961 (the Price syndrome, alas), there was no immediate scramble for a search-and-raise expedition; the boat slumbered on.

Nothing stirred, in fact, until 1975, when the first formal, scientific search for the submarine took place. The Gwynedd branch of the Welsh Association of Sub-Aqua clubs formed an unlikely alliance with Oxford's Laboratory for Archaeology: Dr E.T. Hall wielded his proton magnetometer over a wide area to the west of Rhyl harbour, and found nothing. Everyone went home. Obviously, the task was not as easy as had been thought, even with the wonders of Science to hand. It has never been satisfactorily underlined that equipment like the proton magnetometer, side-scan sonar, bottom-profile sonar and the rest has only ensured that a search that would otherwise have been appallingly difficult can now be classified as merely very difficult indeed. It is also abominably costly, unless one can rely on volunteers to operate complex equipment that is itself usually on loan.

The obvious source of troops and material for such an operation is, of course, the Royal Navy, who expressed a brief flicker of interest (via the Reserve base at Liverpool) in 1981: an unfortunate press statement described the location and recovery of *Resurgam* as 'straightforward' if radar and sophisticated equipment were used. Wrong.

However, before anything sophisticated could come to pass, the rude mechanicals made their presence felt. Early in the morning of 30 March 1983, four men and a bulldozer rumbled over the bridge from Rhyl into Colwyn, bound for Kinmel Bay. Heavily imbued with archaeological zeal, these devoted scientists had been in clandestine correspondence with a local expert (another imbuer, no doubt) who claimed to have found and identified the wreck of *Resurgam* in the sand near Sunnyvale Camp. Following the Rhyl version of standard archaeological procedure, they lumbered down the beach after a ritual blessing from Rhuddlan Borough's Director of Amenities ('We thought we were on to something big') and started digging with all the delicacy and precision that their equipment suggests.

After an hour of excavation, the four heroes were rewarded with a large, old navigation buoy, which seems to have caused a degree of mirth among the assembled sensation-seekers. Disappointed, these heirs to the mantle of Mortimer Wheeler returned to Rhyl for consultations.

The intention of this bizarre adventure had been to dig up *Resurgam* and use her as the centrepiece of what was described as a 'superb maritime history exhibition' at Rhyl. Garrett's sepulchral gyrations, one fears, would have reached gyroscopic speed had this come to fruition. Fortunately, his descendants came to his rescue, and sold the wreck to the Royal Navy Submarine Museum for £1; having dipped into farce, the search for the *Resurgam* was to return to a rational – and National – basis.

In 1982, the Submarine Museum, and more particularly its Director, Commander Richard Compton-Hall, had organised the location and salvage of Britain's first naval submarine, *Holland I*, from the seabed off Eddystone Lighthouse: *Resurgam* looked like a suitable encore. In September 1983, a search was planned as a naval exercise, using helicopters and minehunters, but had to be called off due to bad weather: Rhyl's dreary climate (a result of its total lack of shelter to the north) has been a recurrent and often decisive damper on attempts to salvage the submarine – having, of course, sunk her in the first place. Precisely the same problem emerged during a subsequent expedition in 1985, when it was announced that the boat lay at a position, near Splash Point, that may be too shallow for recovery vessels to approach, on which cheerful note the search was again abandoned.

In August 1987, another serious search was mounted on behalf of the Submarine Museum, this time using the services of the Marine Archaeological Survey, a volunteer organization drawing its personnel and equipment from both (non-bulldozer) archaeology and offshore industry, a potentially superb tool for maritime research. The usual Rhyl climatic problems ensued, exacerbated by equipment malfunctions and various other difficulties: the superstitious may care to consider the implications of the presence of a Mr Garrett (no relation) on board the survey boat when she ran aground. Another failure (this year's failure) seemed inevitable, as MAS, under the command of archaeologist Mark Redknap, gradually combed the search area with magnetometer and side-scan sonar, finding nothing at all.

The search was thorough, but also thoroughly disappointing. However, in the dying days of August, the equipment finally registered a large, buried metallic object, more or less at the spot long thought to be the *Resurgam*'s resting-place. After 107 years, and the very varied efforts of many researchers and seamen, *Resurgam* appeared to be making convincing moves toward living up to her name.

Coincidentally, far to the north, another relic of the Garrett era was taking shape: the last known Nordenfelt car, discovered in 1986 as a bare skeleton, was undergoing restoration at the hands of Mike Holt, an enthusiast in Strathpeffer. The car is an intriguing link between Garrett's century and our own: its engine was made by Bariquand and Marre, manufacturers of the first – unsuccessful – power unit for the Wright brothers' *Flyer*. Somehow, Nordenfelt (indeed, the Nordenfelts) never quite got it right the first time: in the case of the car, there was no second try. Mr Holt's four-wheeled treasure is unique. Fortunately, the car will be no mere museum piece: like many other cars that have been brought back from the rusty tomb (such as Zborowski's *Chitty Bang Bang*, Parry Thomas's *Babs* and the Ridley Special), the Nordenfelt is to be brought back to *running* order.

Perhaps, ninety years after their last meeting, the names Garrett and Nordenfelt are to be reunited, with the return to life of their two greatest failures – the submarine that sank and the car nobody wanted: it would not be the first irony in their story.

George Garrett, lying in a pauper's grave, was denied the

privilege of a headstone, and therefore an epitaph. The name of his submarine – *Resurgam* – stands at the head of the Submarine Memorial in Gosport, both as a prayer for many – *I shall arise* – and as a reminder of Garrett's boat, herself lost, like the many craft listed on the Memorial. Garrett, a clergyman, would only have expected that the day would come when that single word was no longer *Resurgam* but *Resurrexi* – I have arisen.

Notes and References

Notes and References

Chapter One
Throughout, GWG refers to George Garrett, RNSMAG to the Royal Navy Submarine Museum Archive, Gosport, and BVAI to the Bas Vekalet Arsiv, Istanbul. The Cochran papers are in the Museum of Transport, Glasgow.

1. John Garrett, DD: *Two Explanatory Sermons* on Sunday Closing and Other Subjects. Manchester: R.P. Matthews, 1881. Hardly a sermon at all, but an impassioned screed of hate and defiance aimed at Dr Garrett's critics.
2. *Ibid.*
3. Quoted in T.W. Bamford, *The Rise of the Public Schools*.
4. Reference for GWG from E.C. Perry, Vicar of Seighford, 14 April 1870. Author's collection.
5. John Garrett, D.D.: Letter to the *Manchester Courier*, 15 December 1879.
6. *Ibid.*
7. Typescript by John W. Garrett (George Garrett's son), written c. 1950, in RNSMAG. At first sight a valuable first-hand source. However, Garrett Junior was an old man when he came to write it: apparently intended for publication, the article is alive with elementary errors of fact and deeply dubious anecdotes. A minefield for the unwary.
8. *Ibid.*
9. *Ibid.*
10. John Garrett: Letter to *Manchester Courier* (note 4).
11. *Ibid.* It is interesting that Garrett appears to have paid no attention to the all-too-aptly-named French boat *Plongeur* of 1863, perhaps, at 410 wallowing tons, the most monstrous dead end in the history of submarine development. Strictly speaking, her (disastrous) compressed-air propulsion makes her the first mechanically-propelled submarine, but her total, unmitigated failure has relegated her, as here, to the footnotes of history. Oddly, in a neat inversion of what was to be the case with the Nordenfelt submarines, she *anticipated* the Whitehead torpedo in her powering: if the Nordenfelts resembled huge manned Whitehead torpedoes in shape, the Whitehead itself might almost be termed a miniaturised *Plongeur*.
    Dr Garrett also neglects to point out that there had been a full-blown Russian war scare in 1878: Russian naval doings were by no means only of interest to the Turks.

12. Quoted in Donald McCormick, *Pedlar of Death: The Life of Sir Basil Zaharoff*. The Vickers in question was Tom (known to his workforce, somewhat less demotically, as Colonel T.E. Vickers).

Chapter Two

1. UK Patent No 1838 (1878): 'Submarine Boats for Placing Torpedoes, etc'.
2. *Ibid.*
3. *Ibid.*
4. *Ibid.*
5. *Ibid.*
6. *Ibid.*
7. *Liverpool Daily Post*, Friday, 28 November 1879.
8. *Manchester Evening Chronicle*, Friday, 24 February 1916. From an interview with Garrett's brother Dr Thomas Garrett. The First World War U-boat onslaught brought about a sudden (and brief) burgeoning of interest in Garrett's (and therefore Britain's) claim to having built the first true submarine. A similar burst of enthusiasm brought many of Garrett's *Resurgam* collaborators out of retirement and into print in the Liverpool press (see note 15 below and elsewhere).
9. Prospectus, Garrett Submarine Navigation and Pneumatophore Company (1878).
10. *Ibid.*
11. Letter in RNSMAG.
12. GWG To J.T. Cochran, 31 March 1879: Cochran papers. A.J. Dunston (see p. 181) was the Chief Engineer at Portsmouth.
13. *Ibid.*
14. J.T. Cochran to GWG, 11 April 1879: Cochran papers. Launching and ballasting charges came to £181.
15. *Liverpool Weekly Post*, Saturday, 11 March 1916.

Chapter Three

1. *Liverpool Weekly Mercury*, 29 November 1879.
2. 'Old Tugger', *Liverpool Weekly Mercury*, 29 January 1916. One of the many responses to an appeal for information about *Resurgam*. 'Old Tugger' is one of the less exotic *noms-de-plume* employed by the writers, for reasons which now seem not a little obscure: one old salt called himself 'Teana Tamaiti'.
3. *Manchester Courier*, 12 December 1879.
4. *Ibid.*
5. *Ibid.*
6. Dr Garrett's epic letter to *Manchester Courier*, 15 December 1879.
7. *Ibid.*
8. Garrett's log of the *Resurgam* voyage, in Cochran papers. Partially published in *Liverpool Daily Post*, 16 December 1879 and in subtly differing forms elsewhere: the *Post*'s version is the least mangled.

9. Interview with the retired George Price, *Liverpool Echo*, 8 December 1925. This particular resurgence (as it were) of interest was inspired, oddly enough, by the loss of the monitor submarine *M1* the previous month.
10. Garrett log (note 8).
11. Price (note 9)
12. *The Field*, 10 January 1880.
13. Garrett (note 8).
14. Price (note 9).
15. Garrett (note 8).
16. *Manchester Courier*, 13 December 1879.
17. *Rhyl Journal*, 13 December 1879. It has occasionally been remarked that there was a curious (even suspicious) silence in the local Welsh press about the *Resurgam*, a silence which has been cited to support the deliberate-scuttling theory. However, the ill-disguised sarcasm of the reports that *were* published, and Garrett's less-than-parsonical attitude to the locals, indicates a rather more prosaic (and funnier) explanation: Garrett kept the reporters at bay. They were Welsh.
18. 'T.C.O[wen].', *Design and Work*, 2 October 1880. A fascinating late-Victorian popular science weekly that combines astonishingly well-informed articles on ship design (including *Resurgam*), electrical inventions and photography with acres of now-hilarious tripe (such as phrenology). Occasionally, these subjects converge, offering a truly bizarre picture of *Homo Victorianus* as we've never bothered to see him before.
19. *Ibid.*
20. Quoted in interview with J.T. Cochran, *Liverpool Weekly Mercury*, 12 February 1916.
21. Price (note 9).
22. *Ibid.*
23. *Rhyl Journal*, 28 February 1880.
24. Price (note 9).
25. *Ibid.*
26. *Ibid.*
27. *Ibid.*
28. *Rhyl Journal*, 2 February 1880. The unbelievable Russian 'offer' may in fact be a subtle nudge at Garrett's reputation, by way of retaliation against his rather snooty paranoia. Following the 1878 Russian war scare, putting it about that Garrett had nearly sold his fiendish weapon to the Russians at an inflated price was doing him no favours at all.
29. *Galignani's Messenger*, quoted in *Manchester Courier*, 7 May 1880.

Chapter Four
1. T.V. Nordenfelt: lecture to Royal United Services Institute, 5 February 1885. The meeting was chaired by Sir Andrew Clarke, who played an important role in the story of the *Dykeri Pråm*. He also

became chairman of the Maxim Gun Company in January 1887 (the year before the Maxim-Nordenfelt merger): there often are wheels within wheels operating in the superficially uncomplicated professional relationships of the Victorian arms world. Ties between armed services procurement officials and the arms manufacturers had become almost ludicrously blatant by the mid-1880s, in contrast to the relatively ad hoc position of even the late 1860s. The 'military-industrial complex', supposedly a product of the early twentieth century, was in fact largely in place and humming with benevolent diligence by 1885 at the latest.

2. *Ibid.*
3. T.V. Nordenfelt: 'Statement of the Nordenfelt Submarine Boat', 16 April 1885.
4. *Ibid.*
5. *Ibid.*
6. G.W. Garrett, 'From Stockholm to Göteborg with Nordenfelt's Submarine Boat'. Copy of holograph in RNSMAG. Due to a combination of Garrett's non-existent Swedish and changes in Sweden over the last hundred years, many of the proper names in the document (of persons, places and institutions) are incorrect. 'Aetelbolaget' appears to be Garrettese for 'Aktiebolaget' (i.e. 'Ltd'); 'Lake Malar' is Lake Mälaren; 'Södertalje' is Södertälje; 'Braviken'is Bråviken. I am very grateful to Erik Linderoth-Olson for his help in decoding Garrett's fascinating but often very confused account of the geography of the Swedish canal system.
7. *Ibid.*
8. *Ibid.*
9. *Ibid.* 'Skärgärd' is Skärgård.
10. *Ibid.*
11. Affidavit appended to Nordenfelt 'Statement' (note 3).
12. *Ibid.*
13. T.V. Nordenfelt to Hassan Pasha, Imperial Minister of Marine, 29 June 1885. BVAI.
14. Sydenham of Combe (but article unsigned), *The Times*, 1 October 1885. The authorship was revealed when Sydenham summarised his two articles in *The Naval Review* of 1933. Here, he neglects to mention that the submarine actually hit the bottom underneath the *Edda*. Perhaps Garrett and Nordenfelt did not point this out to him. They could both be strangely forgetful in such matters.
15. *Idem., The Times*, 9 October 1885.
16. *Ibid.*
17. *Ibid.*
18. *Ibid.*
19. *Ibid.*
20. T.V. Nordenfelt, letter to *The Times*, 30 October 1885. This weasel-worded nonsense is not at all mitigated by the fact that nobody ever saw so much as the torpedo *tube* at Landskrona: it was fitted

either just before or during the Southampton trials. If it was ever used, Nordenfelt was never anxious to discuss the matter. The boat's outright rejection by the British government was not *entirely* the product of anti-submarine prejudice.

21. *Ibid.*
22. Barthe, Menevée and Tarpin: *Documents Politiques de la Guerre*, quoted in McCormick, *op. cit.* I am *very* suspicious of these 'documents': they virtually scream 'hostile forgery', but for all that they are by no means out of character so far as Zaharoff is concerned. One would need a very peculiar imagination indeed to dream up something that *was* out of character; perhaps he liked dogs. This quote and others like it are offered in the interests of slightly bemused scholarship.
23. *Ibid.*
24. *The Times*, 27 March 1886.
25. Sir Sydney M. Eardley-Wilmot: *An Admiral's Memories.*
26. McCormick, *op.cit.*

Chapter Five
1. Turkish naval ranks have been translated into roughly-equivalent Royal Navy ranks, thus:

Pasha: This honorific – not in itself a rank – was attached to officers of the rank of *Faik Mirliva* ('superior commodore') and above. The highest rank to figure in the story of the submarines is *Ferik*, very roughly rendered as 'admiral' in this account.

Mirliva: commodore
Miralay: captain
Binbashi: commander
Önyüzbashi: lieutenant-commander
Yüzbashi: lieutenant
Mülazim: sub-lieutenant

There was, of course, no such Royal Navy rank as lieutenant-commander until 1914, but this was precisely the position in the hierarchy held by an önyüzbashi.

2. In pre-Atatürk Turkey, non-Islamic dates were rendered according to the Julian calendar, which by this stage was a full 12 days behind the Gregorian. This fact has caused considerable confusion in earlier accounts of the Turkish Nordenfelts, which took the Turkish dates at face value. Many original Nordenfelt documents are dated *both* ways, with the two dates separated by an oblique stroke, to avoid confusion between the sales team in Constantinople and head office.
3. T.V. Nordenfelt, 'Statement' (Chapter Four, note 3).
4. Fred T. Jane, *The Engineer*, 8 February 1901. Jane, by now very disillusioned with the Nordenfelt submarines, is here more or less taking dictation from the equally disaffected Captain D'Alton. There is an unmistakable whiff of recanting heretics about the whole piece, written at a time when Holland's submarines were beyond doubt the true faith. *Nostra culpa* ...

5. Report on the completion and trials of the first Turkish boat, signed by Captain Harty (Chairman), Captain Mehmet Izzet bin Hasan (overseer at Tashkizak) and Esseyid Hosni (engineer); Memorandum to Grand Vezir's Office from Hassan Pasha, summarising the above and commenting on it (and Garrett's supposed illness). Both February 1887: BVAI. Woods Pasha (ultimately Admiral Sir Henry Felix Woods) joined the Turkish Navy in 1870, and was a driving force in the Hamidian reorganisation of the Service, ending his Turkish career as the Sultan's naval aide-de-camp.
6. GWG to Hassan Pasha, 2 June 1887. BVAI.
7. Fred T. Jane, *The Engineer*, 24 June 1887. Young Jane, the believer.
8. *Idem.*, *The Engineer*, 8 February 1901 (note 4). Older Jane, the penitent.
9. *Ibid.*
10. GWG to Jane Garrett, 16 January 1888. Author's collection.
11. GWG to Jane Garrett, 22 January 1888. Author's collection.
12. GWG memorandum, 5 February 1887. In (bad) French, on Nordenfelt Submarine Boats notepaper. Author's collection.
13. Log of submarine trials, Izmit, February 1888. BVAI.
14. GWG memorandum (note 12).
15. Trials log (note 13).
16. GWG memorandum (note 12).
17. *Ibid.*
18. Final trials report, February 1888, signed by Commander Mehmed Rashid, Commander Mehmed, Captain Henry Harty, Commodore Ismail Hakki, Senior Commodore Süleyman ibni Hasan, Admiral Starke, Admiral Süleyman and Admiral Ahmed Ratib. BVAI.
19. *The Engineer*, 24 February 1888. F.T. Jane *in excelsis*.
20. GWG to Hassan Pasha, 28 February 1888. BVAI.
21. Contract between the Imperial Ottoman Government and T.V. Nordenfelt (the man, not the company, interestingly), double-dated 3/15 March 1888 (see note 2). Only the French version, annotated in Ottoman, survives. BVAI.
22. GWG to Jane Barrett, 17 March 1888. The reverend Irish gentleman has also overlooked St Patrick's Day in his excitement. Shame.
23. Harty Bey to GWG (Bey), 7 April 1888. BVAI.
24. *Newcastle Daily Chronicle*, 24 July 1909. One source states that the Greek boat was 'disassembled' in 1901. Not unlikely.

Chapter Six
1. Robert Neumann, *Der König der Waffen*. Herr Neuman is the indubitable Prince of the Zaharoff-bashers, an honourable and entertaining band. As with his colleagues (I am proud to be one), it often seems reasonable to assume that at least the worst Zaharoff stories are true.
2. Hiram Maxim, quoted in McCormick, *op.cit.*
3. *Ibid.*

4. *The Times*, 27 May 1887.
5. Quoted in *Transactions of the Institution of Naval Architects*, 29th Session, 23 March 1888.
6. *The Times*, 27 May 1887 (note 4).
7. *Documents Politiques* ... (Chapter Four, note 22).
8. Sir Hiram Maxim, *My Life*.
9. *The Engineer*, 29 July 1887.
10. *Ibid.*
11. *Ibid.*
12. *The Times*, 23 July 1887.
13. *The Engineer*, 29 July 1887 (note 9). F.T. Jane again.
14. *Ibid.* In his enthusiasm for the *Nordenfelt*, Jane never mentions the lunatic farrago of collisions at the Review which revealed a Royal Naval problem that was somewhat more urgent than the submarine question – incompetent seamanship. The Royal Yacht, three ironclads and a troopship were involved in a series of heavy shunts that caused much mirth in the popular press ('ironclad bumping races', as the *Daily News* put it). The naval architect Edward Reed, once Chief Constructor and now an MP, declared that only six or seven vessels present at the Review were war-worthy. The subsequent efforts to turn these gigantic dodgems into a Navy may well have contributed to the Admiralty's lack of interest in the *Nordenfelt*, which needed a crew of immense talent for her to be handled with any safety.
15. *The Engineer*, 8 February 1901.
16. *The Times*, 21 December 1887.
17. *Ibid.*
18. *Ibid.*
19. *The Daily News*, 21 December 1887.
20. *The Engineer*, 23 December 1887.
21. GWG, reference for Captain Palingen. Copy of holograph in RNSMAG.
22. *The Engineer*, 24 February 1887. Occasionally, one is appalled by the standards of defence journalism in the ironclad High Baroque, and Jane, supposed founding father of naval analysis, is one of the worst offenders. Having published what amounted to a prose poem about the Turkish boats after the gentlest of suggestions from the Sublime Porte, he now publishes raw Nordenfelt propaganda, without bothering to check it for anything as dull as mere accuracy. The Mordovin announcement (note 23) must have had an interesting reception at *The Engineer*'s office. No mention of it appeared in their pages. Short of space, no doubt.
23. *The Times*, 24 September 1888.
24. Quoted in Murray Sueter, *The Evolution of the Submarine Boat*.
25. John Garrett to Thomas James Arm, 27 November 1933. Copy of typed letter in RNSMAG.
26. John Garrett typescript (Chapter One, note 6).
27. John Garrett to T.J. Arm (note 25).

28. John Garrett typescript (Chapter One, note 6).

Chapter Seven
1. *Christ Church Parish Magazine*, February 1865. This is from one of the *better* poems to appear in this often alarming publication, which mixes hard-line Garrettism, Christian instruction, bad verse, adventure stories, children's features and lavish reports of murder trials to produce the authentic seething stew of the Victorian psyche. Like its editor, not for the timid.
2. Neumann, *op.cit.*
3. A.E. Drought to James Parker, 6 April 1893. Author's collection.
4. (Manchester) *Evening News*, 25 September 1893.
5. Katie (Mrs Thomas) Garrett to Jane Garrett, 2 October 1893. Author's collection.
6. H.T. Butler to GWG, 11 December 1895. Author's collection.
7. John Garrett typescript (Chapter One, note 6).
8. Quoted in Alan Burgoyne, *Submarine Navigation*.
9. Henry Cramp (for Cramp and Sons, Ship and Engine Building Co.) to GWG, 1 June 1896. Author's collection.
10. T.V. Nordenfelt to GWG, 7 August 1897. Author's collection. For the 'litérateur' see Bibliography (Forest).
11. GWG to Oliver Garrett, quoted, demanding an explanation, in Oliver's reply, dated 8 December 1897. Author's collection.
12. Oliver Garrett to GWG, 8 December 1897 (note 11).
13. Clipping from unidentified popular New York newspaper in Garrett papers. Copy in author's collection.
14. *Ibid.*
15. *Ibid.*
16. John Garrett to T.J. Arm (Chapter Six, note 25).

Technical Appendix

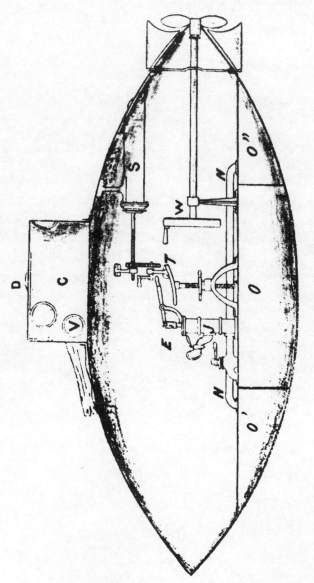

Garrett's 'Egg', 1878.

[This and subsequent drawings preserve the occasionally rather
eccentric labelling codes of the early originals]

C   – Conning tower
D   – Hatch
J   – Ballast pump
O, O', O'' – Ballast tanks connected through distribution pipe N
S   – Compensating cylinder
            (Garrett's term: flooded to dive boat once ballasted down)
T   – Vent valve
V   – Arm holes, with attached leather gauntlets
W   – Hand crank for propeller

The Submarines and Other Inventions
of G.W. Garrett

This Appendix gives the available technical details of Garrett's submarines and other inventions. In the case of the Nordenfelt boats, patent rights were usually assigned either to the Nordenfelt Company or to Nordenfelt himself, sometimes without Garrett's name appearing on the final specification at all (as in the case of the first Nordenfelt boat), but Garrett was the major contributor (see text).

Where applicable, UK patent numbers are given. Dates for submarines are for laying down. Speeds are those *claimed* by Garrett and Nordenfelt.

A: Submarines

1. First Submarine Boat, 1879 (UK Patent No. 1839, May 1878)

Builder: Cochran and Co., Britannia Iron Works, Birkenhead.
Displacement: c.4 tons
Length: 14ft
Beam: 5ft
Hull: Ovoid. Steel plates on iron stringers. Depth controlled by plunger in piston giving directly onto sea.
Machinery: Man-powered. Propeller turned on crank through a flywheel.
Endurance/Speed: No details: probable maximum speed no more than $2\frac{1}{2}$ knots.
Armament: None as built, though specification claims manual mine-fixing capability via rubber sleeves in conning-tower.
Crew: One (Garrett)
Notes: Incorrectly referred to in some sources as 'the first *Resurgam*'. The boat was never given a name. Fate unknown: presumably scrapped at early date.

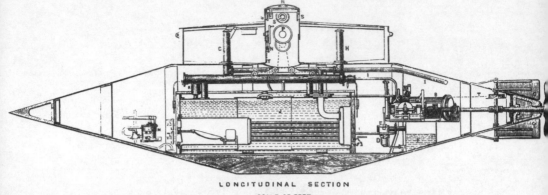

LONGITUDINAL SECTION

SCALE OF FEET

0 1 2 3 4 5   10

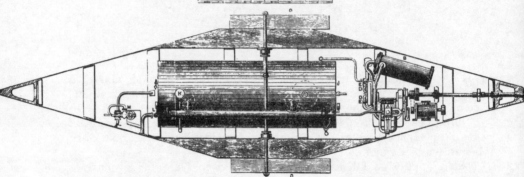

SECTIONAL PLAN

CROSS SECTION IN FRONT OF BOILER

CROSS SECTION THROUGH ENGINE ROOM

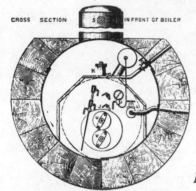

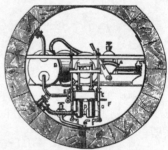

Resurgam, 1879

A	– Cylinder	L	– Blow-off valve
B	– Condenser	M	– Hand force-pump
C	– Blower	N	– Steering wheel
D	– Air and circulating pumps	O	– Side rudders
E	– Feed pumps	P	– Side rudder adjusting wheel
F	– Hot water reservoir	Q	– Rudder
G	– Air pipe with automatic valve	R	– Manhole
H	– Smoke escape valve	S	– Bull's-eye lights
I	– Air pipe to blower	T	– Steering chains
J	– Boiler	U	– Air-tight furnace door
K	– Safety valve	V	– Air-tight ashpit door

2. *Resurgam* (1879)

Builder: Cochran and Co., Britannia Iron Works, Birkenhead
Displacement: c.30 tons (100lb reserve of buoyancy)
Length: 45ft
Beam: 5ft
Hull: Iron plates on iron frames and stringers
Machinery: Return connecting-rod, single boiler: driven when submerged from single Lamm hot-water steam accumulator.
Speed/Endurance: 10 miles at 2-3 knots dived. No details of surface performance.
Armament: None as built, but provision made for external carriage of Whitehead torpedoes (supposedly two) on springs.
Crew: Three
Notes: Lost on delivery voyage off North Wales, February 1880.

3. *Nordenfelt I: Dykeri Pråm En* (1882)

Builder: Aktielbolaget Palmcrantz, Carlsvik, Stockholm. Boat built at Ekensberg yard.
Displacement: 60 tons (dived): 600-800 lbs residual buoyancy.
Length: 64ft
Beam: 9ft (11ft over sponsons): 8ft within hull due to internal width of frames.
Hull: Iron plates, $\frac{1}{2}$in amidships, $\frac{3}{8}$in at bow and stern, on iron frames: frames 3 ft apart, made from angle bars, 3in × 3in × $\frac{3}{8}$in, extreme thickness $\frac{3}{8}$in. Maximum diving depth 100 feet, revised after trials to 50 feet.
Machinery: Compound surface-condensing, two cylinders, 100HP. Forced draught to boiler. Experimental Nordenfelt underwater exhaust system fitted. Two 6HP engines to drive downhaul screws, driven from main plant. Main screw five-bladed, 5ft diameter, 7ft 6in pitch. Depth maintenance by hydrostatically-operated throttle-valve system on downhauls: pendulum-actuated hydroplanes responding to change in boat's longitudinal orientation. Pendulum system could be linked to hydraulic servo system for hydroplanes: pump driven from main plant. Two separate Lamm hot-water steam accumulators, fore and aft. Single ballast tank amidships.
Speed/Endurance: 150 miles at 10 knots surfaced, 16 miles at 4kts awash/dived claimed.
Armament: Single 14in external Whitehead torpedo tube fitted after Landskrona trials, no reloads. Provision for launching guided Nordenfelt torpedo. One single-barrel 25mm quick-firing Nordenfelt gun.
Crew: Three
Notes: Patented in UK and USA under Nordenfelt's name alone. Nordenfelt patented downhaul propeller system and its hydrostatic gear separately in Sweden.

4. *Nordenfelt II: Abdul Hamid* (1886)

Builder: Barrow Shipbuilding Company, Barrow-in-Furness.
Displacement: 160 tons dived. Registered with Board of Trade at 68 gross tons.
Length: 110 ft (Turkish figure – most sources give 100 ft)
Beam: 12ft
Hull: Steel plates on iron frames: measurements as *Dykeri Pråm* above. Maximum diving depth 100 feet.
Machinery: Compound surface-condensing, 250HP. Two 6HP engines for downhaul screws: depth-maintenance as *Dykeri Pråm* above. Single Lamm accumulator forward. Three ballast tanks: one forward, one aft, and third amidships acting as compensating tank for consumed fuel.
Endurance: 150 miles at 10 knots surfaced, 12 miles at 5 knots dived.
Armament: Two 14in Whitehead torpedo tubes. Two single-barrel 25mm quick-firing Nordenfelt guns.
Crew: Five (one source gives *24!*)
Notes: Boat's name now more correctly rendered as *Abdülhamid*.

5. *Nordenfelt III: Abdul Medjid* (1886)

Builder: Des Vignes, Chertsey
Other details as for *Abdul Hamid*. Boat's name now more correctly rendered as *Abdülmecid*.

6. *Nordenfelt IV: Nordenfelt* (1886)

Builder: Barrow Shipbuilding Company, Barrow-in-Furness
Displacement: 160/245 tons (Russian figures: most sources give 230 tons dived)
Length: 125ft
Beam: 12ft
Hull: 5/16ths-in steel plates on steel frames 20in apart. Maximum diving depth 100ft.
Machinery: Two 2-cylinder compound, 1000HP. Lamm accumulators replaced by adapted double-boiler system. Before diving, both boilers employed to establish boat's underwater working pressure in forward boiler, then forward boiler isolated and used as steam reservoir. For normal surface running, only after boiler used. Two 6HP downhaul engines: nine other auxiliary engines for steering, torpedo compressor etc. Depth maintenance as *Abduls* above. Nine ballast tanks, distributed along length of boat.
Speed: 17 knots surface (14 achieved), 5 knots dived (Russian figure).
Endurance: 1000 miles at 8 kts surfaced. 8 tons of coal carried, but maximum capacity 26 tons when ballast tanks used as bunkers, raising

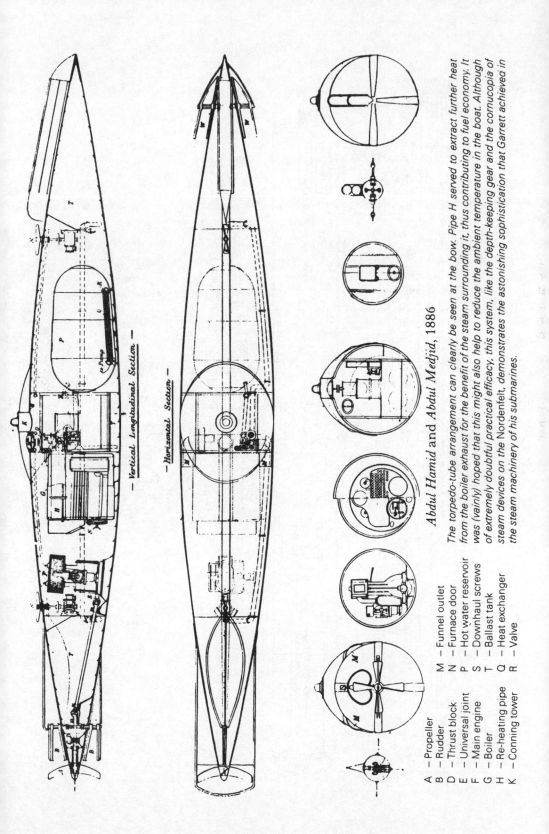

– Vertical Longitudinal Section –

– Horizontal Section –

A – Propeller
B – Rudder
D – Thrust block
E – Universal joint
F – Main engine
G – Boiler
H – Re-heating pipe
K – Conning tower

M – Funnel outlet
N – Furnace door
P – Hot water reservoir
S – Downhaul screws
T – Ballast tank
Q – Heat exchanger
R – Valve

Abdul Hamid and Abdul Medjid, 1886

The torpedo-tube arrangement can clearly be seen at the bow. Pipe H served to extract further heat from the boiler exhaust for the benefit of the steam surrounding it, thus contributing to fuel economy. It was (vainly) hoped that this might also help to reduce the ambient temperature in the boat. Although of extremely doubtful practical efficacy, this system, like the depth-keeping gear and the cornucopia of steam devices on the Nordenfelt, demonstrates the astonishing sophistication that Garrett achieved in the steam machinery of his submarines.

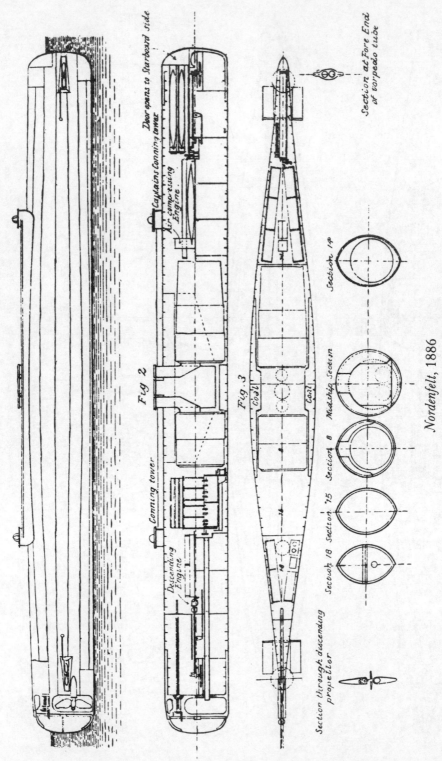

Fig 2

Door opens to Starboard side

Captains conning tower

Air compressing Engine

Conning tower

Descending Engine

Fig. 3

Coal

Coal

Section through descending propeller

Section at Fore End of torpedo tube

Section 14

Midship Section

Section 8

Section 75

Section 78

Nordenfelt, 1886

An early semi-technical drawing of the boat

nominal endurance to 2,000 miles+.

Armament: Two bow Whitehead torpedo tubes, two reloads. Two 2-pounder quick-firing Nordenfelt guns incorporated in design, but not fitted.

Notes: Lost on delivery voyage off Jutland, November 1888.

German Nordenfelt Boats (1890: see Chapter Six)

6a: U1

Builder: Howaldswerke, Kiel
Displacement: 200/212 tons
Length: 34.85m/114ft
Beam: 3.65m/11ft
Hull: All-steel construction as in two *Abduls*, but no details available.
Machinery: As *Dykeri Pråm* above (?)
Endurance: As *Dykeri Pråm* above (?)
Speed: 12 knots surfaced, 6 knots dived (but see below)
Armament: As *Dykeri Pråm* above (?)
Notes: On trials, reached a maximum of 9.3 knots awash, 6.5 knots submerged. Sueter (see Bibliography) gives speed as $11/4\frac{1}{2}$ knots, but above breakdown into submerged and awash speeds (Burgoyne, see Bibliography) suggests a better source.

6b. U2

Builder: Kaiserliche Werft, Danzig
Details as for *U1* above.

B: Garrett's Other Inventions

1. Pneumatophore (1872-6)

Closed-cycle breathing apparatus, combining a carbon-dioxide scrubbing unit of Garrett's invention (using caustic potash, KOH, as reducing agent) with standard diving suit. Widely demonstrated by Garrett, and the eponymous product of the Garrett Submarine Navigation and Pneumatophore Company, but no examples, specifications or drawings have survived. Abandoned by late 1883 (see Chapter 4).

2. Vapour Generator (UK Patent No. 6489)

Key component of the 'Garrett Motor' (the putative 'Beam Engine') (see Chapter Seven).

An adaptation of an ordinary surface condenser. Steam, hot water or other liquid is passed through the condenser tubes, and liquid with a lower boiling point and lower specific heat than the water or other liquid in the tubes (such as petroleum spirit) is passed or sprayed over the tubes. The volatile liquid vaporises at a higher vapour tension (giving a higher pressure) than steam or water at the same temperature, and can be used to drive an ordinary expansive steam engine.

Not known to have been demonstrated, though Garrett contracted to do so in April 1901 (demonstration to have taken place in or about late June).

Garrett also contributed suggestions for the Nordenfelt Compound Rotary Engine (UK Patent No.2834, 1883), but these were minor: the engine was of Nordenfelt's own design.

Select Bibliography

Select Bibliography

While most of this book has been based on unpublished documents of one kind or another, I have consulted many contemporary periodicals and books, most of the latter written soon after Garrett's death. Submarine histories apart, other works were consulted for general background and the occasional minuscule detail of daily life, so necessary if the planet one evokes is to have an atmosphere. This list is necessarily selective, though largely complete with respect to newspapers, the often maddeningly contradictory starting point for most recent history.

Submarine histories have brief comments appended, for the guidance of the reader.

Newspapers and Periodicals

Brassey's Naval Annuals
Christ Church Parish Magazine
The Daily News
Design and Work
The Engineer
The Graphic
Liverpool Echo
Liverpool Weekly Mercury
Liverpool Weekly Post
Manchester Courier
Maritime Wales
P.S.N.C. Magazine
Rhyl Journal and Advertiser
The Times
Warship (There is an excellently-researched, broadly accurate paper on the Nordenfelt submarines by Lt.-Cmdr John Maber in Issue 32)

Books

T.W. Bamford: *The Rise of the Public Schools*. London: Nelson, 1967.
Robert F. Burgess: *Ships Beneath the Sea*. London: Robert Hale, 1976. Readable, popular submarine history, mainly from the American point of view: contains virtually nothing on Garrett.
Lt-Col Alan H. Burgoyne, MP: *Submarine Navigation, Past and Present*. 2 Vols, London: Grant Richards, 1903. One of the classic early

241

submarine histories, a prime reference source for the subject. Rather quirky, however (as one would expect from a man who christened his daughter John). While chapters on Garrett are largely based on D'Alton's hostile reminiscences, Burgoyne still includes an astonishing statement from D'Alton stating that the *Nordenfelt* was 'the best submarine ever constructed'. Conscience?

Cmdr Richard Compton-Hall: *Submarine Boats*. London: Conway Maritime Press, 1983. By far the best modern popular submarine history, bringing together a great deal of otherwise obscure material to form an instantly comprehensible broad picture. Splendidly illustrated and very well written. Chapters on Garrett have been overtaken by more recent research, but the book as a whole is indispensable.

Cmdr William H. Cracknell, USN: *United States Navy Monitor of the Civil War* (*Warship Profile* 36). Windsor, Berks: Profile Publications, 1973.

Rear-Adm Sir Sydney M. Eardley-Wilmot: *An Admiral's Memories: Sixty-five years afloat and ashore*. London: Sampson Low, Marston and Co., Ltd., n.d. (c.1927). Standard I-was-right stuff, but he *did* see the *Dykeri Pråm*.

Lieut-Col and Brevet-Col Cyril Field: *The Story of the Submarine, from the earliest times to the present day*. London, Sampson Low Marston and Co., 1908. Interesting mainly for being an early popular submarine history, drawn, I suspect, mainly from Burgoyne, Fyfe and Sueter. Useless, almost childish illustrations. Contains material on Garrett, but is mostly of curiosity value.

Forest and F. Noalhat: *Les Bateaux Sous-marins*. 2 Vols, Paris, 1900. One of these two gentlemen, I strongly suspect, was the *littérateur* who visited Nordenfelt in 1896, but little seems to have been gained from the visit.

Herbert C. Fyfe: *Submarine Warfare*. London, 1907. Another important early text, drawn mostly from contemporary journalists' accounts (but badly scrambles the *Resurgam* story).

John Guthrie: *Bizarre Ships of the Nineteenth Century*. London: Hutchinson, 1970. Includes witty, perceptive naval architect's assessment of Garrett's submarines.

J.R. de S. Honey: *Tom Brown's Universe: The Development of the Victorian Public School*. London: Millington, 1977.

G.W. Hovgaard: *Submarine Boats*. London: E. and F.N. Spon, 1887. One of the very earliest submarine books (*Nordenfelt* was still under trial when it was published). Now very rare indeed, but a vital insight into the submarine mentality of its period.

G.W. Hovgaard: *Modern History of Warships*. London: E. and F.N. Spon, 1919. Chapter on submarines includes interesting updating on the previous book.

F.T. Jane: *Jane's Fighting Ships* (1898-)

F.T. Jane: *The Imperial Russian Navy* (1899). Reprinted, London: Conway, 1983.

Robert H. Kargon: *Science in Victorian Manchester*. Manchester: MUP, 1977.

John Halladay Latané: *America as a World Power 1897-1907*. New York: Harper, 1907.

Richard Lewinsohn: *The Man Behind the Scenes: the Career of Sir Basil Zaharoff, 'The Mystery Man of Europe'*. London: Gollancz, 1929.

Bernard Lewis: *The Emergence of Modern Turkey*. Oxford; OUP, 1961.

Donald McCormick: *Pedlar of Death: The Life of Sir Basil Zaharoff*. London: Macdonald, 1965.

R.B. McDowell and D.A. Webb: *Trinity College Dublin 1592-1952. An Academic History*. Cambridge: Cambridge University Press, 1982.

Binbasi Yazan Rasit Metel: *Türk Denizaltıcilik Tarihi*. Istanbul, 1960. A very remarkable work of scholarship, written by a Turkish submarine commander. Never translated into English (and highly unlikely ever to be so), it also leaves documents in (transliterated) Ottoman. It therefore needs almost as much effort to read as it did to write, but a key work and a so far ignored challenge to other navies, whose own internal submarine histories are nothing like as complete.

Milford Docks Company: *History of Milford Docks*. Milford Haven, n.d.

Robert Neumann: *Der König der Waffen*. Zürich, 1951.

Cmdr Murray Sueter, RN: *The Evolution of the Submarine Boat, Mine and Torpedo*. Porstmouth: Griffin, 1907. Much the most comprehensive early history. Subject (like all the early books) to Nordenfelt propaganda and D'Alton spite, but essential reading.

Index

Index

Rossall School, 23-4, 193
Rothschild, Lord, 174, 200
Royle, Mrs Peter (Christ Church parishioner), 52-3
Rozhdestvensky, Lt Zinovi, 35-6, 66
Russell, John Scott (naval architect), 44, 89
Russo-Turkish War (1877-8), − torpedo-boats in Danube, 33-5, 117

Sadler, William (Submarine Company director), 56
Salonik, 140-1
von Sanders, Gen Liman, 151
Seawolf, USS, 56
Seymour, Adm, 111-2
Seymour, Capt, 161
Shafter, Gen, 205
Singer, Adm Morgan, 161
Skoda (munitions manufacturer), 164
Smiles, Samuel (popular philosopher), 20
Smith, Capt Edward (of *Titanic*), 88-9
Smith, John Abel (politician), 23-5
Spanish-American War (1898), 203-7
Starke, Adm, 126-139
Steward, Gen Harding, 161
bin Süleyman, Adm Hassan Sabri, 128, 139
'Swede Anderson', 178
Sydenham of Combe, Lord, 105-9, 116, 123
Symon, Randolph (Maxim's partner), 153

Tahir, Cmdr, 138
Tamar, HMS, 165
Tashkizak (shipyard), 121, 124ff, 193
Temeraire, HMS, 113
Tercümani Hakiket Gazet, 137, 149
Teutonic, RMS, 189
Timsah (pioneer Turkish submarine), 117; − des Vignes torpedo boat, 121
Titanic, RMS, 89
Toledo, SS, 112
Torpedo, mine, 34; Nordenfelt, 101; spar, 35, 43; towed, 34, 35-6; Whitehead, see Whitehead,

Robert; first submarine torpedo launch, 136
Tosun Pasha, 127
Trikoupis, Kharilaos (Greek Prime Minister), 114
Trinidad, SS, 124
Trinity College, Dublin, 27, 29-30, 172
Turbinia, 165

U1 (German para-Nordenfelt submarine), 183
U2 (German para-Nordenfelt submarine), 183
Upottery (Devonshire), − duck-pond, 36

van Drebbel, see Drebbel
Vancouver('s) Island, Russian threat to, 33, 67
Verne, Jules, − *20,000 Leagues Under the Sea*, 45, 55, 88
Vernon, HMS, 162, 181
Vickers, Albert (arms and steel manufacturer), 120, 176, 155, 183, 201
Vickers, Col T.E. ('Tom') (arms and steel manufacturer), 37, 155
Victoria, Queen, 166-7, 205
Victoria and Albert (Royal Yacht), 167
des Vignes, G.F.G. (shipbuilder), 120; − shipyard (Chertsey), 120-1, 122-4, 127, 144
Villafranca, Duchess of, 187, 204, 210

Wales, Prince of − see Edward
Waddington, James, and *Porpoise*, 175
Warrior, HMS, 47
Watts, William Marshall (chemist), 26
White, W.H. (Director of Naval Construction), 168
Whitehead, Robert (torpedo designer), 35; torpedo, 35-6, 46, 85, 94, 171
Wilkins, John (Bishop of Chester), 15-16
Willes, Adm Sir George, 161
William, Archduke, Austrian War Minister, 154
Willis, Gen Sir George, 161; − Lady, 161
Woods, Adm Sir Henry Felix (Woods Pasha), 128, 139, 144
Zaharoff, Sir Basil(eos), becomes